MARIHUANA

Merrill Sociology Series

Under the editorship of

Richard L. Simpson
University of North Carolina at Chapel Hill

and

Paul E. Mott
University of Pennsylvania

MARIHUANA

edited by
STANLEY E. GRUPP

Illinois State University

Charles E. Merrill Publishing Company
A Bell & Howell Company
Columbus, Ohio

ISBN: 0-675-09834-3

Library of Congress Catalog Card Number: 72-157698

1   2   3   4   5   6   7   8   9—76   75   74   73   72   71

Printed in the United States of America

Contents

INTRODUCTION   1

1
ITS NATURE AND USE

DRUG DEPENDENCE OF CANNABIS
(MARIHUANA) TYPE

*Nathan B. Eddy, H. Halbach, Harris Isbell,
Maurice H. Seevers*   7

MARIHUANA SMOKING IN THE UNITED STATES

Donald D. Pet and John C. Ball   9

SOCIAL AND EPIDEMIOLOGICAL ASPECTS
OF MARIHUANA USE

Gilbert Geis   24

CANNABIS

Advisory Committee on Drug Dependence   37

MARIHUANA AND HEALTH

National Institute of Mental Health   53

v

2
VALUE PERSPECTIVES

CHILDREN OF THE DRUG AGE

William Simon and John H. Gagnon   65

THE DANGERS OF MARIHUANA—FACTS
YOU SHOULD KNOW

Federal Bureau of Narcotics   78

DEPENDENCE ON CANNABIS (MARIHUANA)

American Medical Association   85

MARIHUANA AND SOCIETY

Council on Mental Health   94

THE GREAT MARIJUANA HOAX

Allen Ginsberg   98

MARIJUANA: THE REAL PROBLEMS AND THE
RESPONSIBILITIES OF THE PROFESSIONS
IN SOLVING THEM

Joel Fort   112

3
RESEARCH REPORTS

ADVERSE REACTION TO MARIHUANA

Martin H. Keeler   123

BECOMING A MARIHUANA USER

Howard S. Becker   129

CLINICAL AND PSYCHOLOGICAL EFFECTS
OF MARIHUANA IN MAN

*Andrew T. Weil, Norman E. Zinberg,
Judith M. Nelsen*   142

EXPERIENCES WITH MARIHUANA IN A
SAMPLE OF DRUG USERS

    Stanley Grupp   165

THE EFFECTS OF A SYNTHETIC MARIHUANA-
LIKE COMPOUND ON MUSICAL TALENT AS
MEASURED BY THE SEASHORE TEST

    C. Knight Aldrich   178

THE ASSOCIATION OF MARIHUANA SMOKING
WITH OPIATE ADDICTION IN THE
UNITED STATES

    *John C. Ball, Carl D. Chambers
and Marion J. Ball*   182

COMPARISON OF THE EFFECTS OF
MARIHUANA AND ALCOHOL ON
SIMULATED DRIVING PERFORMANCE

    *Alfred Crancer, Jr., James M. Dille,
Jack C. Delay, Jean E. Wallace
and Martin D. Haykin*   200

THE MARIHUANA PROBLEM IN THE
CITY OF NEW YORK

    George B. Wallace   209

4
THE QUESTION OF CONTROL

POT BUST AT CORNELL

    David Sanford   219

THE MARIHUANA PROBLEM—
MYTH OR REALITY?

    Alfred R. Lindesmith   226

MARIJUANA AT ISSUE

    Lee Berton   243

ENFORCEMENT TECHNIQUES

*Allan S. Morton, John Mueller, Joel Ohlgren,
Roger W. Pearson and Sheldon Weisel*   249

COMMONWEALTH V. LEIS AND WEISS

Chief Justice Tauro's Opinion   277

LEGISLATIVE AND JUDICIAL TRENDS IN
MARIHUANA CONTROLS

Donald E. Miller   297

INTRODUCTION

The marihuana problem has today become the "marihuana muddle." Few, if any, social problems have received so much attention and resulted in so little agreement about what we should do to ameliorate the situation. As the use of marihuana expands in the middle and upper classes, officials are increasingly confronted with questions concerning the effects and dangers of marihuana use. Unfortunately, the answers that can be given are limited. Perhaps the most decisive point that can be made is that the possession and sale of marihuana is against the law. The focus of the "marihuana muddle" revolves around this fact. Were it not for its illegality and the increasing number of persons who are being arrested and prosecuted, an increase in use notwithstanding, the subject would undoubtedly receive conspicuously less attention than it does today.

It should be emphasized at the outset that in today's society the question of marihuana use and control is important to everyone, affects our entire society, and the manner in which we deal with it does have far-reaching legal and ethical implications. Similarly, the "marihuana muddle" poses interesting questions for those interested in the theoretical and practical problems of social control. A few examples will point up these facts. There is an ingrained assumption in our society that marihuana use and sale can be controlled by the criminal law. Note, for example, that many of those who argue that our marihuana laws are too tough are interested in seeing marihuana possession laws reduced to a misdemeanor but *not* entirely eliminated. The assumption that marihuana can be controlled by criminal law continues today in spite of rapidly increasing use of marihuana and growing tolerance for it on the part of many citizens. As this use increases we increasingly have a prohibition-like condition. Examples of police purposely ignoring marihuana smokers because of the sheer impossibility of applying the law even to the extent of making an arrest, are not uncommon. This comes at a time when the problems for law enforcement agencies are increasingly magnified both in terms of their deteriorating image and their capacity to perform their traditional functions. What are the consequences of this situation for the criminal law and the system for the administration of justice?

Regardless of one's personal standards with respect to use or non-use of marihuana, one of the questions which must be addressed is what criteria should be used to determine when a given behavior circumstance is made criminally sanctionable? Can respect for the law be built and sustained in our citizens when in fact there is such a glaring disparity between what is said and what is done? Or should it be argued that the expectations as outlined by the criminal law do set the moral-ethical tone for the society whether or not we can realistically expect reasonable consistency in the enforcement of the law? After all, no code of conduct is adhered to all the time.

Professional and public opinion about marihuana, as any reader of his daily paper knows, is sharply divided. Differences are especially acute with respect to the meaning of the expansive use of marihuana and the question of what should be done about it. The readings in this volume direct themselves to these areas.

Myths and quasi-myths abound in the literature and discussions about marihuana. It is not uncommon for the exceptional case to be generalized to the entire population of persons who have had experience with marihuana. Reasoning of this sort is not, of course, unique to the marihuana problem; it is, as a matter of fact, quite commonplace in discussions and literature related to the entire drug abuse field.

Ironically, however, it is sometimes difficult to separate fact from myth and at times the entire matter takes on the form of a verbal sideshow specializing in symbolic gymnastics, characterized by charges and countercharges.

One interesting case in point is the prevalent assertion that our marihuana laws punish too severely and the accompanying claim that the response to the marihuana law violator has been increasingly punitive in recent years. Unfortunately, hard data is not available in many areas of the United States which permit an examination of these claims. Theoretically, the laws do permit relatively stiff prison sentences. Based on information from California, the only state that systematically collects and reports this type of data, it can be said that while prison sentences are indeed possible, the fact is that overall they represent an increasingly smaller and smaller proportion of the sentences generated. Most violators are placed on probation. While we do not know for certain, it is probable that similar patterns characterize other states. This disposition pattern hardly seems consistent with the assertion that we are increasingly harsh in dealing with marihuana law violators.

Any selection of materials on marihuana from the vast reservoir that is available must to some extent be arbitrary. Much of what is said waxes emotional or is a monotonous repetition of statements either favorable or opposed to marihuana. In making the selections for this volume, however, I have tried to avoid the insipid as well as the sentimental and have emphasized well-argued and clearly-presented materials which reflect the range of viewpoints that are espoused on the subject. This, of course, is a matter of judgment. Inevitably one tends to feel positive about those points of view which reflect his biases. It is the stance one takes with respect to the control dilemma where we are most apt to find controversy. In this regard, we would only say that it is not easy to locate articulate statements that defend the status quo.

Materials have been organized around four major themes in such a way as to provide both an introduction to the subject as well as in-depth reading. Marihuana is spelled both marihuana and marijuana. In all instances we have retained the preferred spelling of each author. In the first section the nature and use of marihuana is considered. Each of the statements by experts present what they feel is known about marihuana.

The second section concerns value perspectives. Our concern here is on position papers whose major thrust is that of analyzing and understanding marihuana problems. In view of the fact that the illegality of marihuana serves as a focal point for this subject it is inevitable that legal questions are touched on here, but they are not the primary focus. A variety of papers are presented including some by medical spokesmen, some from representatives of the law enforcement segment, and a range of other viewpoints.

A similar stance is taken in the third section in which we present seven reports of research studies. Several disciplines as well as research methodologies are represented. Research reports involving marihuana offer a fertile ground for a discussion of research strategies and methodo-logical problems. The subject is a research challenge offering all of the problems posed by deviant research and more. Depending on one's research objectives the problematical enforcement situation, the sampling problems posed by the unknown universe, the surreptitious nature of the behavior, and the variable quality and effects of marihuana itself all pose formidable problems.

The final section deals with the question of control. A variety of opinions are presented. Selections were chosen because of their concern with the problem of control, especially legal concerns. Although some of the statements also reflect a value perspective, their thrust concerns the legal question.

PART 1
ITS NATURE AND USE

DRUG DEPENDENCE
OF CANNABIS (MARIHUANA) TYPE

Nathan B. Eddy, H. Halbach,
Harris Isbell, Maurice H. Seevers

It is not known with absolute certainty which of the chemical structures that have been isolated from *Cannabis sativa* L. is responsible for the typical cannabis effects, but these can nevertheless be described as constituting an entity that varies in degree according to the concentration of the active principle or principles in the plant and the preparations obtained therefrom, and to the mode of application. These effects are also producible by certain synthetic substances of similar chemical structure.

Among the more prominent subjective effects of cannabis, for which it is taken occasionally, periodically or chronically, are: hilarity, often without apparent motivation; carelessness; loquacious euphoria, with increased sociability as a result; distortion of sensation and perception, especially of space and time, with the latter reinforcing psychic dependence and being valued under special circumstances; impairment of judgement and memory; distortion of emotional responsiveness; irrita-

Reprinted from "Drug Dependence: Its Significance and Characteristics," *Bulletin of the World Health Organization* 32 (1965): 728–29.

bility; and confusion. Other effects, which appear especially after repeated administration and as more experience is acquired by the user, include: lowering of the sensory threshold, especially for optical and acoustical stimuli, thereby resulting in an intensified appreciation of works of art, paintings and music; hallucinations, illusions, and delusions that predispose to antisocial behaviour; anxiety and aggressiveness as a possible result of the various intellectual and sensory derangements; and sleep disturbances.

In the psychomotor sphere, hypermotility occurs without impairment of co-ordination. Among somatic effects, often persistent, are injection of the ciliary vessels and oropharyngitis, chronic bronchitis and asthma; these conditions and hypoglycaemia, with ensuing bulimia, are symptoms of intoxication, not of withdrawal.

Typically, the abuse of cannabis is periodic but, even during long and continuous administration, no evidence of the development of physical dependence can be detected. There is, in consequence, no characteristic abstinence syndrome when use of the drug is discontinued.

Whether administration of the drug is periodic or continuous, tolerance to its subjective and psychomotor effects has not been demonstrated.

Whereas cannabis often attracts the mentally unstable and may precipitate temporary psychoses in predisposed individuals, no unequivocal evidence is available that lasting mental changes are produced.

Drug dependence of the cannabis type is a state arising from chronic or periodic administration of cannabis or cannabis substances (natural or synthetic). Its characteristics are:

(*a*) Moderate to strong psychic dependence on account of the desired subjective effects.

(*b*) Absence of physical dependence, so that there is no characteristic abstinence syndrome when the drug is discontinued.

(*c*) Little tendency to increase the dose and no evidence of tolerance.

For the individual, harm resulting from abuse of cannabis may include inertia, lethargy, self-neglect, feeling of increased capability, with corresponding failure, and precipitation of psychotic episodes. Abuse of cannabis facilitates the association with social groups and sub-cultures involved with more dangerous drugs, such as opiates or barbiturates. Transition to the use of such drugs would be a consequence of this association rather than an inherent effect of cannabis. The harm to society derived from abuse of cannabis rests in the economic consequences of the impairment of the individual's social functions and his enhanced proneness to asocial and antisocial behaviour.

MARIHUANA SMOKING
IN THE UNITED STATES

Donald D. Pet and John C. Ball

Marihuana smoking is a topic of considerable public interest in the United States. One may observe a growing controversy of spirited opinion ranging from the view that marihuana is beneficial and should be legalized, to warnings that catastrophic harm is the direct consequence of marihuana use. In this controversy, the abuse of known information about marihuana may be as important an issue as the abuse of the drug itself. Dr. J. D. Reichard's review of marihuana knowledge in his article for *Federal Probation,* October–December 1946, was primarily intended to dispel many of the myths of that time which had come to be associated with the drug. Similarly, this review is intended to provide a contemporary perspective of marihuana use within the broader drug abuse situation that will have practical use for probation and parole officers.*

The term marihuana refers to any part of the hemp plant (Cannabis

---

* Acknowledgement is expressed by the authors to Donald R. Jasinski, M.D., of the Addiction Research Center, Lexington, Ky., for his helpful comments and advice.
Reprinted from *Federal Probation* 32 (September 1968): 8–15, with the permission of the publisher.

9

Sativa) or its extract which is pharmacologically active in man. A resin obtained from the flowering tops of the female plant contains most of the active ingredients. This resin, known as "hashish" in Arab countries, is far more potent than the dried leaves and flowering shoots. The potency of the active ingredients of the cannabis plant vary with the region of growth. In the United States, the horticultural conditions are generally unfavorable for the production of high resin content.[1] Common names for cannabis include: bhang, ganja, charas (India); kif (Morocco); dagga (South Africa); anascha (Russia); maconha (Brazil); tea, pot, sticks, grass, joints, reefers (U.S. slang).[2]

While marihuana may be taken orally, as a tea, a confection, or even whole, in this country it is primarily smoked. Absorption is more rapid by the latter route, intoxicating effects appearing shortly after smoking begins.[3] Most investigators have agreed that the effects of marihuana are due to tetrahydrocannabinols. Although physiologically active substances had previously been extracted, a substance of *known* chemical structure has only recently been isolated and evaluated under laboratory conditions.[4] Differences in the potency of drug samples and the inadequate methods of laboratory analysis have contributed to the present confusion concerning the effects of marihuana use. Thus, the voluminous literature on marihuana is difficult to evaluate, almost as though one were comparing the effects of wine and whiskey, or beer and gin, without considering alcohol content or amount of consumption. Marihuana, for the most part, has yet to receive the more thorough pharmacological evaluation given to drugs of accepted medical use.

EFFECTS IN MAN

The effects of a drug depend in part on the dose. The smoking of marihuana is a process in which the active ingredient is taken in small portions with each inhalation. The experienced user thereby has a greater opportunity to achieve a "controlled" high than with drugs customarily

---

[1] Samuel Allentuck and Karl M. Bowman, "The Psychiatric Aspects of Marihuana Intoxication," *American Journal of Psychiatry*, Volume 99, September 1942, p. 248.

[2] For further nomenclature and discussion, see: Robert P. Walton, *Marihuana* (New York: J. B. Lippincott Co., 1938); R. N. Chopra and I. C. Chopra, *Drug Addiction* (New Delhi: Delhi Press, 1965).

[3] Samuel Allentuck, "Medical Aspects: Symptoms and Behavior," *The Marihuana Problem in the City of New York,* ed. Mayor's Committee on Marihuana. Lancaster, Pennsylvania: The Jacques Cattell Press, 1944, pp. 35–51.

[4] Harris Isbell, *et al.,* "Effects of (–) Delta [9] -Trans-Tetrahydrocannabinol in Man," *Psychopharmacologia (Berl.),* Volume 11, 1967, pp. 184–188.

taken in a single dose such as the ingestion of LSD or the "shooting" of opiates into the vein.

Acute physical symptoms frequently include conjunctival vascular injection, dryness of the mouth and pharynx, irritation of the throat, increased sensitivity to light, sound, touch, and pain stimuli, and such changes in the autonomic nervous system as increase in pulse, blood pressure, and tendon reflexes. Ataxia, the impaired ability to coordinate voluntary muscular movements, may also occur. Appetite is often stimulated. There is no evidence that marihuana increases sexual potency. There are as yet no recognized lasting ill effects directly attributed to the brief use of marihuana nor has a death been reported in this country due to overdosage.[5]

The mental changes following marihuana use are variable and depend in part upon the expectations and prior drug experience of the user and the social setting at the time of use; thus, the meaning of the experience is largely socially acquired.[6] Marihuana is primarily classified as a hallucinogen even though intoxication may include both early stimulant and later depressant effects. A decreased sense of fatigue, relaxation, and increased self-confidence has been described. There may be a distortion of affect toward omnipotency and a perception of "insight" rarely shared by the unintoxicated. The individual is often garrulous, giggly, and talk is disconnected. Associated with a period of euphoria, or well-being, there may be distortions of time, space, color, and other sensory perception with increased dosage.

Depersonalization, the perception of the physical body as not self, has been described with use. While this distortion might be expected to increase the likelihood of self-injury, we know of no documentation to confirm this expectation.

Increased suggestibility, decreased judgment, and change of affect may be followed by depression and sleep. There may also be delusions, hallucinations, suspiciousness, panic, and fear of death. Violent or aggressive behavior is unusual. While occasional persons may be especially sensitive to even small doses, with the result that a psychotic-like state is produced, there is recent evidence that almost all persons are so affected with sufficient dosage.[7] A puzzling observance is that many of

---

[5] Jerome H. Jaffe, "Drug Addiction and Drug Abuse," *The Pharmacological Basis of Therapeutics,* ed. Louis S. Goodman and Alfred Gilman (New York: Macmillan Co., 1965), p. 300.

[6] Howard S. Becker, "Becoming a Marihuana User," *American Journal of Sociology,* Volume 59, November 1953, pp. 235–242.

[7] Isbell, *et al., op. cit.,* p. 186.

the persons who have had frightening episodes in their marihuana experience wish to repeat it.[8]

In summary, the acute effects of marihuana smoking commonly include a euphoric state accompanied by motor excitation and mental confusion. These reactions are often followed by a period of dreaminess, depression, and sleep. The wide variety of individual reactions appears to be more closely related to personality differences (including expectations and emotional arousal) and the cultural setting of use than to any specific property of the drug itself. Recognizing this variability, one user remarked that "every person has the dream he deserves."

Even though there are an estimated 200 million users worldwide,[9] predominantly in Africa and Asia, the long-term effects of marihuana use have not been sufficiently studied to permit valid generalization. While physical deterioration, lethargy, and social degradation have been observed among the chronic cannabis users of India and Africa, it has not been established that the deleterious effects were not related to inadequate nutrition, disease, subcultural norms, or other influences.

No research has been done in the United States to establish the presence or absence of a chronic marihuana syndrome. Thus, the absence of a well-defined chronic syndrome among cannabis users at the present time does not establish that marihuana is safe. The extent of long-term ill effects may be determined by the duration and frequency of use, and the potency of the drug abused. The absence of a well-defined chronic syndrome in the United States might be accounted for by restricted availability of the drug, the practice of smoking only to a "controlled" high, or other factors.

Though repeated use of cannabis seems to attract the emotionally unstable, there is presently no adequate evidence that it causes permanent mental disorders. More sophisticated studies will eventually reveal whether marihuana causes changes in the chromosomal patterns (as recently reported with respect to LSD), or other subtle physical changes.

MEDICAL USE

There is no presently accepted medical use for marihuana.[10] In this regard, marihuana differs from the opiate drugs in that the latter are ex-

---

[8] Martin H. Keeler, "Adverse Reaction to Marihuana," *American Journal of Psychiatry,* Volume 124, November 1967, p. 677.

[9] William H. McGlothlin, "Cannabis: A Reference," *The Marihuana Papers,* ed. David Solomon (New York: Bobbs-Merrill Co., 1966), p. 402.

[10] Committee on Alcoholism and Drug Dependence of the American Medical Association, "Dependence on Cannabis (Marihuana)," *Journal of the American Medical Association,* Volume 201, August 7, 1967, p. 108; World Health Organization, Technical Report Series, No. 211, *Eleventh Report of the Expert Committee on Addiction-Producing Drugs* (Geneva, 1961), p. 11.

tensively used to alleviate pain. Marihuana may have some effect as a tonic, diuretic, antibiotic, anticonvulsant, sedative, and pain reliever, but none of these properties is of sufficiently demonstrated effect or reliability to compare favorably with other available drugs. We believe marihuana deserves further experimental investigation.

IS MARIHUANA ADDICTING?

This question generally leads to confusion because there is a discrepancy between the medical, legal, and social definitions of addiction. One can more meaningfully discuss this question of addiction if certain basic drug effects are understood. To consider first the medical viewpoint, a chart has been prepared to provide the reader with a framework for identifying psychoactive drug types and noting their addictive properties (see page 16).

Drug addiction is commonly described medically with respect to the three properties of tolerance, physical dependence, and psychological habituation.[11]

Tolerance is the decreased effect produced with repeated use of a drug, with the result that the original effect can only be obtained by repeatedly increasing the dose. Thus, an opiate addict may require a dose which is several hundred times the normal therapeutic measure in order to achieve a "high." Similarly, he might be immune to the toxic effect of a large dose of opiates which would be sufficient to kill a nontolerant person, such as you or me.

Physical dependence refers to an altered physiological state in which absence of the drug from the body causes illness. In the addicts' language, he has a "habit," or is "hooked." There is a characteristic "withdrawal sickness" for each class of drugs. The two groups of drugs that unequivocally produce physical dependence are the narcotics (opiates) and sedative-hypnotics (barbiturates, minor tranquilizers, and alcohol).[12]

The opiate drugs give rise to a withdrawal sickness resembling influenza with diarrhea, cramps, sweating, muscle aches, and so on, but this sickness infrequently results in death. Sudden alcohol or barbiturate withdrawal is medically more dangerous in that hallucinations, convulsions, and death are not uncommon. With medical supervision, withdrawal from addicting drugs is generally safe and withdrawal symp-

---

[11] John C. Krantz and C. Jelleff Carr, *The Pharmacologic Principles of Medical Practice* (Baltimore: Williams and Wilkins Co., 1958), p. 547; Harris Isbell, "Medical Aspects of Opiate Addiction," *Bulletin of the New York Academy of Medicine,* Volume 31, December 1955, pp. 886–901.

[12] William R. Martin, "Drug Addiction," *Drill's Pharmacology in Medicine,* ed. Joseph R. Di Palma (New York: McGraw-Hill Book Co., 1965), p. 278.

toms are markedly reduced. At the National Institute of Mental Health Clinical Research Center at Lexington, Ky., the withdrawal period from opiate drugs is usually accomplished within 10 days; alcohol and barbiturates often require a longer period of withdrawal.[13]

Psychological dependence (or habituation) refers to a persistent need or craving for a drug, or the conditions associated with its use. Tobacco and coffee are familiar examples of habituation. In the case of "hard narcotics" (the opiate drugs) habituation is marked and accounts, in part, for the relapse of opiate addicts following hospitalization.

Thus, a medical definition of an addicted person is one who will experience withdrawal sickness without the drug, tends to increase the dose as tolerance develops, and has a compelling desire to continue use of the drug. With respect to marihuana, use does not produce physical dependence and rapid tolerance has not been observed.[14] Medically, then, marihuana is best described as habit forming rather than addicting.

Recently the World Health Organization [15] has attempted to resolve the confusion often associated with the words "addiction" and "habituation" by replacing these terms with "drug *dependence*" of a specified type—as "morphine type," or "amphetamine type." In this classification, habitual marihuana use is referred to as "drug dependence of the cannabis type."

Social definitions of drug addiction have included consideration of whether use of a drug is detrimental to the individual or to society. Legal definitions vary according to local, state, or federal jurisdiction. Marihuana is often included in such definitions of addiction.[16]

IS MARIHUANA DANGEROUS?

Unfortunately this question frequently is answered with an impassioned, unqualified "yes" or "no." Marihuana is a pharmacologically potent drug. It is an intoxicant. Small doses may precipitate psychosis

---

[13] Harris Isbell, "Manifestations and Treatment of Addiction to Narcotic Drugs and Barbiturates," *Medical Clinics of North America,* Volume 34, March 1950, pp. 425–438.

[14] Edwin G. Williams, *et al.,* "Studies on Marihuana and Pyrahexyl Compound," *Public Health Reports,* Volume 61, July 19, 1946, pp. 1059–1083; Mayor's Committee on Marihuana, *The Marihuana Problem in the City of New York* (Lancaster, Pennsylvania: The Jaques Cattell Press, 1944), pp. 144–146.

[15] World Health Organization, Technical Report Series, No. 273, *Thirteenth Report of the WHO Expert Committee on Addiction-Producing Drugs* (Geneva, 1964), p. 9.

[16] For a discussion of legal issues, see: William Butler Eldridge, *Narcotics and the Law* (Chicago: American Bar Foundation, 1962).

in the susceptible person.[17] Yet, advocates are of the opinion that marihuana intoxification is a beneficial experience for most users.

We believe that danger exists less in drugs themselves than in their
misdirected use—in the "misuser." Danger, then, must be considered
with regard to the individual user as well as the larger social and cultural
system of which he is a part. False expectations about the properties of
a drug or the need for which it is taken constitute an important part
of the danger liability. Few drugs score so high as marihuana on
unsubstantiated claims attributed to the drug and misguided expectations by the user. Popular myths abound and these are associated with
the reported effects of marihuana use itself. Stripped of its folklore, the
layman's picture of marihuana might be considerably changed.

DOES MARIHUANA LEAD TO CRIME?

The possession or sale of marihuana is a criminal offense in the United
States.[18] Thus, the use of marihuana, in fact, makes one a lawbreaker.

Beyond this, the question arises as to whether marihuana use is
associated with other types of criminal behavior. Does the violation
of marihuana laws predispose or compel an individual to commit other
illegal acts, or does this illicit behavior have no further consequences?

There is no evidence to suggest that marihuana, or any drug, has a
direct causal relationship with criminal behavior in the sense that its
use invariably compels an individual to commit criminal acts. The relationship is more complex as the behavioral consequences depend upon
the age and sex of the user, his mental state and associates, his socioeconomic status, and the extent of his involvement in and identification with
drug abuse as a way of life. In the last instance, it is obviously one thing
to experiment with marihuana smoking once or twice and quite another
thing to habitually use the drug, actively proselyte for initiates, or sell
marihuana for profit.

Habitual use of marihuana is often associated with other illicit acts.
First, many persons who are otherwise delinquent or criminal may also
smoke marihuana. Second, marihuana use is often pursued in a hedonistic peer-group setting in which laws are violated. Third, use of more
dangerous drugs is frequently preceded by the use of marihuana.[19]
On the other hand, use of marihuana is not necessarily associated with
other illicit acts and the extent to which occasional users go on to the

---

[17] Harris Isbell, *et al., op. cit.,* p. 186.

[18] The Marihuana Tax Act [26 U.S.C. Sec. 4741 et seq., (1958)].

[19] John C. Ball, "Marihuana Smoking and the Onset of Heroin Use," *British
Journal of Criminology,* Volume 7, October 1967, pp. 408–413.

CLASSIFICATION OF PSYCHOACTIVE DRUGS, WITH MEDICALLY ADDICTIVE PROPERTIES AND EXAMPLES OF EACH TYPE

Drug Effects*	Opiate Narcotics	Stimulants	Minor Tranquilizers (Sedative hypnotics and depressants)	Major Tranquilizers	Antidepressants	Hallucinogenic (Psychotogenic or "mind expanding")	Cannabis
Physical Dependence	+	−	+	−	−	−	−
Tolerance	+	+	+	−?	−	+	−?
Psychological Dependence	+	+	+	−	−	+	+
Examples of each Drug Type	Heroin Morphine Meperidine (demerol) Methadone (dolophine) Hydromorphine (dilaudid) Codeine Paregoric	Cocaine Amphetamine (dexedrine, benzedrine) Methamphetamine (methedrine)	Barbiturate (pentobarbital, phenobarbital, amytal, seconal) Gluethamide (doriden) Meprobamate (equanil, miltown) Chlordiazepoxide (librium) Chloral hydrate Peraldehyde Alcohol	Phenothiazines (thorazine, mellaril, stelazine)	Imipramine (tofranil) Amitriptyline (elavil)	LSD STP DMT Mescaline (peyote) Psilocybin Morning glory seeds	Marihuana Hashish

* In considering the medically addictive properties of each drug type, "−" represents slight or no effect; "+" that the property is present, and "?" that the effect is not clearly established.

NOTE.—For a further discussion of psychoactive drug effects, see Samuel Irwin, "A Rational Framework for the Development, Evaluation and Use of Psychoactive Drugs," in *Drug Therapy*, Supplement to the *American Journal of Psychiatry*, Volume 124 (February 1968), pp. 1–19.

use of more dangerous drugs or become involved in criminal activity is unknown.

Available evidence suggests that marihuana use in the United States is a type of behavior which is often associated with criminal activity.[20] Although most juvenile delinquents do not go on to become professional criminals, most professional criminals have been delinquents. The question remains, then, as to how many marihuana smokers are involved in a transitory episode of delinquency and how many become enmeshed and committed to a drug oriented way of life.

DOES MARIHUANA USE LEAD TO OPIATE ADDICTION?

We do not know the percent of marihuana users who do not abuse other drugs. We do know that 70 percent of 2,213 opiate addicts admitted to the U.S. Public Health Service Hospitals at Lexington and Fort Worth during 1965 reported a history of marihuana use. From interviews with 337 of these patients, it was found that the dominant sequence of events was marihuana smoking followed by opiate use.[21]

Although marihuana use is neither a necessary nor sufficient condition for opiate addiction, it may be a contributory influence. The self-administration of one illicit drug predisposes the user to try other drugs, especially when this is done in a group setting for hedonistic purposes. Thus, it is not uncommon for the neophyte to be introduced to both marihuana and heroin by the same group of friends:

> *Case No. 211.*—The very first time he tried drugs, it was marihuana. It happened one night . . . he was going out with a couple of friends to a party. One of them got hold of some cigarettes and they decided to try it. At first, he didn't get any "kicks" out of it, but the others seemed so excited, he decided to keep trying it. After that first night they would get together mostly on weekends and smoke marihuana. About 3 months later he tried heroin. (Year of Onset: 1958.)

> *Case No. 147.*—The subject had his first experience with marihuana at age 22 while in New York City after his discharge from the Army.

---

[20] Eli Marcovitz and Henry J. Myers, "The Marihuana Addict in the Army," *War Medicine,* Volume 6, 1944, pp. 382–391; Lee N. Robins and George E. Murphy, "Drug Use in a Normal Population of Young Negro Men," *American Journal of Public Health,* Volume 57, September 1967, pp. 1580–1596; Solomon Kobrin and Harold Finestone, "Drug Addiction Among Young Persons in Chicago," in *Gang Delinquency and Delinquent Subcultures,* James F. Short, Jr., ed. (New York: Harper and Row, 1968), pp. 110–130.

[21] John C. Ball, Carl D. Chambers, and Marion J. Ball, "The Association of Marihuana Smoking With Opiate Addiction in the United States," *Journal of Criminal Law, Criminology and Police Science,* Volume 59, June 1968.

He said he was living in a neighborhood where most of the kids were using marihuana. He was going around with this crowd until one night he decided to try it himself. They went up to one of the fellow's rooms and smoked marihuana. He went on using marihuana almost every day for a couple of months before he used heroin. He used heroin with the same crowd. He said that two of the fellows were heroin addicts, and they were also selling. (Year of Onset: 1954.) [22]

What is not known at present is the long-term effects of continual marihuana use upon the persons who use this drug and who do not graduate to hard narcotics. What will happen to the college student who becomes a daily marihuana user? Is the solitary user different from the more common peer-group abuser? Does continued marihuana use lead to an alienated and nihilistic orientation to life, to hippie deviancy? Is it of no consequence? Or, conversely, does alienation lead to marihuana use?

IS MARIHUANA USE INCREASING?

It appears that marihuana use has increased in the United States considerably during the past 30 years, and particularly during the past several years. With respect to marihuana use among opiate addicts, the evidence suggests that this has increased markedly. The absence of reference to marihuana use in 1928 [23] and the finding in 1937 [24] that only a few Lexington patients had used marihuana before opiates seem significant when contrasted with the dominant pattern of marihuana use followed by opiate abuse reported in recent years. [25]

Newspaper and magazine reports suggest that marihuana use has markedly increased among high school and college students. Although these journalistic accounts cannot be utilized to estimate the extent of marihuana use (incidence rates), police arrest figures for marihuana offenses [26] and clinical reports from school health authorities support

---

[22] John C. Ball, "Marihuana Smoking and the Onset of Heroin Use," paper reported to the Committee on Problems of Drug Dependence, National Academy of Sciences, National Research Council, Lexington, Ky., February 16, 1967.

[23] Charles E. Terry and Mildred Pellens, *The Opium Problem* (New York: Bureau of Social Hygiene, 1928).

[24] Michael J. Pescor, "A Statistical Analysis of the Clinical Records of Hospitalized Drug Addicts," *Public Health Reports,* Supplement No. 143, 1938, pp. 1–30.

[25] Isidor Chein, *et al., The Road to H.* (New York: Basic Books, Inc., 1964), Chapter VI; Robins and Murphy, *loc. cit.*

[26] President's Commission on Law Enforcement and Administration of Justice, *Narcotics and Drug Abuse* (Washington, D.C.: U.S. Government Printing Office, 1967), p. 3.

the observation, as do verbal reports of increasing use of marihuana by America's youth. The extent of this increase is unknown.

CREATIVITY AND MARIHUANA

There appears to be considerable curiosity and an increase in marihuana use among college students. Some users even claim to be striving for Truth. The issue of creativity and marihuana use is such an important and current one that we would like to elaborate our views in this regard.

Some persons "give witness" to creative insights and a new found purpose and zeal in life following drug use. Many users even become "marihuana missionaries." Consider these "natural laws" of a leading missionary, Timothy Leary: [27]

I. Thou shalt not alter the consciousness of thy fellow man.
II. Thou shalt not prevent thy fellow man from altering his own consciousness.

Leary claims he did not invent these commandments:

> They are revealed to me by my nervous system, by ancient, cellular counsel. . . . Ask your DNA code. I urge you to memorize these two commandments. . . . Nothing less than the future of our species depends upon our understanding of and obedience to these two natural laws.[28]

The assertion that marihuana is a mind expander, that it "turns on" creativity, may well turn out to be an insidious liability. While there is some foundation for the view that marihuana produces a *feeling* of creativity, this is quite different from creativity.[29] For example, musicians perceive that they do better when high, but the available evidence suggests just the reverse.[30] If artists' and musicians' fame were dependent upon marihuana-inspired creativity, our belief is that they would for the most part remain unrecognized, save possibly to an audience intoxicated with marihuana.

The ordinary creative process in society, as found in literature, art, music, and science has been viewed as consisting of four stages.[31] (1) A

---

[27] Timothy Leary, "The Politics, Ethics and Meaning of Marijuana," *The Marihuana Papers,* ed. David Solomon (New York: Bobbs-Merrill Co., 1966), p. 90.

[28] *Ibid.,* p. 89.

[29] Williams, *et al., loc. cit.*

[30] C. Knight Aldrich, "The Effect of a Synthetic Marihuana-Like Compound on Musical Talent as Measured by the Seashore Test," *Public Health Reports,* Volume 59, March 31, 1944, pp. 431–433; Williams, *et al., op. cit.,* p. 14.

[31] Eliot D. Hutchinson, *How To Think Creatively* (Nashville: Abingdon Press, 1949), p. 97.

stage of *preparation* often requiring years of effort in the acquisition of technical skills. (2) A stage of *frustration* characterized by rising emotionality, restlessness, feelings of inferiority, neurosis, and even abandonment of the problem for other activities in the sheer defense of emotional balance. (3) A stage, or moment, of *insight* accompanied by a flood of ideas, almost hallucinatory vividness of thought and feelings of exaltation. (4) A stage of *verification,* or confirmation, in which the new found "insight" is checked against external realities and exaggeration and overstatement are modified.

Supposing marihuana *does* cause a feeling which mimics the period of insight of Stage 3 without the genuine work and time required in the creative process. We might then predict that the marihuana user will wish to repeat the pleasant experience for hedonistic purposes, but woe to his attempt to communicate to others the value of drug induced "creative insight."

We believe marihuana may uncover longings for omnipotency and success as well as provide a false sense of self-confidence. This is illustrated in the following recorded experience of an intoxicated person who believed he was creating a great novel:

> "I'm giving you the thoughts; slap them down, we'll make a fortune and go whacks. We'll make a million. . . . Take down everything that is significant—with an accent on the *cant*—Immanuel Kent was a wise man, and I'm a wise man; I am wise, because I'm wise." In spite of all the gabble concerning the volume that was to bring fame and fortune, not even one line was dictated by the inspired author. In fact he never got beyond the title: "Wise is God; God is Wise." [32]

This feeling of accomplishment and superiority was noted in a study of 35 confirmed marihuana users who were failures in the Army.[33] They were referred during World War II for medical treatment because of inadequate performance of their duties. Nonetheless, many of them felt themselves "superior" to their fellow soldiers. In this regard, the following account of the 35 subjects' thoughts and attitudes is pertinent:

> The rest of the world, the "squares," allowed themselves to be limited to the earth, whereas they [the marihuana users] could transcend it. In this they take on the traditional attitude of the creative artist or the "Bohemian" but without the need of even making a pretense of creating. They themselves are the supreme creation, and they do not feel any

---

[32] Victor Robinson, "Experiments With Hashish," *The Marihuana Papers,* ed. David Solomon (New York: Bobbs-Merrill Co., 1966), p. 203.
[33] Marcovitz and Meyers, *loc. cit.*

need to justify their existence by soiling their hands with work. They repeatedly state, "I don't go for work," or "I wasn't cut out for work."

There were repeated statements that marihuana improved their health, increased their strength, enhanced their sexual potency and gave them feelings of power over women and over other challenging situations.[34]

In short, the use of marihuana seemed to enhance their self-image and make them unconcerned with the real world and its dangers.

Some observers report that the use of hallucinogens by college students leads them to feel superior to their professors and to regard examinations as beneath them; the outcome may be that they become college dropouts. Says Leary:

> The new cult of visionaries. They turn on, tune in, and often drop out of the academic, professional and other games-playing roles they have been assigned. They do not drop out of life, but probe more deeply into it, toward personal and social realignments characterized by loving detachment from materialistic goals.[35]

Those who preach that marihuana promotes insight might be opening a Pandora's Box with regard to creativity. We believe this would be especially so if the user has the illusion that marihuana will be a substitute for adequate preparation and the frustrations often associated with the creative process. The assertion that marihuana causes a user to "tune in" and "turn on" a creative experience is no more justified than the statement that marihuana leads one to "fade out" and "turn off" with respect to recognizable creative accomplishment.

The majority of persons of recognized creativity deny the value as well as the use of drugs to assist their creativity.[36] While it is true that some persons do attribute their creativity to drug use, it also appears that such persons have studiously prepared themselves and have been creative *before* the use of drugs.

IS MARIHUANA LESS HARMFUL THAN ALCOHOL AND SHOULD MARIHUANA BE LEGALIZED?

Is marihuana less harmful to the individual and to society than alcohol? Should marihuana be legalized? Arguments have been advanced

---

[34] *Ibid.*, pp. 386, 388.
[35] Leary, *op. cit.*, p. 88.
[36] Hutchinson, *op. cit.*, p. 133.

that the answer to both questions is "yes." [37] While this *might* be the case, we believe sufficient data for such a decision is lacking.

Let us not forget that alcoholism afflicts over 5 million people in the United States and it is one of our most enigmatic social problems. The widespread use and abuse of alcohol is a reality. While we cannot easily change existing folkways and mores concerning the consumption of alcohol, we may have a greater degree of freedom to wisely legislate policy on marihuana.

There has been extensive controversy as to whether the existing legal code pertaining to marihuana use should be changed. Differing views on this subject have been presented by others. [38]

WHAT METHODS OF PREVENTION ARE EFFECTIVE?

This question is often asked. We must say that know-how in prevention is lacking. Most efforts have been directed at the established user with such methods as limiting drug supply, heavy penalties, and long probation for offenders. [39] Unfortunately, insufficient effort has been directed toward the development of methods which would promote more informed opinion among potential drug users. While many states require drug education by law, organized programs are the exception with the result that mass media reports based on personal impressions often go unchallenged as expert opinion.

The last point suggests a potential role for the probation officer. Open discussions and forums with *active* student participation have promise if accurate scientific information is made available. [40] The probation officer, if he is well informed, could be a key person to stimulate such activities and assist as a resource person. General principles of education to follow include the avoidance of preaching and an effort to present

---

[37] *The Marihuana Papers,* ed. David Solomon (New York: Bobbs-Merrill Co., 1966) *passim.*

[38] Foreword, Introduction, and Book One, *The Marihuana Papers;* for an opposite viewpoint, see: Donald E. Miller, "Narcotic Drug and Marihuana Controls," paper presented to the National Association of Student Personnel Administrators Drug Education Conference, Washington, D.C., November 7–8, 1966.

[39] For discussion favoring strong enforcement laws, see: U.S. Treasury Department, Bureau of Narcotics, *Prevention and Control of Narcotics Addiction* (Washington, D.C.: U.S. Government Printing Office, 1966), pp. 23–30.

[40] The following source material is suggested: Helen H. Nowlis, *Drugs on the College Campus* (Detroit, Michigan, National Association of Student Personnel Administrators, 1967); National Education Association, *Drug Abuse: Escape to Nowhere* (Philadelphia: Smith Kline and French Laboratories, 1967); John A. O'Donnell and John C. Ball (eds.), *Narcotic Addiction* (New York: Harper and Row, 1966); Time-Life Special Reports, *The Drug Takers* (New York: Time, Inc., 1965); David P. Ausubel, *Drug Addiction* (New York: Random House, 1958).

information objectively. The World Health Organization has suggested that education improperly done may stimulate rather than prevent abuse.[41] One local health educator reported that "after being scared in a high school assembly program about the evils of narcotics, four girls took up marihuana smoking the following day." [42]

There are the beginnings of a comprehensive health education curriculum for use in public schools.[43] In this approach, marihuana smoking is recognized as a symptom rather than an illness and will be related to the greater drug abuse problem, as well as to the problems of school dropouts, suicide, venereal disease, out-of-wedlock pregnancy, homosexuality, delinquency, and even boredom and unhappiness.

SUMMARY

To recapitulate, the danger liability of marihuana with respect to our society is largely unknown. A danger does exist, however, in that individuals with personality problems often are attracted to abuse of drugs. Frequent reasons given by users for beginning are thrills, boredom, desire for a change, to be one of the gang, curiosity, or because it's illegal. It seems to us that the use of any drug to satisfy transitory needs in an effort to relieve the immediate discomforts of life is a poor substitute for facing reality and building a durable and meaningful way of life.

---

[41] World Health Organization, Technical Report Series, No. 363, *Fourteenth Report of the WHO Expert Committee on Mental Health* (Geneva, 1967), p. 36.

[42] Geoffrey W. Esty, "Preventing Drug Addiction Through Education," *Public Health News,* Volume 47, April 1966, pp. 87–90.

[43] For example, see: San Mateo County Board of Education, *Family Life Education* (Second Revised Working Copy), Redwood City, California, 1967.

SOCIAL AND EPIDEMIOLOGICAL ASPECTS OF MARIHUANA USE

Gilbert Geis

To a sociologist, the marihuana picture today borders on the surrealistic. Much discussion concerns the pharmacological properties of marihuana and the consequences—short- and long-term—of its usage. Additional debate centers about the adequacy and/or fairness of legal sanctions and judicial dispositions for marihuana offenses. Both of these items, however, beg the central issue regarding marihuana use today, an issue that is fundamentally social and epidemiological: It is the fact that respected and respectable people are themselves smoking marihuana or are facing the fact that their children do so or are likely to do so.

It matters not much, I think, whether marihuana will prove to be somewhat more or somewhat less harmful than we now believe it to be. There are things much more dangerous than marihuana that remain well beyond the reach of the criminal law. It may be noted, for instance, that self-indulgence in food presents considerably more serious problems for

Reprinted from *Journal of Psychedelic Drugs* 2 (Fall 1968): 67–77, with the permission of the publisher. Originally presented at the Illinois State Medical Society National Symposium on Psychedelic Drugs and Marihuana, Chicago, Illinois, April 11, 1968.

the well-being of our society than use of marihuana. Overweight people kill themselves prematurely, make poor soldiers, and waste valuable commodities. Yet nobody seriously proposes the creation of new crimes, labeled first- and second-degree obesity, or the establishment of an S.S. corps (for Supermarket Surveillance), or restrictions on the import of Israeli halvah, Swiss chocolate, or Italian spaghetti, items poisoning the bloodstream of our population, and making us vulnerable targets for a foreign takeover.

What does matter, excruciatingly so, is that marihuana is becoming embedded as part of the way of life of obviously responsible, obviously otherwise conforming persons. The implications of the epidemiological situation pose problems regarding tactical withdrawal from an entrenched moral position. Our problem with marihuana is not unlike (if a political aside may be permitted) the long-standing problem of our official position in Vietnam. It is not by chance alone, in this respect, that Congressional attention has to be drawn in recent months to the supposedly high rate of marihuana use among American troops in Vietnam. Like sex indulged in under the banner of tomorrow-we-die-on-the-battlefield, marihuana use by combat troops raises delicate questions of a "moral armistice," in the manner that terminal cancer patients are permitted to have as much morphine or LSD as is necessary for their comfort. Presumably, as graduate students are drafted in large numbers into the armed forces, the marihuana problem will become aggravated; perhaps films such as "The Menace of Marihuana" will replace those on venereal disease as leading candidates for military cinema Oscars.

HOW THINGS WENT TO POT

It hardly needs saying that the precise parameters of marihuana usage are very difficult to locate. The well-publicized episode of a 58-year-old elementary school principal in a northern California town who recently told a legislative committee that it had been her habit for the past 18 years to come home from the classroom to a puff of pot illustrates what is undoubtedly a widespread phenomenon of regular and undetected marihuana usage. In the same vein is the story of a California law school dean who suggested that the statutes against marihuana would undoubtedly be repealed within the next ten years. It was his understanding that a large number of his students were currently using marihuana, and his presumption that many of these persons would be elected to the state legislature in coming years.

Anecdotal material does not, however, provide adequate fare for an epidemiological inventory regarding marihuana. Such an inventory might begin by noting that Chinese and Indian sources report on the presence of marihuana as far back as the 1300's. The drug was adopted in literary, intellectual, and artistic circles in Europe about 1800. It then made its way to Latin-America and Mexico, but was virtually unknown in the United States until the 1920's.

Enactment of the Marihuana Tax Act in 1937 clearly set the ground rules for official handling of the drug. In 1930, when the Federal Bureau of Narcotics was established, only 16 states had outlawed marihuana, and theirs were relatively mild prescriptions, rarely enforced.[1] In 1933, the ill-fated Volstead Act and Prohibition were abandoned, though by 1937, virtually all states had declared marihuana illegal. The Congressional hearings in that year on the Marihuana Tax Act represent illustrations of the federal legislative process at its poorest; with single-minded dedication committee members moved from an untenable set of original postulates to a fallacious set of preordained conclusions, making certain to push aside any refractory material along the way.[2]

Fundamental to passage of the Marihuana Tax Act and to state laws was an unstated linkage between marihuana and the behavior and repute of groups then using the drug in the United States. As we shall see, acts viewed as unattractive, family patterns seen as unappetizing, and similar conditions believed to be unesthetic, items which were indigenous to Negro and Spanish-speaking groups, were implicitly related to the presence of marihuana. It was the same process by which the idiosyncracies of the aberrant in other times and other places have been tied to such things as their style of dress, their heresies, and their ceremonies. Today, in similar manner, campaigns against crime in the streets often represent camouflaged methods for retaliatory tactics against minority group members, who most often commit such crimes, but against whom frontal assaults are no longer fashionable.

THE LITTLE FLOWER AND POT

Mayor Fiorello LaGuardia of New York City, while serving in the House of Representatives, had been impressed by testimony that use of

---

[1] David Solomon, "Marihuana Myths," in Solomon, ed., *The Marihuana Papers,* Bobbs-Merrill, Indianapolis, 1966, p. xv.

[2] U.S. House of Representatives, Committee on Ways and Means, Hearings on the Taxation of Marihuana, 75th Cong., 1st Sess., 1937. See also: Joseph S. Oteri and Harvey A. Silverglate, "In the Marketplace of Free Ideas: A Look at the Passage of the Marihuana Tax Act," in J. L. Simmons, *Marihuana: Myths and Realities,* Brandon House, North Hollywood, Calif., 1967, pp. 136–162; and Howard S. Becker, *"The Marihuana Tax Act,"* in *The Outsiders: Studies in the Sociology of Deviance,* Free Press, New York, 1963, pp. 595–846.

marihuana among troops in Panama posed no serious problem either
to mental health or discipline. Given this background, LaGuardia tended
to doubt the horror stories regarding marihuana, and he therefore arranged for a medically-supervised investigation of the subject. The
subsequent report of the work of the Mayor's Committee, begun in 1939
and published in 1944, provides by far the best epidemiological material
we have on marihuana for this period.

Field work for the sociological segment of the Mayor's Committee
report was undertaken, oddly enough, by six officers from the Narcotic
Squad of the police department. Their investigation was directed toward
answering six questions. The first two concerned the extent of marihuana
usage in New York and the method by which marihuana was distributed.
They found use heaviest in Harlem and secondarily in one section of
midtown Manhattan, although marihuana was employed somewhat in
other areas of the city as well. Most of the users were either Negro or
Latin-American, were in their twenties, and were unemployed. There
were an estimated 500 peddlers in Harlem, and about 500 "tea-pads"
where marihuana was consumed on the premises.

The third question dealt with how users viewed marihuana. The smokers felt that it made them feel better and that it was not harmful in any
way. Persons would voluntarily cease using marihuana for long periods
without signs of discomfort. Finally, it did not appear that marihuana
served as a stepping-stone to heroin or other addictive drugs.

Because of claims that marihuana use was responsible for sexual
degeneracy and sex crimes, the field workers looked for possible relationships between marihuana and eroticism. They found none. The
evidence also failed to substantiate the existence of a causal relationship
between marihuana use and crime. In cases where an individual both
smoked marihuana and engaged in crime, it appeared that the criminal
activity came first. Finally, the study looked into the relationship between
marihuana use and juveniles. It found very little marihuana use in the
New York high schools or junior high schools, and no tendency for
juvenile delinquency to develop out of the little use there was. The
report on the sociological segment of the study concluded that "the publicity concerning the catastrophic effects of marihuana smoking in New
York City is unfounded." [3]

Issued almost midway in the second World War, the sound and so-

---

[3] See Dudley D. Shoenfeld, "The Sociological Study," in *Mayor's Committee on
Marihuana, New York City,* Cattell Press, Lancaster, Pa., 1944, pp. 1–25. The summary of the report has been taken in large measure from the excellent presentation
by David O. Arnold, "The Meaning of the LaGuardia Report: The Effects of Marihuana," in Simmons, *op. cit.,* pp. 111–135.

phisticated material in the Mayor's Committee report has never received the careful attention it merits, though its conclusions regarding the non addictive qualities of marihuana are widely-known.

Both support for and perversion of the approach of the Mayor's Committee is, however, nicely illustrated by a number of wartime studies of marihuana use by military personnel. All, for instance, note a disproportionate number of Negroes among marihuana users referred to neuropsychiatric services. In a study of patients at Fort McClellan Alabama, for instance, 55 were Negroes, one white;[4] all but one of the 35 marihuana cases at March Air Field Base in California were Negroes, and 95 percent of the marihuana cases among servicemen in India were also Negroes.[6]

The Fort McClellan study illustrates, as well as anything might, the ofttimes feudal and futile process of generalizing from a sample whose characteristics are not measured by adequate sampling or control techniques. Thus, for instance, the Fort McClellan researchers concluded that "the preponderance of Negroes is due, we believe, to the peculiar need marihuana serves for them." Marihuana, they felt, "enables the Negro addict to feel a sense of mastery denied him by his color,"[7] a conclusion made somewhat less than prescient by the spread of use today to persons who possess an obvious sense of mastery of both themselves and the world about them.[8] In addition, the Fort McClellan study went on to detail a panorama of personal and background horrors found among the users that, three decades later, sounds like nothing more than a description of life and its consequences for a large part of the population of the Negro ghetto.

The LaGuardia report and the clinical material from the military doctors have been further supplemented by studies of marihuana use among jazz musicians, members of an occupational group that perhaps more than any other has traditionally been associated with a pattern of heavy recourse to drugs.

A study by Winick indicates that jazz musicians were heavy users

---

[4] Sol Charen, and Luis Perelman, "Personality Studies of Marihuana Addicts," *American Journal of Psychiatry,* Vol. 102, March 1946, pp. 674–682.

[5] Eli Marcovitz and Henry J. Myers, "The Marihuana Addict in the Army," *War Medicine,* Vol. 6, December 1944, pp. 382–391.

[6] Herbert S. Gaskill, "Marihuana, An Intoxicant," *American Journal of Psychiatry,* Vol. 102, September 1945, pp. 202–294.

[7] Charen and Perelman, *op. cit.,* p. 674.

[8] "Fifteen percent of the students at Princeton admit smoking pot—two-thirds of them in the upper academic 20 percent, a third of them members of varsity athletic teams." Antoni Gollan, "The Great Marihuana Problem," *National Review,* Vol. 20, No. 4, January 30, 1968, p. 78.

of alcohol in the early years of this century, but moved toward marihuana during the 1930's. Following the second World War, however, heroin began to gain popularity. From interviews conducted during 1954 and 1955 with 357 jazz musicians, whose average age was 33, regarding the drug use habits of their colleagues, Winick estimated that 82 percent had used marihuana at least once, 54 percent were occasional users, and 23 percent were regular users. More than half had tried heroin, 24 percent used it occasionally, and 16 percent regularly. Though a majority of the musicians tended to believe that marihuana hindered rather than improved performing ability, a number pointed out that use of the drug seemed necessary for them to face the demands of their job; that without it they would be unable to perform at all. The study also indicated that marihuana may aid in buttressing occupational solidarity and insularity. If true, for instance, the story often told Winick that a jazz band had performed such marihuana-euphemistic numbers as "Tea for Two" and "Tumbling Tumbleweed" at a police benefit dance must have been a source for great ingroup merriment.[9]

Using a similar group of subjects, interspersed with marihuana users other than musicians, Becker has contributed the view that contained recourse to marihuana depends upon a sequential series of events, beginning with learning to smoke the drug in a manner which will produce real effects and proceeding to learning to enjoy the perceived sensations. "In short," Becker suggests, "the marihuana user learns to answer 'Yes' to the question: Is it fun?" The further direction that his drug experience will take then comes to depend upon intervening factors, including such things as moral judgments, availability, arrest, and social reactions.[10]

OUT OF THE FRYING POT

It is only in the past year that we have acquired adequate longitudinal information with which to examine the continuing careers of persons in the lower socio-economic class who have constituted the bulk of marihuana users until very recent times. This information comes from a St. Louis study by Robins and Murphy which indicated more widespread use of marihuana than many persons had suspected as well as a striking diminution of marihuana use with advancing age.

---

[9] Charles Winick, "The Use of Drugs by Jazz Musicians," *Social Problems,* Vol. 3, Winter 1959–1960, pp. 240–253; Winick, "Marihuana Use by Young People," in Ernest Harms, ed., *Drug Addiction in Youth,* Pergamon Press, New York, 1965, pp. 19–35.

[10] Howard S. Becker, "Becoming a Marihuana User," *American Journal of Sociology,* Vol. 59, November 1953, pp. 235–242.

Study subjects were young Negro men who had been born in St. Louis between 1930 and 1934, had attended local elementary schools, and were residing in St. Louis in 1966. Of the 221 persons interviewed in the study, 109 had tried at least one of four drugs during his life; 103 had used marihuana, 28 had used heroin, 37 had used amphetamines, and 32 had used barbiturates. It is noteworthy that all the heroin addicts, as distinguished from heroin experimenters, had arrest records, and that all addicts admitted their heroin use to study interviewers who themselves were previously unaware of it. In regard to marihuana, only a very small percentage of either occasional or regular users had ever come to the attention of the police. It is notable that half of the marihuana users had never employed any other drug, that three out of four of the heroin users began with marihuana, and that one out of four of the marihuana users began with the drug prior to his sixteenth birthday. Sixty-nine percent had begun using by the time they were twenty years old, and only nine percent from age 24 and afterwards.[11]

During the year preceding that in which they were interviewed, twenty-two of the men (about ten percent) reported that they had used drugs. Three had used heroin, while a fourth, then imprisoned, had been using heroin prior to his arrest.[12]

The drug use rate uncovered by the St. Louis investigation may be slightly inflated by omission of rural and small town migrants, but it indicates nonetheless a quite pervasive pattern of marihuana use among a minority group in a midwestern city where drugs are not considered as notable a problem as they are in seaports and Mexican border cities.

WEED-FILLED RECREATION SITES

Marihuana use today has obviously moved from its concentration among socially and economically segregated segments of our population into our demographic mainstream. The spread of marihuana to the middle and upper strata of the society is, however, a quite recent phenomenon, one that makes the most penetrating numeration outdated in short order. As a *recent* magazine recently put the matter: "Statistics on the problem are non-existent, and its extent is tough to gauge. School officials normally ignore it or hush it up; students with first-hand knowledge are prone to boastful exaggeration; arrests are relatively rare." [13]

---

[11] Lee Robins and George E. Murphy, "Drug Use in a Normal Population of Young Negro Men," *American Journal of Public Health,* Vol. 57, September 1967, pp. 158–159.

[12] *Ibid.,* p. 158.

[13] "The Pot Problem," *Time Magazine,* March 12, 1965, p. 49.

Despite this situation, however, we do have some information regarding marihuana use currently that provides underpinning for observations about the direction in which such usage is likely to proceed.

It is necessary, first, to continue to look at lower socio-economic groups, partly because they constitute so heavy a usage enclave, and partly because they provide the liaison to marihuana use in other segments of the society.

The clearest insight into present drug customs in deprived areas must certainly be that reported by Blumer and his colleagues last year. Blumer's work had been designed to induce youthful drug users to abstain from further usage, a mission in which it totally failed. "The real reason for the lack of success," Project workers noted, "was the strong collective belief held by the youths that their use of drugs was not harmful and their ability to put up effective arguments, based usually on personal experience and observation, against claims of such harm." [14]

Frustrated by reformers, the Project team decided to become researchers. As such, by their rather immodest appraisal, they were pre-eminently successful. "We believe," they write, "that we have penetrated more deeply and fully into an analysis of the world of youthful drug users than is true of any published accounts."

Two major types of drug users were identified among youths in the Oakland flatlands, an area populated primarily by lower-class Negroes and Mexican-Americans, where the Project was run. These youths were labeled either as *rowdy* or as *cool*. Rowdies, a small minority of youths, were aggressive, used any and all drugs, but preferred alcohol. Cool youths fell into three types. There were the pot heads (or weed heads), the mellow dudes, and the players. Mellow dudes, by far the most prevalent group, would "try anything once" but did not seek out drugs. Their orientation was hedonistic, their pleasures primarily sexual. They used pills and crystals (methamphetamine hydrochloride or methedrine) as well as marihuana.

The pot head, member of a sizeable group, is exclusively a user of marihuana. He has been described in the following terms:

> He uses no drugs other than marihuana and may even prefer soda-pop to drinking alcohol. He is respected by other adolescents, presenting an image of a calm, sensible, solitary figure, soft-spoken, personable, and thoroughly knowledgeable about what is "happening" in the adolescent world. He takes pride in his appearance, always wearing sharp

---

[14] Herbert Blumer, Alan Sutter, Samir Ahmed, and Roger Smith, *The World of Youthful Drug Use,* Add Center Project Final Report, School of Criminology, University of California, Berkeley, January 1967.

slacks and sweaters, is interested in taking things easy, having a good time, and fostering relations with the opposite sex. He is likely to be involved in conventional life activities, participating in various school functions, athletics, and conventional work.[15]

The pot head is apt to smoke a joint when he awakens, and a second after breakfast, after he has "eaten his high away." A third cigarette might be used in the early afternoon and others in the evening, depending upon the social agenda. Like members of all types of youthful drug users, the pot head looks down on heroin addicts as persons who have "blown their cool."

Initiation into marihuana use by pot heads was regarded by the Project researchers as something other than a fulfillment of a personality predisposition or a motivational syndrome. Various conditions were found to keep the neophyte from access to drugs, primarily conditions relating to others' estimate of his integrity and his "coolness." Many pot heads were "turned on" by older brothers, intent upon preventing them from "sniffing glue, drinking wine, or risking the chance of being arrested." [16]

Finally, the Oakland study team assailed standard personality theories of drug use, finding them "ridiculous." It is "primarily the defining response of associates that leads to the formation of whatever motives may be attached to drug use," it was claimed. The study evidence was said to show "overwhelmingly that the great majority of youngsters become users not to escape reality but rather as a means of embracing reality" in a setting where drug use is extensive and deeply-routed.[17] It was the guess of the research team that most pot heads would be assimilated into conventional life as adults, though their drug experience might lead a few of them into more serious narcotics involvement.

Further light has been shed on the subsequent careers of young dangerous drug users by a follow-up study of a selective group, 866 persons under 18 arrested for the first time on a non-opiate drug charge during 1960 and 1961 by the Los Angeles Police. Subsequent arrest records of each person were examined from the date of his initial apprehension through the following five years.

Of the 866 youths, 58 percent had no subsequent recorded arrest for drug involvement. Thirty percent were subsequently arrested on marihuana and/or dangerous drug charges only (the same offense for which they had initially been apprehended). Only 12 percent of the youths

[15] *Ibid.*, p. 79.
[16] *Ibid.*, p. 49.
[17] *Ibid.*, p. 59.

were subsequently arrested for opiate involvement. These findings contradict the notion that later opiate use is necessarily a consequence of marihuana or dangerous drug involvement.[18]

WHERE THE GRASS IS GREENER

Given the heavy saturation of segments of lower class life with the marihuana use in the past decade, it is likely that the striking recent increase in police seizures of marihuana [19] and the skyrocketing arrest rates for marihuana offenses, represent at least in considerable measure the movement of middle and upper class citizens into marihuana use. Much less well studied to date, this group nonetheless, as indicated at the outset, presents the major ideological challenge to marihuana laws, and the major rebuff to traditional explanations of marihuana use.

A general overview of available epidemiological material by Yolles indicates that perhaps 20 percent of high school and college students have had some experience with marihuana. More men than women students report involvement, and of those students reporting use 65 percent say they smoked marihuana fewer than ten times, with the most common response being "once or twice." It was noted as particularly interesting that fully 50 percent of the students who had tried marihuana indicated that they experience no effects from it. Four explanations were offered for the situation: (1) the agent may not have been potent, (2) frequently effects are seen only after repeated use, (3) the expectation of the user has a significant effect on what he experiences, and (4) the social setting in which use takes place has an effect on the response.[20]

More detailed information than that supplied by Yolles may be gained from surveys of drug use patterns among high school students on either coast of the United States. In a study at two senior high schools in Great Neck, New York, an affluent suburb with a school system considered among the best in the nation, some 207 of 2,587 students

---

[18] Dimitri Polonsky, George F. Davis, and Chester F. Roberts, Jr., *A Follow-Up Study of the Juvenile Drug Offender,* Institute for the Study of Crime and Delinquency, Sacramento, October 1967, p. ix.

[19] Bulk seizures of marihuana by federal enforcement authorities totaled 5,641 kilograms in 1965, as against 1,871 kilograms in 1960. President's Commission on Law Enforcement and Administration of Justice, *Challenge of Crime in a Free Society,* Government Printing Office, Washington, D.C., February 1967, p. 213.

[20] Stanley F. Yolles, "Statement on LSD, Marihuana, and Other Dangerous Drugs," Statement to U.S. Senate, Committee on the Judiciary, Subcommittee on Juvenile Delinquency, March 6, 1968, pp. 14–15.

(8 percent) self-reported smoking marihuana. Fifty-five had tried LSD.[21] On the West Coast, in a senior class of a high school in San Mateo County, California, more than twenty-five percent of 288 boys and almost ten percent of 220 girls reported that they had used marihuana at least once, with more than half of both groups indicating use on three or more occasions. It is interesting in this connection that the San Mateo survey made note of the following item:

—There is less accurate and less medical information about marihuana than any of the other dangerous drugs or narcotics.
—Youth do not trust adults' information regarding marihuana.
—Many youth maintain that the use of marihuana is no more harmful, and probably less harmful, than the use of alcoholic beverages.[22]

It is also interesting in connection with the high school surveys that a recent Harris Poll indicates that only five percent of the nation's parents report knowing a teenager who smokes marihuana, and that of all activities, the smoking of marihuana is forbidden for their own children more than any other, with 85 percent of the parents saying that they would forbid marihuana, against 84 percent who would ban LSD, 70 percent who would rule out drinking hard liquor, and 66 percent who would object to a two-week trip alone by the youngster.[23]

It may be, though, we have no tight information on the subject as yet, that a disproportionate number of the high school drug users do not matriculate. Among those most deeply-immersed into drug culture, some may migrate to such renowned citadels as the Haight-Ashbury district in San Francisco, where research is currently being undertaken to gain a profile of summer transients and permanent residents. Preliminary Haight-Ashbury reports, incidentally, indicate that the largest amount of marihuana use occurs among persons regularly using methedrine. Such persons employ marihuana to put themselves in a more tranquil condition after recurrent methedrine experiences or, in their terms, at the "end of a run." It is the methedrine group as well that reports in Haight-Ashbury the highest rate of personal problems as such problems are measured by prior contact with or referral to psychiatric services [24] though it is possible, research logicians would note, that the

---

[21] United Press International, February 16, 1967.

[22] Juvenile Justice Commission, *Narcotics Inquiry Report for San Mateo County,* November 16, 1967, p. 5.

[23] *Los Angeles Times,* March 4, 1968.

[24] David E. Smith and J. Fred E. Shick, "Marihuana and Its Relationship to Other Drug Practices," paper presented at National Marijuana Symposium, San Francisco, March 24, 1968.

psychiatric experiences drove the youths to methedrine rather than that a preexisting disordered state led both to psychiatric referral and to later drug use.

The sparse data available on marihuana use in colleges also indicates a dropping off from the rates among high school seniors at the surveyed schools. A news report has indicated that, on some basis, it was decided that 15 percent of the student body at the University of Miami had had some experience with marihuana and that 8 percent of the total group had used marihuana more than ten times.[25] More useful is the result reported by McGlothlin and Cohen of a questionnaire profile of 121 male graduate students responding to an advertisement for study subjects in January 1965. Thirteen of the respondents indicated some experience, generally of an infrequent nature, with marihuana. The advertisement, it should be noted, gave no indication that the experimenters were interested in drug issues, though it is still not unlikely that there could have been a significant under-reporting because of possible loss of the opportunity to acquire work. In either case, the current nature of our information on marihuana use by college students is clearly inadequate and obviously colored for the *New York Times.* Four years ago, he writes, a Harvard student turned in his roommate to the authorities for smoking marihuana in order to save him. Today, "it would be embarrassing for a student to admit that he hadn't at least tried pot—just as it would be embarrassing to admit that he was a virgin." [26]

SUMMARY: POTPOURRI

Our analysis suggests that early and continued use by dispossessed elements in American society may have contributed to the present legal position of the drug, just as it suggests that shifts in use patterns may be contributing to a re-examination of that position. It has not been our intention to reargue well-argued polemical points regarding the proper position for the law, the medical profession, or the lay public to take regarding official policies on marihuana or personal use of the drug. Rather we have attempted to marshall what concrete data exists concerning the social and epidemiological nature of marihuana usage, and to let that material speak for itself. Ultimately, of course, the attitude that society chooses to take regarding marihuana must emerge from a

---

[25] Reuter's March 18, 1968.
[26] William H. McGlothlin and Sidney Cohen, "The Use of Hallucinogenic Drugs Among College Students," *American Journal of Psychiatry,* Vol. 122, November 1965, pp. 572–574.

weighing of unquantifiable values. It is only worth noting, in concluding, that that attitude itself will then become, as it has been in the past, one of the most important items shaping the epidemiological patterns and the consequences of such patterns in regard to marihuana use.

CANNABIS

*Advisory Committee on
Drug Dependence*

CANNABIS AND ITS CLINICAL FEATURES

Cannabis is the generic name of Indian hemp (C.Sativa). Cannabis drugs are obtained from the unfertilized flowering tops and the leaves of the plant, which can be grown in climates varying from temperate to tropical. Cannabis Sativa is one species which may be divided into two groups: (i) C.Indica, which is grown in the Indian sub-continent or from seeds originating there, and (ii) C.non-Indica, which originates and is grown elsewhere. The potency does not differ as between these groups, provided that the conditions in which they are grown are the same. To yield a potent drug a high temperature and low humidity are necessary, and these conditions are seldom available naturally in the United Kingdom.

There are many local names for preparations of cannabis, e.g. the dried leaves may be termed marihuana, or dagga; the resin obtained from

---

Reprinted from *Cannabis,* London, 1968, pp. 5–16 with the permission of the Controller of Her Brittannic Majesty's Stationery Office.

the flowering tops is usually called hashish, or charras. The Anglo-Saxon countries also have an extensive and continually changing vocabulary.

Cannabis contains a number of identifiable constituents. Recent research indicates that the tetrahydrocannabinols (THC) are active principles: some have been shown to be highly potent. . . .

Clinical Features

In the following paragraphs we try to portray, so far as possible in layman's language, the effects of cannabis smoking (a) in moderation, (b) in excessive use on a particular occasion, leading to acute intoxication, and (c) in chronic use. This digest reflects the experience of a number of different cultures. In Section III we try to relate United Kingdom experience to this picture.

The effects of drugs which act upon the central nervous system are not determined solely by the drug and its dose. They are dependent also upon the person taking it, upon the immediate setting in which it is taken, and upon the cultural background. These are liable, in certain persons and in certain situations, to produce unexpected effects. Any account of the effects of a drug can only be fully appreciated if this possibility is borne in mind. Some people can even take opiates regularly and become physically dependent on them without obvious deterioration in their health or social efficiency.

The response to cannabis may vary according to the form in which it is taken, and to the dose consumed. Where it is smoked, the effect normally comes on within half an hour, and lasts for two or three hours. When it is taken by mouth the onset is delayed sometimes up to two or three hours, and the effect may last twice as long. Because of the relatively rapid onset when the drug is smoked, experienced smokers can adjust their dosage to achieve the effect that they seek. When the drug is taken by mouth this adjustment is less easy to achieve. Apart from these considerations there does not appear to be any significant difference in effect between the many different forms of cannabis that are used throughout the world.

The taking of cannabis does not normally result in any characteristic physical effects except that of redness of the eyes. When the drug is smoked there may be some initial rawness and burning in the throat, and tightness in the chest. Upon occasions, particularly when the subject is initially anxious, headache may result. There may be nausea and vomiting. Once the effect of the drug has worn off there may be an increase in appetite, even ravenous hunger. There have been isolated reports in which death has been attributed to cannabis, but these are very rare and their validity cannot be confirmed.

The effects of cannabis in moderate amounts are predominantly psychological. They begin with a sense of excitement or tension, sometimes with apprehension or hilarity, followed as a rule by a sense of heightened awareness: colours, sounds and social intercourse appear more intense and meaningful. A sense of well-being is then usual. After this a phase of tranquility and of passive enjoyment of the environment normally follows until, after a few hours, fatigue sets in and the subject sleeps. Although a "hangover" may follow this is not a common occurrence.

When the amount consumed is more considerable, or the subject is of a nervous disposition, or in an uncongenial social setting, symptoms of anxiety may be the first effects. These may be expected to settle, and the subject enters the euphoric or the passive state described above. On occasions, however, the anxiety may mount and symptoms suggestive of a deluded state ensue. As a rule these effects are not overwhelmingly intense. In most cases the subject retains his sense of contact with reality and remains aware of the fact that he is under the influence of a drug whose effects will pass off. On rarer occasions, usually with a heavy oral administration, the disturbance may be more profound.

The untoward effects of over-dosage as described above appear, in the great majority of cases, to pass off uneventfully as the drug clears from the system. They would be described in medical language as a toxic psychosis. There have been reports of a psychotic state persisting longer, even in rare cases giving place to what appears to be a prolonged schizophrenic illness, but it is difficult from these reports to assess the exact role of the cannabis in these circumstances.

Having reviewed all the material available to us we find ourselves in agreement with the conclusion reached by the Indian Hemp Drugs Commission appointed by the Government of India (1893–1894) and the New York Mayor's Committee on Marihuana (1944), that the long-term consumption of cannabis in *moderate* doses has no harmful effects.[1]

There have been reports, particularly from experienced observers in the Middle and Far East, which suggest that *very heavy long-term* consumption may produce a syndrome of increasing mental and physical deterioration to the point where the subject is tremulous, ailing and

---

[1] "The moderate use (of hemp drugs) practically produces no ill effects. In all but the most exceptional cases, injury from habitual moderate use is not appreciable"—Indian Hemp Drugs Commission.

"From the study as a whole, it is concluded that marihuana is not a drug of addiction, comparable to morphine, and that if tolerance is acquired, this is of a very limited degree. Furthermore those who have been smoking marihuana for a period of years showed no mental or physical deterioration which may be attributed to the drug"—New York Mayor's Committee.

socially incompetent. This syndrome may be punctuated on occasions with outbursts of violent behaviour. It is fair to say, however, that no reliable observations of such a syndrome have been made in the Western World, and that from the Eastern reports available to us it is not possible to form a judgment on whether such behaviour is directly attributable to cannabis-taking.

In Western society cannabis is sometimes taken with other drugs. There is no evidence to suggest that cannabis in man in customary doses enhances the effect of other drugs. When combined with another drug, cannabis in man does not cause this to exert an effect quantitatively greater than that which would result from the use of that drug alone in the same dosage; when cannabis is used with other drugs such as L.S.D., or occasionally alcohol, it is their effects, rather than those of cannabis, which predominate. Some persons who have taken L.S.D. frequently are apt to get a recrudescence of the hallucinogenic experience as a consequence sometimes of quite small doses of cannabis.

Those who believe that there is a syndrome of chronic excessive cannabis-taking describe symptoms of physical deterioration such as yellowing of the skin, tremor, wasting and unsteadiness of gait. Here again it is very difficult to make a confident judgment as to the role played by the drug and the changes brought about by other factors such as malnutrition. There is no evidence that in Western society serious physical dangers are directly associated with the smoking of cannabis.

CANNABIS IN THE UNITED KINGDOM

Prevalence

In 1956 the United Nations Commission on Narcotic Drugs observed that it was clear that consumers of cannabis, as of opium, numbered millions in the world, and that geographically it was the most widespread drug of addiction.[2] Few countries have published numerical estimates of consumers or consumption, preferring to rely on such data as the quantities of drug seized and the number of convictions, for demonstrating the nature of their cannabis "problem." These details often reflect altered emphasis in enforcement and are not a reliable guide to scale or trends, without supplementary evidence about what is not being detected.

Our witnesses considered that there had been a gradual growth in cannabis use in the United Kingdom over the past 20 years, and the

---

[2] Official Records of the Economic and Social Council, Twenty-second Session, Supp. No. 8 (E/2891), para. 133.

relevant statistics so far as they go are consistent with this. The following table shows the numbers of convictions for cannabis offences and of seizures by H.M. Customs and Excise, and the amounts seized, in each year since the end of the Second World War:

	Convictions	No. of Customs Seizures	Amounts Seized *
			Kg
1945	4	4	0
1946	10	?	2
1947	42	?	8
1948	46	32	13
1949	60	38	25
1950	79	65	41
1951	127	46	48
1952	87	70	19
1953	83	44	27
1954	144	68	118
1955	115	48	82
1956	103	37	114
1957	51	36	237
1958	99	32	101
1959	185	36	282
1960	235	84	126
1961	288	66	107
1962	588	60	105
1963	663	68	150
1964	544	96	336
1965	626	84	250
1966	1,119	72	258
1967*	2,393	87	192

* Before 1967 amounts seized by the police were not comprehensively recorded and do not figure in the table. In 1967 the total amount of cannabis involved in 2,734 prosecutions was 102–681 Kg. and 457 cannabis plants. The weights shown are simple aggregations of reported quantities of herb and resin.

In the early part of the period, most seizures were of green plant tops, found in ships from Indian and African ports and thought to be destined for petty traffickers in touch with coloured seamen and entertainers in London docks and clubs. By 1950 illicit traffic in cannabis had been observed in other parts of the country where there was a coloured population. In 1950, however, police raids on certain London jazz clubs produced clear evidence that cannabis was being used by the indigenous population; by 1954 the tendency for the proportion of white to coloured offenders to increase was well marked, and in 1964 white persons constituted the majority of cannabis offenders for the first time. The recent trend can be seen from the following figures:

Cannabis offenders	1963	1964	1965	1966	1967
White	296	284	400	767	1,737
Coloured	367	260	226	352	656

Several witnesses discounted the significance of immigrant influence on cannabis-use, and asserted that international movement of young people and new attitudes to experimentation with mood-altering drugs were the main explanation of increased cannabis use by white persons in the United Kingdom since 1945.

> The Times advertisement on 24th July 1967 claimed that
> "The use of cannabis is increasing, and the rate of increase is accelerating. Cannabis smoking is widespread in the universities, and the custom has been taken up by writers, teachers, doctors, businessmen, musicians, artists and priests. . . . Smoking the herb also forms a traditional part of the social and religious life of hundreds and thousands of immigrants to Britain. . . . Uncounted thousands of frightened persons have been arbitrarily classified as criminals. . . ."

We invited witnesses to estimate the numbers of people who had tried cannabis and of those who used it regularly. Only guesses were forthcoming and these ranged between 30,000 and 300,000. We could find no basis for constructing estimates of our own. It is clear from the convictions recorded that such use of cannabis as there is, is widely spread throughout the country. Most witnesses felt that cannabis-use would continue to be popular and to spread for some time yet. As to speed of growth, we doubt whether the annual doubling of convictions in 1966 and 1967 reflects a corresponding growth in the use of cannabis in that period. One explanation might be that the formation of drug squads in many police areas in the past three years has been responsible for more successful police action against cannabis offenders than previously.

Supply

The annual volume of seizures by the Customs has been fairly steady over the past decade or so. Individual cases have shown that large supplies have been brought in by highly organised smuggling. According to witnesses, however, there is also a substantial traffic in small amounts carried by persons returning from holidays abroad, or sent—mainly to immigrants—by post from their home countries. Several witnesses felt that "amateur" smuggling was now becoming more organised, with a more standardized drug in the illicit market. Lebanon, Pakistan and Cyprus were mentioned as major sources. It was suggested that hashish now formed some eighty per cent of the traffic.

Within the United Kingdom, we were told, the competition of the "amateur" smuggler has made the illicit traffic a very loosely organised and often casual activity not exploited to any significant extent by professional criminals. We were informed that the price of cannabis on the illicit market has shown little fluctuation in recent years beyond what might be expected for varying quality, and that there has been no shortage of supplies.

Users

All our witnesses were agreed that cannabis-smoking in the United Kingdom was a social rather than a solitary activity, casual and permissive like the taking of alcohol. Friend introduced friend; the drug was readily enough available; if it did not suit the initiate, no one was the loser. The collective impression was that cannabis "society" was predominantly young and without class barriers. It resented middle-aged society's judgment on alcohol and cannabis. It was not politically inclined and our witnesses saw no special significance in the popularity of cannabis among members of radical movements.

Some witnesses thought that it was possible to distinguish particular social groups within cannabis "society" and mentioned staff and students in universities and art schools, jazz and pop musicians and entertainers, film makers and artists, and others engaged in mass media of publicity. They explained this part of the pattern by the particular appeal of the drug to those interested in creative work and self-expression. But they also mentioned that there were growing numbers of workers in unskilled occupations who smoked cannabis for pleasure at week-ends as their equivalent to other people's alcohol. The aspect that some of our witnesses thought most worthy of note was the broad similarity of attitude to cannabis and its dangers amongst all these groups.

The "professional" group, for example, was described to us as fundamentally law-abiding; discriminating in the use of cannabis for introspection and elation as well as for social relaxation; "involved in life," often to the point of social protest; not much interested in experiments with L.S.D.; generally disinclined to take amphetamines or alcohol (which was regarded as much more damaging than cannabis); and tending to stop the use of cannabis on marriage, or when the risk of prosecution was felt to be inimical to career prospects. The "unskilled" group was said to be similarly industrious and law-abiding and to see nothing wrong or harmful in its use of cannabis.[3]

Outside these groups the picture was much more confused and in flux. There were young people who had failed to adjust to university life or professional training or regular work, and who had "dropped out"; actively discontented and rebellious teenagers, looking for "kicks," who were prepared to take any drug offered to them; their weaker associates who took cannabis to avoid rejection by the group; and a few who were severely unstable and sought escape from their problems in a multiple drug use that included cannabis.

None of our witnesses felt able to estimate the relative sizes of the groups that they identified. We judged that they considered the responsible law-abiding regular users to be in the majority. They could tell us little about the use of cannabis by immigrants and we did not find any clear links between this and cannabis-smoking by other groups. Proportionately to their numbers there have been more convictions recorded against immigrants than indigenous United Kingdom nationals and we have no doubt that a number of those who have recently come to this country from areas where cannabis-smoking has been traditional have not given up their habit. We made special enquiry without success in an attempt to discover whether the smoking habits of immigrants made them particularly vulnerable to enforcement or caused unusual problems of social adjustment with local communities.

Use and effects

Witnesses knowledgeable about patterns of use told us that although some people smoked every day without interference to work or social life, the typical user probably took the drug once or twice a week, aiming at a "high" of 2 or 3 hours. More intensive daily smoking tended to make the user withdraw from other activity, particularly if he was not

---

[3] A similar picture of attitudes was found by investigators in Oakland, California, who obtained the confidence of youngsters, mostly Mexicans and Negroes, through providing them with club amenities without strings. The youngsters were firm in their conviction, based on their own experience, that the use of such drugs as marihuana resulted in harmless pleasure and increasing conviviality, did not lead to violence, madness, or addiction, was less harmful than alcohol, and could be regulated. They cited case after case of individuals known to them who had not been harmed in health, school achievement, athletics or career as a result of a habit of smoking marihuana; and they were not themselves interested in being helped to abstain from the drug. Most had taken up marihuana-smoking from a simple desire to emulate older boys, and not by reason of emotional disturbance or social stress. On the contrary the group regarded those who took drugs to excess as having a weak personality, and marihuana-users generally as making a positive effort to be in the main stream of organised society and reality.

in a full-time occupation. Some people responded badly to the drug and a small number of initiates gave up smoking quickly because they disliked feelings of nausea or burning in the chest. There was little bias as between leaves or resin, but most smokers were interested in distinctive effects and there were individual preferences for material from particular sources. Experience and the heightened suggestibility due to the drug allowed the regular smoker to achieve the elation he sought with successively smaller doses. There was no physical tolerance; and "hangovers," although occasionally severe, were extremely rare.

We found a large measure of agreement among witnesses about the principal subjective effects of the drug. Most gave chief emphasis to its relaxing and calming effect. Several medical witnesses speculated that it had appeared to be beneficial for young patients during depression and also to have helped ex-addicts to abstain from heroin. Others contested this. Some suggested that cannabis tended to concentrate the user's attention on his anxieties, aches and pains, without helping him to resolve them, and to induce passivity without removing suffering. Apart from relaxation, the main sensations looked for were euphoria, tolerance of environment, and—at a more intellectual level—heightened awareness of self. Much reference was made to the varying influence of the circumstances in which the drug was used, little to altered visual or sensory perception. It was generally agreed that it was dangerous to drive a motor vehicle under the influence of cannabis not so much because driving ability was over-estimated (as with alcohol) as because of possible distortion of perception of depth and perspective.

We were told by more than one medical witness that cannabis-users did not seek treatment, and, when seen for other reasons, did not feel that treatment was needed for a cannabis habit. One medical witness mentioned having seen a few cases of acute psychosis following cannabis-use, but did not feel completely satisfied that cannabis had been the cause. The same witness was impressed by evidence of severe disturbance in a sample of chronic cannabis-users, but as this group was self-selected this information seemed to be of doubtful relevance to the generality of experience of cannabis-taking. A review carried out by the Ministry of Health has been reported to us as showing that 82 cases were admitted to hospital in 1966 with the diagnosis of drug addiction where cannabis was mentioned as the only or one of the drugs concerned. Further data were obtained in 79 of these cases. In 29 cases further evidence as to the significance of cannabis in leading to admission to hospital was inconclusive because of inadequate data or the patients' concurrent misuse of other drugs. Of the remaining cases, 8 had psychoses or confusional states, and 9 had other mental symptoms (not psychoses), which appeared to be attributable primarily to using cannabis, although other drugs might have been taken. Twenty cases showed evidence of a way of life in which cannabis had played a significant part in the social deterioration which had led to admission, although acute symptoms had not been the immediate cause. In this group the concurrent misuse of other drugs was a significant consideration. In 13 cases cannabis appeared to be irrelevant as a reason for admission to hospital. Thus in 42 cases the evidence was inconclusive or irrelevant and in the other 37 other drugs might also have been used.

SOCIAL ASPECTS OF CANNABIS USE

Much of the main controversy about the dangers of cannabis has attached to the claims that its use leads to opiate addiction and to the commission of violent crime. We paid particular attention to these aspects in our review of the salient literature and of evidence as to United Kingdom experience.

Progression

Hitherto discussion of the question whether there is a progression from cannabis to heroin has relied chiefly upon evidence from retrospective investigations of the previous habits of heroin-users. In the nature of the case such evidence can never be conclusive. On the assumption that the use of cannabis is still confined to a fairly small section of the population, evidence that a high proportion of heroin addicts have previously taken cannabis would only suggest that the marihuana-smoker is more likely than the non-smoker to take to heroin; what it cannot do is to give any clue to the frequency of such a progression among marihuana-smokers generally. For what they are worth, such retrospective investigations (which incidentally more commonly deal with American than with British experience) indicate that many heroin addicts have previously sampled other drugs including cannabis.

Most observers discount any pharmacological action disposing the cannabis-smoker to resort to other drugs, and look for other explanations. Some have suggested that in order to obtain their supplies cannabis-users must inevitably resort to the criminal underworld where opiates are also available. According to our witnesses supplies of cannabis in this country are not necessarily obtained in the same places as heroin. However, social mixing of some cannabis and some opiate-users takes place and involvement with opiates could thus occur on a socio-cultural basis.

Others suppose that dissatisfaction with the relief or pleasure to be obtained from cannabis leads users on to other drugs, and a minority postulate a predisposition to cannabis which is also a predisposition to heroin. These suggestions arise because most observers obtained their information from drug-users who are patients or offenders. These are often the multiple drug-users who rarely avoid trouble and are frequently to be found in clinics and before the courts. There appears to be a particular group of emotionally deprived, disturbed personalities who have tried most of the illegal drugs (including cannabis) before becoming heroin addicts. In fact most heroin addicts are multiple drug-users and have the emotionally impoverished family background not infrequently found in other delinquent groups, such as high incidence of broken homes, poor school record, police record, unemployment and work-shyness. Cannabis-users with similar personalities and backgrounds may have a predisposition to heroin, amphetamines and other illegal drugs. It is the personality of the user, rather than the properties of the drug, that is likely to cause progression to other drugs.

It can clearly be argued on the world picture that cannabis use does not lead to heroin addiction. So far as the United Kingdom is concerned no comprehensive survey has yet been made, but a number of isolated studies have been published, none of which demonstrate significant lines of progression. Our witnesses had nothing to add to the information already available, and we have concluded that a risk of progression to heroin from cannabis is not a reason for retaining the control over this drug.

Crime

Published statements on links between cannabis and crime tend to confuse the consequences of enforcing legal restrictions on non-conforming drug users with alleged criminogenic effects of cannabis-smoking itself. Since possession of cannabis is generally prohibited, the user found in possession automatically acquires a criminal record. To obtain his supply, an illicit source must also be involved.

A main charge against cannabis overseas, but not in this country, has been that its use makes people commit crimes of violence, because it removes inhibitions. There have been reports of outbursts of wild agitation and unprovoked violence by chronic users. Other observers have denied any direct link with violent crime. The Indian Hemp Drugs Commission concluded that "the connection between hemp drugs and ordinary crime is very slight indeed," but that excessive use did, in some very rare cases, make the consumer violent; 600 witnesses were asked by the Commission whether they knew of cases of homicidal frenzy, and very few did. A considerable majority of these witnesses did not consider that the drug produced unpremeditated crimes of violence, and some said, as other writers have since, that there is a negative relation because cannabis makes men quiet as a rule. The New York Mayor's Committee reported to similar effect: many criminals might use the drug, but it was not the determining factor in the commission of major crimes.

Probable reasons for this divergence of views are: criminals in some countries have based their defence on alleged cannabis-intoxication which provoked behaviour which they could not remember and for which they could not be held fully responsible; many of these users had combined cannabis with opium, heroin, amphetamine, barbiturate or alcohol, and it was impossible to identify which of these if any was to blame for an individual's criminal behaviour; samples of persons investigated have mostly been small and the history of drug-taking, its duration and its degree in each individual has been provided exclusively by the man himself, who often believed it to be in his interest to lie about it.

The most that emerges from the welter of conflicting statements is that an excessive dose of cannabis may lead to an attack of disturbed consciousness, excitement, agitation, or panic, and reduce self-control. The extent to which the affected person may commit a violent crime in this state of mind depends much more on his personality than on the amount or preparation of cannabis which he has been taking. The evidence of a link with violent crime is far stronger with alcohol than with the smoking of cannabis.

In the United Kingdom the taking of cannabis has not so far been regarded, even by the severest critics, as a direct cause of serious crime. It is not, of course, disputed that a number of criminals take cannabis as many do alcohol. We sought further evidence on these matters, but we found that for lack of reliable methods of detecting cannabis in the body the police were not in a position to offer any information.

A COMPARISON OF CANNABIS AND OTHER DRUGS

Cannabis has intrinsically different effects from most other drugs. As with most other drugs its effects are very variable, and depend not only on the substance consumed but on the person and his social setting. To this extent it is not easy to make any close comparison between cannabis and other drugs in common social use. Nevertheless, science, the law and social attitudes tend to create a common frame of reference for all drugs and, provided the risks of oversimplification are borne in mind, comparison of cannabis with other substances that affect the mind is relevant to our study even though it must necessarily be in broad terms.

Unlike the "hard" drugs, such as heroin, cannabis does not produce tolerance. Consuming the same, sometimes even a smaller, amount of cannabis continues to produce the original effect. Unlike heroin, cannabis does not cause physical dependence and withdrawal effects do not occur when its use is discontinued. The majority of users regard cannabis as pleasurable and so continue its use, but if they decide to give it up they do not usually experience difficulty. Here it might be said is a form of psychological dependence, but it is of a different order from the intense psychological dependence which normally follows the use of the "hard" drugs. The "hard" drugs are also physically dangerous: the direct result of over-dosage may be death, and possible indirect results are ill-health and even death, from pneumonia, malnutrition and infection due to dirty syringes. The social effects of taking opiates and cannabis are very different. The opiate-user frequently gets drawn into a "junkie" sub-culture where obtaining the drug and all that goes with it becomes a way of life, and this inexorably leads to gross deterioration. This is not true of cannabis, the use of which by itself does not appear to impair the subject's efficiency. In Western society it is clear that some adolescents form aberrant social groups around cannabis-taking; but where these are personally or socially deleterious it is not clear that the cannabis itself is primarily to blame. The use of other drugs as well as cannabis is often to be found in such groups and the social implications of adolescent alienation are probably of greater significance than the actual drugs.

In this country the barbiturates and the so-called minor tranquilizers such as meprobamate and chlordiazepoxide are widely prescribed by doctors and are all capable of producing varying degrees of tolerance and physical and psychological dependence. Over the last ten years the death rate from barbiturate poisoning (both accidental and suicidal) has doubled and cases of self-poisoning necessitating hospital admission have trebled. The amphetamines are also widely prescribed, and tolerance, psychological dependence and psychosis have become increasingly recognised as a consequence of their excessive use. Misuse of intravenous methylamphetamine (Methedrine) and related compounds carries with it the same risks of syringe-transmitted infections as are associated with heroin. No similar hazards have been observed to result from the use of cannabis.

We shall in due course be submitting a report on our study of L.S.D. and therefore do not propose to deal with it at length here. Suffice it to say that L.S.D. and other hallucinogens have for some while had a limited role in research and in experimental psychiatry. It is only in the last few years that these drugs have been used illicitly. It is still not easy to reach a clear assessment of their effects and dangers in this context, and it is therefore extremely difficult to make a clear comparison between them and cannabis. The subjective reports of those taking hallucinogens, both in clinical and in illicit conditions, suggest a response that is very much more intense. Under the influence of L.S.D. subjects may be so dangerously deluded that serious, even fatal, accidents occur, but there are no reliable reports of similar episodes among those who have taken cannabis alone.

Cannabis is often described as an "intoxicant" and frequently compared with alcohol. Both produce relaxation and euphoria; both, taken in excess, impair judgment, speed of reaction, and co-ordination. Cannabis more readily distorts perception of time and space. Unlike alcohol, cannabis is not known to enhance the effects of certain other drugs, induce a limited degree of tolerance or, over the long term, cause physical damage to body tissues directly or by dietary deficiency. Cannabis may well, however, be at least as dangerous as alcohol as an influence on driving or other responsible activity. This sharpness of similarity and contrast is considerably blurred by the effects of very different social settings. Alcohol in our culture is in general use and not illegal. Cannabis is used by a minority, and mostly against the law. Drinking patterns vary widely by country and by social class. Though many drinkers, particularly those who can be regarded as alcoholics, drink to get drunk, alcohol-users normally take a small amount, seeking only mild effects and a little social relaxation. The patterns of cannabis-smoking are more obscure. Experienced cannabis-users often smoke cannabis for a mild intoxication that they feel will improve their performance in a particular social setting or activity, e.g. playing jazz. Many smokers, however, take the drug in anticipation of a few hours of intense mental elation without the aggressive impulses often associated with taking large amounts of alcohol. All in all, it is impossible to make out a firm case against cannabis as being potentially a greater personal or social danger than alcohol. What can be said is that alcohol, with all its problems, is in some sense the "devil we know"; [4] cannabis, in Western society, is still an unknown quantity.

Tobacco-smoking is, of course, the most widespread "drug-addiction" in our society. The immediate effects are well known and substantially harmless. Physical dependence does not appear to occur, but habituation is intense, and people find great difficulty in giving up smoking. The long-term dangers of smoking in inducing cancer of the lung, in exacerbating chronic bronchitis and in contributing to coronary thrombosis are great. Nevertheless the danger that smoking may produce lung cancer

---

[4] In 1966, 66,468 males and 4,031 females were convicted of offences of drunkenness.

was for a long while not apparent. It is not possible to say that long continued consumption, medically or for pleasure, of cannabis, or indeed of any other substance of which we have not yet had long experience, is free from possible danger.

To make a comparative evaluation between cannabis and other drugs is to venture on highly subjective territory. The history of the assessments that have been given to different drugs is a warning against any dogmatic judgment.

Tobacco was once the object of extreme judgments. In the 17th century a number of countries attempted to restrict or forbid its use, but without success. In 1606 Philip III of Spain issued a decree restricting its cultivation. In 1610 in Japan restrictions were issued against planting and smoking tobacco, and there are records of at least 150 people apprehended in 1614 for buying and selling it contrary to the Emperor's command, who were in jeopardy of their lives. At the same time, in Persia, violators of the laws which prohibited smoking were tortured, and in some cases beheaded. The Mogul Emperor of Hindustan noted "as the smoking of tobacco has taken a very bad effect in health and mind of so many persons I order that no person shall practice the habit." Smokers were to have their lips slit. In 1634 the Czar of Russia forbade smoking, and ordered both smokers and vendors to have their noses slit, and persistent violators to be put to death. Medical reports of the period are full of accounts of its deleterious effects on mental and physical health.

Even non-alcoholic beverages that are now in common use have, in their time, been regarded as gravely dangerous. As late as the beginning of this century the Regius Professor of Physic at Cambridge along with the most distinguished pharmacologist of the time described in a standard medical textbook the effects of excessive coffee consumption: "the sufferer is tremulous and loses his self-command; he is subject to fits of agitation and depression. He has a haggard appearance.... As with other such agents, a renewed dose of the poison gives temporary relief, but at the cost of future misery." Tea was no better. "Tea has appeared to us to be especially efficient in producing nightmares with . . . hallucinations which may be alarming in their intensity. . . . Another peculiar quality of tea is to produce a strange and extreme degree of physical depression. An hour or two after breakfast at which tea has been taken . . . a grievous sinking . . . may seize upon a sufferer, so that to speak is an effort. . . . The speech may become weak and vague. . . . By miseries such as these, the best years of life may be spoilt."

With such earlier judgments in mind we do not wish to make any formal or absolute statement on a comparison of cannabis and the other drugs in common social use. All we would wish to say is that the gradations of danger between consuming tea and coffee at one end of the scale and injecting heroin intravenously at the other, may not be permanently those which we now ascribe to particular drugs.

MARIHUANA AND HEALTH

In this, the first detailed report to the Congress on Marihuana and Health, an attempt has been made to accurately describe the present state of our scientific knowledge concerning this issue. Not unlike a rather elaborate jigsaw puzzle, however, there are many research "pieces" whose relation to one another is not obvious. Moreover, many of the most important pieces that are required are not yet available. Some of the technical data that have been accumulated remain obscure for the present, particularly in providing a picture comprehensible to the layman. The ultimate meaning of past, present and future research will only become clearer as the various parts can be related to an emerging whole.

The purpose of this summary is to try to translate the present disparate elements into as reasonable an answer as can currently be framed to the question: What are the health implications of marihuana use for the

Reprinted from *Marihuana and Health,* National Institute of Mental Health, A Report to the Congress From the Secretary of Health, Education, and Welfare, January 31, 1971, pp. 5–17.

American people? It does not attempt to evaluate broader legal, economic or social issues including the consequences of law enforcement for personal marihuana use even though they are important and must be considered in a complete discussion of the overall problem.

As we examine the drug in its various natural and synthetic forms, however, it becomes evident that the deceptively simple question posed is highly complex and marihuana is not a single, simple substance of uniform type. It consists of varying mixtures of different parts of the plant, Cannabis sativa, with psychoactive properties ranging from virtually nonexistent to decidedly hallucinogenic in its stronger forms and at high doses. Unfortunately, much of the discussion in lay and sometimes scientific forums ignores this very basic and important fact. Most of our American experience has been limited to the widespread relatively infrequent use of a rather weak form of marihuana. Early research dealing with the drug is inevitably faulted by the fact that it is difficult to be certain just what potency material was involved and at what dose level. Although the principal active ingredient in the plant is thought to be Delta-9-tetrahydrocannabinol, much remains to be learned about the chemistry of marihuana and related substances.

Even the form in which the drug is consumed may make a difference in the consequences of use. It is quite possible, for example, that when smoked the material taken into the body differs significantly from orally consumed drug. The route of absorption, whether through the lungs or the digestive tract, may also make a significant difference in the consequences of use.

Virtually all of the American data indicate that use of marihuana has rapidly increased over the past several years. While the number of those who have tried the substance at some point in their lives remains a minority of the population it is continuing to increase rapidly. In some high school or college settings it is virtually certain that a majority have at least tried marihuana. By the end of 1970 about one college student in seven was using it on a weekly or more frequent basis. High school use has generally lagged behind that of colleges and universities, although in areas of high use as many as a third to a half have experimented with it. While comparable data are not available for non-school attending youth there is reason to believe that levels of use are at least comparable and for school drop outs are probably higher. In some west coast high schools which have had relatively high levels of use there is evidence that the increase in use may be decelerating and even declining. The likelihood of continuing, persistent use over an extended period of time by large numbers is not known at the present time.

Middle class users have tended to be individuals from higher income families attending larger, non-religiously affiliated urban universities rather than small, denominational colleges. However, as the number of users increases they become less clearly distinguishable from the more general youthful population. As use becomes more widespread there is reason to believe still younger as well as older populations are becoming involved.

Rather than being restricted to our own affluent society, marihuana use as a recent source of concern is a problem in many countries of the world. In at least three other English-speaking countries this concern has led to the appointment of commissions to examine the problem and to issue reports (Canada, England and New Zealand). While in 1956 the United Nations Commission of Narcotic Drugs estimated that over two hundred million people made regular use of cannabis, it is very likely the number is now substantially larger.

The bulk of this report makes clear that while there is much yet to be learned about cannabis, there is a substantial body of information at present available. Much of it is, however, of only limited immediate relevance to the question of the long-term health implications of use.

SUBJECTIVE EFFECTS

A range of studies have been conducted of the drug's acute effects. As is true of other drugs, generally the effects are closely related to the amount that is consumed. There is general agreement that at the usual levels of social usage the typical subjective effects are: Alteration of time and space perception, sense of euphoria, relaxation, well being and disinhibition, dulling of attention, fragmentation of thought, impaired immediate memory, an altered sense of identity, exaggerated laughter and increased suggestibility. Other less common effects are dizziness, a feeling of lightness, nausea, and hunger. As doses higher than the typical social dose are consumed more pronounced thought distortions may occur including a disrupted sense of one's own body, a sense of personal unreality-of being unreal, visual distortions, sometimes hallucinations and paranoid thinking. The more marked distortions of reality or psychotic-like symptoms become increasingly common if the dosage used becomes extremely high. Most users smoke to the point of "high" which they find pleasurable and at which they are able to control the effect. It is, however, difficult to predict individual reactions. Rarely, individuals may become quite anxious or panicky on even low doses. When eaten, effects are less predictable and more difficult for the user to control

In addition to the amount of the drug that is consumed, the set and setting of use are important factors in determining marihuana's subjective effects. Set refers to the attitudes, mood, expectations and beliefs which the individual brings to the drug using experience. Setting represents the external circumstances surrounding the experience. Thus a relatively emotionally neutral laboratory setting may evoke very different responses at a given dose level than might a more typical setting of social usage surrounded by other drug users. A situation in which the individual is depressed or apprehensive about the drug's effects differs markedly from one in which the user is more sanguine and looks forward to the drug experience with eager anticipation. The degree of personality integration, psychological rigidity and the presence or absence of psychopathology are all important contributors to one's subjective reactions to marihuana or other psychoactive drugs.

All of these psychological aspects also play a role in what is often referred to as the "placebo effect." The placebo effect is the response to the substance based not on its pharmacological activity but on the totality of expectations brought about by the set and setting of use. It is not uncommon for individuals consuming a psychoactively inert material to experience subjective effects which they erroneously attribute to an active drug. This same placebo effect may complicate results in a laboratory setting, in which the placebo is so compounded as to resemble the active material in all respects except for the presence of the psychoactive constituents. Particularly at low doses, it may be difficult to be certain to what extent an effect is brought about by the drug itself or placebo effects.

PHYSIOLOGICAL EFFECTS OF ACUTE MARIHUANA USE

Physiological changes accompanying marihuana use at typical levels of American social usage are relatively few. One of the most consistent is an increase in pulse rate. Another is a reddening of the eyes at the time of use. Dryness of the mouth and throat are uniformly reported. Although enlargement of the pupils was an earlier impression, more careful study has indicated that this does not occur. Blood pressure effects have been inconsistent. Some have reported slightly lowered blood pressure while others have reported small increases. Basal metabolic rate, temperature, respiration rate, lung vital capacity and a wide range of other physiological measures are generally unchanged over a relatively wide dosage range of both marihuana and the synthetic form of the principal psychoactive agent, delta-9-THC.

Neurological examinations consistently reveal no major abnormalities during marihuana intoxication. However, some investigators have found a small decrease in leg, hand and finger strength at higher dosages. Some decrease in hand steadiness and the ability to maintain balance occurs as dosages increase. Although users often report enhanced sensory awareness in the drugged state, objectively measurable improvements in visual acuity, brightness discrimination, touch discrimination, auditory acuity, olfactory threshold or taste discrimination have not been found. Some small changes in electroencephalograph (EEG) findings have been detected but the significance of these results is in doubt.

From the standpoint of lethality, cannabis products must be counted among the safer of the drugs in widespread use. Death directly attributable to the drug's effects is extremely rare even at very high doses.

ACUTE PSYCHOTIC EPISODES

Acute psychotic episodes precipitated by marihuana intoxication have been reported by a number of investigators. These appear to occur infrequently, usually at high dosages, but may occur, even at levels of social usage, in particularly susceptible individuals. Heightened susceptibility appears to be more likely in those who have previously had a marginal psychological adjustment especially in the presence of excessive stress.

INTELLECTUAL AND MOTOR PERFORMANCE

Changes in time sense have definitely been shown to take place during marihuana intoxication. There is a tendency to overestimate the passage of time particularly while engaged in some activity.

A wide range of tests of intellectual functioning and of psychomotor performance (the ability to precisely coordinate sensory perception and muscular performance) have been carried out under conditions of intoxication. As might be expected, the degree of impairment is dose related. It also varies during the period of intoxication.

Generally, the more complex and demanding the task to be performed the greater is the degree of impairment. Simple and very familiar tasks such as reciting the alphabet or repeating a brief series of numbers are least likely to be affected at relatively low dose levels. As the task becomes more complicated, however, decrements in performance do become apparent. Inexperienced users tend to show greater decrements than do experienced marihuana users.

Because of the importance the automobile assumes in our society, the effect of marihuana on driving performance is of fundamental interest.

One widely reported finding using a driver simulator was that the per formance of marihuana using drivers was equal on the average to tha of a non-intoxicated control group. It is, however, important to not that this was based on a single study of intoxicated drivers under tes conditions that might be expected to be highly motivating. In addition half the drivers in the experimental group did more poorly than did th control group. This suggests that the ability to compensate for th effects of marihuana—to suppress the "high"—may differ markedly from individual to individual. The relevance of this work to more typica driving conditions is not known.

It is noteworthy that in another series of studies not directly concerne with driving, marihuana intoxicated subjects consistently answered "No!" when asked, "Do you think you could drive a car now?" Pre liminary results of a study of attention skills believed to be among th best predictors of actual driving performance have shown performance decrements under marihuana use similar to those found when drivers have consumed moderate amounts of alcohol. Additional much needed research on driver performance and other complex motor tasks is cur rently in progress.

Marihuana users consistently report that their short-term and imme diate memory while under the influence of the drug is interfered with. Systematic research evaluation generally confirms this. More complex functions such as learning a number code, using such a code for encoding a series of numbers, understanding a written paragraph or spoken speech are all interfered with even at the moderate levels of typical American social usage. This is believed to reflect difficulty in retaining, coordinating and indexing over time those memories, perceptions and expectations demanded by the task being performed.

MARIHUANA AND BIRTH DEFECTS

A basic concern with any drug substance coming into wide use is the possibility that it may affect fetal mortality or fetal development (i.e. may be teratogenic) in such a way as to bring about abnormal offspring of pregnant users. It may also conceivably affect unborn generations by causing chromosomal changes (i.e. may be mutagenic) that persistently alter the genetic heritage. Thus far there is little evidence that marihuana or related materials do this. While preliminary studies of the effects of injecting relatively large quantities of cannabis or related substances have found some indication of fetal abnormalities in rats, other re searchers have been unable to duplicate such findings. There is no evidence to suggest that marihuana use in humans affects fetal develop-

nent. Despite the present absence of such evidence, it is obviously unwise for anyone to use any drug of unknown teratogenic or mutagenic
properties during the child bearing years. Use during pregnancy is particularly unwise.

EFFECTS OF LONG-TERM CHRONIC USE

While a good deal is known about the acute effect of cannabis use
and the laboratory findings to date generally correlate well with user
reports, much less is known about the implications of long term chronic
use. In few experimental studies has marihuana been administered to
humans for extended periods. These periods have been limited at most
to a few weeks. In addition, earlier studies of both acute and chronic
use have provided no indication of the exact amounts of psychoactive
material involved and so it is difficult to compare those findings with
those of contemporary research. Over a period of just under six weeks,
one investigator found only small physiological changes when individuals
were permitted to consume the drug freely in whatever quantity they
chose. A daily mean of 17 cigarettes each was consumed by this group
of prisoners. There was some mild confusion under those conditions of
continued intoxication with slight impairment of performance on general
intelligence testing during the period. While mild changes in electroencephalograph findings were found, these returned to normal five days
after discontinuing the drug. There was no evidence of withdrawal
effects (i.e. physical symptoms precipitated by discontinuing the drug)
after this duration of use.

It should be emphasized that early attempts at evaluating the effects
of long-term use of cannabis suffer from multiple scientific defects.
Whether they tend to indict or to absolve cannabis from causing chronic
physical or psychosocial consequences, it is difficult to be certain of the
validity of their observations. The Indian Hemp Commission Report,
for example, although a careful, systematic study for its day (the
1890's), can hardly be regarded as meeting modern epidemiological research standards. Subsequent studies such as those of the group appointed by the then Mayor LaGuardia in New York City can also be
easily faulted for their scientific deficiencies. While psychoses presumably resulting from heavy cannabis use have been reported, these studies
do not generally meet modern scientific standards.

The fact that there are many worldwide reports of heavy, chronic
cannabis use resulting in loss of conventional motivation and in social
indifference is of particular interest in that there are now some reports
of somewhat similar findings among American heavy users of marihuana.

Unfortunately, American use patterns are frequently contaminated by the use of other drug substances, making interpretation difficult. It is not certain to what degree this "amotivational syndrome" is the result of marihuana use *per se* or of a tendency for those who lack conventional motivation to find drugs unusually attractive. If one confines his use of the term to a description of the present American scene one must conclude that present evidence does not permit the establishment of a causal relationship between marihuana use and the amotivational syndrome. There is, however, increasing evidence that frequent, heavy marihuana use is correlated with a loss of interest in conventional goals and the development of a kind of lethargy. Research in humans is being conducted in an attempt to determine to what extent this observed correlation is due to alteration in brain functioning.

The issue of long-term mental deficit is an exceedingly complex one in which the lack of sufficiently sophisticated methodology may be crucial. The problem of determining harmful effects of chronic use and especially of psychological harm as a result of using a drug substance whose effects are not dramatic is very difficult. Unless the type of deficit is especially distinctive, it is likely that the same symptoms will be exhibited by many non-drug users. Furthermore, unless the harm done to the user is so gross as to be noticeable in a high percentage of users, it may readily be attributed to other factors such as poverty or poor nutrition. Tobacco furnishes an apt example of the difficulties encountered in demonstrating even physical hazards of use. It was only after many years of use by a substantial segment of the population that the role of smoking in the development of various types of diseases was recognized. It should be noted that concern has been expressed that marihuana when smoked in large quantities might be expected to have similar carcinogenic effects to those associated with cigarette smoking. There is, however, no present evidence to suggest that marihuana is cancer-producing.

MARIHUANA AND THE USE OF OTHER DRUGS

It is generally conceded that marihuana use does not necessarily lead directly to the use of other drugs. On a worldwide basis there is little evidence of a progression from the use of marihuana to that of opiates or hallucinogens. However, those who find use of marihuana highly attractive, may also be attracted to the use of other drug substances which may be popular among their peers. These may include stronger hallucinogens, amphetamines and the opiates. While it is true that a high percentage of heroin addicts have used marihuana as well, most marihuana users both here and abroad do not appear to be attracted to the use of heroin.

FUTURE RESEARCH DIRECTIONS

It is evident that much remains to be learned about marihuana, hashish and related materials. Little is as yet known about the implications of chronic use particularly at lower dose levels and less frequent intervals. Although much can be learned from animal research, in the final analysis the most crucial information with respect to long-term human use can only be obtained by careful observations of chronically using groups here and abroad. Such research is currently being carried out.

It is important that we learn more about the possible interactions between marihuana use and that of a wide range of other drugs. This includes not only such drug substances as caffeine, tobacco and alcohol, but also other drugs of abuse and a wide spectrum of therapeutically employed drugs. As use of marihuana comes to include a wider spectrum of the population it is important that we learn its effects on those whose physiological functioning is to some degree impaired or who suffer from physical or psychological disabilities. Such effects must be studied over a wide dosage range and in various use patterns.

From a psychosocial point of view it is essential that we come to better understand the different patterns of drug use, their implications for social functioning and those factors which contribute to such use. These include parental attitudes, child rearing practices and peer pressures as well as those aspects of subcultural and cultural practices that may affect use. Finally, it is imperative that we determine what are more effective prevention and education techniques that serve to avert drug abuse of all types including that of marihuana.

PART 2

VALUE PERSPECTIVES

CHILDREN OF THE DRUG AGE

William Simon and John H. Gagnon

The use of marijuana has leaped from the peripheral zones of the society to its very center. Just a few years ago marijuana was limited to the ghetto scene, jazz circles, and the highly alienated young in flight from families, schools, and conventional communities. Today, one finds an increasing incidence of marijuana use among young—and not so young —adults otherwise pursuing ordinary careers, among high school students who remain relatively conformist in most other regards, and even among the culturally underprivileged fraternities and sororities on a number of college campuses. More importantly, there is good reason to assume that it will not emerge and fade like some passing fad, but rather that it will both persist and spread. Marijuana use is very likely to become a continuing fact of life for American society.

These new patterns of marijuana use, for all their apparently unpre-

Reprinted from *Saturday Review,* September 21, 1968, pp. 61–63 and 75–78, copyright 1968 *Saturday Review,* Incorporated with permission of the publisher and William Simon.

dictable and perhaps revolutionary character, must be seen in terms of their continuity with general trends in contemporary American culture. One of these trends—one that is almost something of a cliché in "pop" sociology—is the fact that we have become, as a nation, a population of pill-takers. Both the actual miracle and the myth of modern medicine have made the use of drugs highly legitimate, as something to be taken casually and not only during moments of acute and certified distress. Our children, in being casual about drugs—particularly casual in their acceptance of them and their promises—far from being in revolt against an older generation, may in fact be acknowledging how influential a model that generation was.

A second factor is that marijuana as an idea and possibility has become a widely available cultural fact; this article, in itself, is a part of this. For our generation and older generations, exposure to marijuana even as a concept was highly limited. To gain a knowledge of marijuana beyond a few jokes about jazz musicians, one had to journey to the margins of conventional society, and to experience the drug, one had to carry hard-earned credentials. Now, seemingly all at once, it has become a proper topic for the mass media. Major magazines discuss the problem at great length. TV comedians and film-makers have at it. It is a commonplace in the imagery and lyrics of youth culture, upon which so much of adult culture seems to draw.

The irony is that, in something of a re-creation of the absurdities as well as costly stupidities of the prohibition era, "pot" has become an object of information and entertainment exchanges all over the society at the same time that its possesssion or sale remains a felony offense at both the state and federal level. Once out of the cultural pockets of secret knowledge—the ghettos that no one ever saw or the jazz musicians that no one ever knew personally—marijuana use becomes almost universally available *as an idea*. This development may or may not be deplored. However, the question raised by those for whom censorship is an answer remains moot, for marijuana has become a general cultural institution. The fact is that the cat is out of the bag or, as one might say, the pot is out of the cat.

The very nature of marijuana itself facilitates the development of this trend. Unlike other both "hard" and "soft" drugs, marijuana requires no sophisticated technology nor complex organizational structure for either production or distribution. Unless the policing of marijuana sales becomes more efficient or repressive than anyone presently contemplates, it will probably remain a relatively low-cost drug and will continue to be available from numerous, relatively unorganized sources.

These factors combine to give us predisposition to use, knowledge of the idea of use, and growing access to opportunities for use of marijuana. Little appears on the social horizon to suggest that the presence of these mutually reinforcing factors will not produce patterns of increased marijuana use in our society. However, it is important to understand that the effect of changing patterns of marijuana use upon the society and—more immediately—upon the quality of life in this society remains somewhat open-ended. Only the most hysterical or self-interested talk in terms of necessary or predictable outcomes, and these outcomes invariably involve decay and disaster for both the individual users and the society. Our sense of possible general and social effects is very much like our sense of the effects of immediate use: Marijuana tends to produce the kinds of feelings in the user that the user has been trained to expect. In line with this, we suspect that much of what will follow by way of impact upon the society will depend upon how the society chooses to respond. And what one comes to fear is the possibility of a continued societal reaction of employing old rigidities and old assumptions in dealing with new patterns of use by new populations.

A crucial population to consider is that of high-school-age users and potential users. They are crucial in several senses. First, the young are often in the forefront of social innovation, and in this case, so much of the current public imagery of concern about marijuana use focuses upon the teen-ager. Second, they are important because much of the meaning of the marijuana experience is derived from the language of contemporary youth culture. Perhaps because it is a relatively new phenomenon in the human experience to have youthful adults—youthful well into what used to be called middle age—we have to turn to the presently young for images of self. As part of this, adult culture seems increasingly to feed off youth culture. This is suggested by several elements of both men's and women's current fashions. The language of youth culture is found in the current idioms of adult language. How many of us are "doing our thing?" How many of us casually describe ourselves or others in terms of this or that "bag?" Third, and most important, we should give particularly serious consideration to the young because they require our protection; indeed, following Erik Erikson, one might say that the very meaning of adolescence in our society is to be defined by the protected status we extend to the young while they manage the uncertainties of both changing senses of self and changing social expectations.

Along the same line, our concern for teen-age drug use requires special considerations because for this population the drug experience and the attending attachment to drug-using subcultures is more likely to be an *ego-forming* experience. Drug use has a greater potential for becoming an organizing pivot during adolescence than during any subsequent stage in the life cycle. In talking to the youthful marijuana user, for example, one cannot help but be struck with how strongly the imagery of that experience influences ideas of the good and the desirable, how quickly it becomes the standard of happiness, how effectively it impoverishes the rewards and rewarding experiences that the larger society appears to offer. On this latter point, one might consider that the ease with which such rewards or rewarding experiences have been supplanted indicates the degree to which they are the unrealistic and unrealizable illusions of an older generation.

What, then, can be said of high-school-age marijuana users? In very specific terms, the answer must be: not very much. There are no real estimates of the number of young people that one is talking about. Much of the blame for this lack of knowledge must fall upon uneasy parents and timid school administrations who have "protected" their children from responsible inquiry and in doing so have also protected our ignorance. There is little one can say on this except that the weight of observations and impressions is that the rate of increase in teen-age drug use has been substantial and that most indicators point to further increases. At this point, one must begin, if unable to specify numbers, to tentatively specify some of the characteristics of the populations involved.

Clearly, if marijuana use among teen-agers in the urban ghettos has increased in recent years—and it may have—this is not the source of renewed societal concern. Marijuana use has long been prevalent in the urban ghettos; it was just that no one really cared. It was only when Holden Caulfield came face to face with Claude Brown—only when marijuana became desegregated and upwardly mobile—that there was an increase in societal attentiveness. The new population of teen-age users, from all indications, appears to be from social backgrounds that are substantially middle class or higher. The appearance of marijuana among working-class or lower-middle-class youth, who—for the moment —lack both social and intellectual connections to marijuana, seems to be slower in coming. This tendency for marijuana use to appear among middle-class and upper-middle-class youth was reflected in a recent survey reported by Louis Harris. One in six parents with substantial incomes and some degree of higher education reported knowing at least one teen-ager who used marijuana. The parents also reported holding values increasingly less hostile to such use.

One of the characteristics of marijuana use—as is true for many other drugs—is that the idea of use creates availability and rarely the reverse. Early experiments with marijuana rarely produce desirable effects. Indeed, as Howard Becker has observed, for marijuana to produce markedly pleasurable effects often requires a great deal by way of social learning and social support. Relatively few users at any age level come to marijuana in isolation or practice its use in isolation; to become and remain a major phenomenon marijuana use requires a sustaining culture. The crucial question becomes: Who or what are the carriers of marijuana culture? And once one abandons the simple-minded imagery of the dirty old man standing outside the high school or the profit-crazed crime syndicate, the "infectious carriers" turn out to be aspects of public culture that are fully legitimate and social relationships that involve persons very much like the potential marijuana user.

As we have already indicated, much of the imagery surrounding "pot" use is transmitted increasingly through the mass media, especially that part of the commercial media that serves the youth market. Lyrics of popular songs refer to the drug itself or the drug experience in barely coded terms, often coded just enough to establish an illusion of membership among the listeners. Elements of the music are described as having an additional message *if* the hearer is properly turned on. More crucial is the fact that the media—frequently in articles and programs designed to "inform" and "warn" an adult audience, as well as to excite its fantasies—provide an ideology and a definition of self that makes marijuana use legitimate; it is somehow tied to a "new spirit," a new honesty, a new quest for substantial values and experiences, a children's crusade organized around the reinvention of Rousseau, Thoreau, and Lawrence. In this way the mass media provide not only a basis for legitimating the use of pot, but also a structure of rationalizations after the fact of use. One cannot help but be struck by the uniformity of explanations for the use of marijuana given by the young—a uniformity of response not only in the expected environments like Haight-Ashbury or the East Village, but in the suburbs of major cities across the land and in relatively small college towns.

However, the general availability of marijuana as a cultural possibility is not automatically translated into active use; what is required is an effective, intermediate link, and this most often turns out to be peers or near peers. One significant point of entry for marijuana use in particular high schools is the intersection between the college experience and high school experience. Our best current estimate is that between 10 and 15 per cent of college students have ever used pot, about a third of these using it fairly regularly. Marijuana is frequently introduced to high school culture by high school students with close siblings at college, older girls who have begun to date college boys, or youngsters who are drawn to intellectual, political, or artistic activities that are shared with college students. This latter group is of course increased if there is a college

campus close at hand or a relatively handy location where such commit-
ments can be acted out—Haight-Ashbury in San Francisco, the East
Village in New York, Old Town in Chicago, Plum Street in Detroit, and
the like. And with the current affluence of America's middle class and
the utilization of "youth fares" offered by major airlines, even a relatively
provincial city can claim several who have made the pilgrimage to one or
more of these communities.

It should be noted that while high school students who are involved
with the intellectual, political, or artistic activities common to college
students may be predisposed to drug use, they are also likely to be more
intellectually and even more emotionally mature than most of their immediate peers. This kind of teen-ager will tend to be among the least
likely to conform to the naïve image of the adolescent that elicits the
adult world's response to the teen-ager. They are even less likely to conform to the self-consciously dishonest image that elicits the response of the
American high school. For them the way to marijuana will be encouraged
partly by the refusal of significant adults to respond to their discovery of
the world with candor and an equal sense of commitment. This group,
it should be acknowledged, may also contain many whose "vulnerabil-
ity" to drug use was increased by psychological stresses of a more individual genesis.

The probable pattern of use of marijuana among high school students
is not a simple one. To say that X per cent of high school students may
be using it does not mean X per cent in all or even most high schools
have been "turned on to pot." The proportion of high school students
who are users is at the moment probably very small and the proportion
of high schools even smaller. While the mass media may make the idea of
marijuana almost universally available, not all high schools possess appropriate actualizing mechanisms. Thus it is likely that the vast majority
of high schools in the country have yet to directly encounter the marijuana issue. In a much smaller group of high schools—those in major
metropolitan areas and smaller college towns—use may be limited to a
very small and self-isolating minority. In another relatively small group
of schools, use may have become fairly widespread, with students who
use marijuana remaining fairly conventional, not particularly "hip" or
"cool."

This gives us three distinct types of high school populations: those
without experience and for whom marijuana exists only as a culturally
available idea, those who have begun experimenting with marijuana but
who remain attached to conventional values and social relationships, and
those for whom use is associated with entry into an unconventional social
framework and perhaps ultimately into an alienated subculture. This

latter group deserves particular attention not only because they may well contain many of our brightest children, but because the long-term costs to them may be the highest.

All of the students—users and nonusers—for whom the marijuana issue is salient will have one thing in common: they will all be interested witnesses to the larger society's response, and for many of them it can only be a demoralizing spectacle. Initially, they are confronted with a mass of claims and counter-claims; the "scare" rhetoric by those who would advocate more repressive actions is matched by the counter-arguments of those advocating more permissive policies, who deny a cause for alarm and, in many instances, claim a potential for joyful and mind-expanding experience. For those without immediate reference to experience—either their own or that of close peers—this debate can only increase a sense of distrust, if not cynicism. For those with experience for reference, the arguments of the permissives—even if they promise more than marijuana can deliver—turn out to be confirmed more often than not. For many other drugs, including alcohol, much of the negative imagery surrounding their use, which in many cases serves to inhibit use, is actually confirmed by the experience of the teen-age experimenter or someone in his immediate environment. Alcohol does tend to make you sick, produces wild, acting-out behavior, and leaves you feeling "hung-over." There is a growing negative imagery surrounding LSD use beyond what remains for the present solely a claim that it damages chromosomal structure. There is the experience of the "bad trip" and "freaking out" for uneven and unpredictable lengths of time. Use of the amphetamines is now associated with experience that suggests its addictive qualities, its damaging effects upon the body, and the unpleasant depression that follows use which has become known as "crashing." But if marijuana use is damaging to the young, it is clearly not damaging in the ways that many of its hysterical critics allege that it is.

One dangerous by-product of using excessive scare tactics is that it produces the "wolf-wolf-wolf" or boomerang effect. The discrediting of the illegitimate claims made for the dangers of marijuana use tends to rub off on legitimate claims for the dangerous effects of other drugs. Among the young who are involved with drugs, a credibility gap exists that is far greater than that associated with government pronouncements on the Vietnam conflict. Moreover, this credibility gap extends not only to research undertaken by government agencies, but also to academic research that is supported by governmental agencies. Exaggerated and disprovable claims for the effects of marijuana may actually encourage experimentation with more immediately dangerous drugs by discrediting all warnings.

If one of the functions of largely unsubstantiated claims about the dangerous character of marijuana use is educational—educating against use—it has obviously failed and failed almost totally. However, it has another apparent function: that of maintaining and justifying the present repressive legal sanctions against use, possession, and sale. On this level, the campaign has been far more successful, but successful because its appeal has not been to users or potential users, but to anxiety-ridden adults whose observations are often filtered through the hysteria of some part of the mass media, as well as their own uneasiness, confusion, distrust, and even envy of the presently young. This helps to sustain a structure of law enforcement that is at best erratic in its application. One consequence of this is to produce a dangerous sense of invulnerability on the part of many users: they know it happens but not very often. One young user equated the risk of arrest with "that of being hit by something falling from a window." Moreover—since the pattern of enforcement is either accidental, capricious, or hostile—when the sanctions imposed are severe, they are defined as unreasonably punitive (and beyond hypocrisy when joined with the language of reform and correction), and when the sanctions imposed are minimal they are viewed as an admission that the society does not believe its own pronouncements about the dangers of drugs.

In general, then, the entire population of high school youth, particularly those who are middle-class in background, is part of a potential audience highly critical of what is often defined as the older generation's hypocrisy or denial of reality. This kind of reaction, of course, obtains in areas well beyond drugs—two that come to mind immediately are politics and sex. It is even possible that we have trained the young in this kind of ideological response; increasingly one notes adult commentators, journalists, educators, and liberal religionists who appear all too eager to confess the guilt of the adult world on this count—often confessing long before the accusation is made. But nonetheless, we must bear in mind that the response of the society to marijuana use is another situation in which the young may learn an attitude toward the society. Even for the young person with little or no likelihood of marijuana use, the response of the organized community is instructive about the community's capacity to be rational, honest, or humane.

There will also be, as we have already observed, a growing number of young persons using marijuana who are, in the terms of their generation, otherwise fairly conventional. They will be the equivalents in many respects of their peers who are experimenting with drinking during this same period. To date, there is no evidence that suggests that the pot user will necessarily come to worse ends than those who to varying degree experiment with alcohol. From what little we currently know about the effects of marijuana, it is possible that the marijuana users may well fare better. They are less likely to become hostile and aggressive, wildly uninhibited, and they would have to work very hard to equal the impressive record of the young who drink and drive.

Again, the greatest risk this group runs may not have anything to do with the effects of the drug as such, but with the quality of societal response to marijuana use. For many of the youthful users of pot—young people for whom use itself and the frequency of use may vary considerably—a dreadful cost factor may suddenly emerge as a result of the vagaries of law enforcement. The possibilities of being found "in possession" (or being caught "holding") are both many and few. These possibilities include a momentary loss of "cool," being investigated for something other than marijuana use, and the like. But once the possibly casual user is caught, he or she ceases to be a casual user and becomes a socially defined user and often a legally liable user. As a result, school careers are often interrupted as suspension or expulsion becomes the response of nervous school administrators. This is something that typically does not follow with equal severity when a liquor violation is reported. It is almost as if such school administrators act to ward off an incipient epidemic, instead of realizing that such arrests are a late symptom of the drug's arrival and diffusion.

Financially costly, emotionally disturbing, and socially stigmatizing contact with the courts is also common. In both, the schools and the courts a language is used to describe the seriousness of the offense that bears little resemblance to what the individual "offender" or his witnessing peers feel about themselves or what they are doing. Thus, an experience that in itself carries little direct potential for alienating the young person from conventional or orderly process of development, may all at once—in an unpredictable way—become profoundly and even traumatically disordering and alienating.

The present legal status of marijuana also increases the risks of social dislocation by pushing the youthful users into contacts with highly alienated subcultures that are sources not only for marijuana but also for hard and soft drugs whose effects are either unknown or known to be dangerous. In a sense, by trying in dubious ways to protect the young from the "ravages" of marijuana we may actually have increased their possible exposure to still other, more dangerous drugs, and we do this at a time when we have also been successful at minimizing our own credibility.

Possibly the smallest, but at the same time most visible group of high-school-age marijuana users are those for whom drug use has become an important subcultural value, young people for whom pot use has taken on both ego-forming and ideological aspects. These are boys and girls for whom drug use is not an occasional adventure into the forbidden or a kick, but an important part of the context of values and the reordering of relationships that impinge directly upon the emerging sense of self-identity of the young person. Disproportionately, this group will include many of the brightest and potentially the most creative of our young people. They tend to come from home environments culturally rich, sophisticated, and socially concerned. They are often young people with the kind of endowment that enables them to ask the hard questions of a society that the society either evades or responds to with the most fatuous of answers. It is extremely important that we understand something of these young people, because they are often the cadres who, more than merely responding to "youth culture," generate new forms of "youth culture."

The main focus of this essay has been on marijuana. This leads to something of a distortion. While drugs—marijuana as well as the others —appear to play an important part in the current experience of the young, they may well be more symptom than cause. Indeed, it is some-how comforting to adult observers to worry about the young in terms of something as alien to them as "the menace of drugs." It is almost as if some totally remote and strange factor emerged to threaten our young people. We, the adult world, need not be implicated or if implicated, it is only because we have been remiss in developing the proper defense against this menace. While this is not the appropriate place to raise the question of the general condition of the society and its ability to cope with its major problems, it is necessary to indicate that such an examina-tion is the minimal context within which the problem of the young and drugs must ultimately be considered.

Here we suffer from many things, but not from a communication gap. If anything, the adult world has said both too much and too little, and the young have really been listening. The young did not, out of some innocent wisdom, suddenly invent the idea that the contemporary Ameri-can education industry on all levels has failed its clients—both its pupils and the society at large; there is an abundance of data to that very effect and a large number of adult critics have been saying so for a long time. If there is a difference, it is that while many adults know it, many of the young know it and have to experience it at the same time. (On a per-sonal level, a dilemma of one of the authors, who is in the process of completing a study of the college experience, is to try to persuade a teen-age son to continue his education while the data suggest a great deal of the experience may be meaningless and some aspects of it even destructive. How does one do this without appeals to the purely personal and the purely opportunistic?)

The young did not invent the horrors of segregated society or the ghetto; they did not even invent the description of those horrors. Similarly with the cynicism that surrounds the wedding of statement of national purpose with what we are presently doing in Vietnam. Even the very language of alienation, which many of the young have learned so well, has derived from the more articulate anguish of an adult world. If many of the young have learned to distrust the police, it has to do with more than the drug question. How many of us trust the police when it comes to civil disturbances, civil rights, or peace demonstrations? And if many of the young feel that little can be done and that purely personal solutions should properly be pursued, how many of us—particularly those of us who try to link the character of the recent Presidential primaries and public opinion polls with the ultimate choice of candidates and programs—are about to offer them a viable and effective alternative? We seem to have none for ourselves.

And insofar as much of what is new in the current pattern of drug use is that its users come from homes of affluence and not deprivation, it is important to resume a consideration of the pathologies of affluence that we, as a nation, began to consider out loud before we were shamed into silence by the specter of poverty that still haunts the society. The fact that the poor suffer does not lessen or make less painful the wounds of affluence. In many ways, we have made the world costly for the children of the middle class by essentially making most achievements relatively inexpensive. Earlier generations could strive for achievement (something we have transformed into some kind of universal truth) even if the experiences or rewards of achievement were kindly left unspecified because the consequences of failure were so terrifyingly real; it was perhaps enough merely not to have failed. One aspect of achievement was a capacity for pleasure, for accumulating a capacity for what appeared to be personal experiences. These, too, we left hazy and unspecified. We accumulated this capacity for pleasure very much like a check that no one wanted to cash; we rarely, if ever, wanted to scan the landscape on the far side of achievement.

A generation is now emerging that tests our imagery of failure and finds it even more mythic than our imagery of achievement. It is possible that the affluence that exists for a large section of our society has allowed a Deweyian commitment to survive its brutalization and banalization at the hands of professional educators. What the young in some cases want, and what appears to adults as unreasonable, is that the prize be located at the top of the Cracker Jack box, not at the bottom. When they find that the prize is not a meaningful social experience, they are prepared to seek out experiences whose dimensions are almost totally personal and private. The attraction of drugs and subcultural activities within which the "drug experience" plays an important role is precisely that they allow the illusion of intense and immediate experience that is almost totally and safely referential to the self and not to the world. Unfortunately that sense of self remains pathetically thin and unsubstantial for there is little that is intrinsic to this private world. It is not that they "drop out," but that they haven't as yet been "turned on" by the world. Even with the drug experience, with its supportive and learned rhetoric of intense experience, they continue to ask: what is there to do? It is not that they are frantic or full of inner turmoil, but that they are bored.

For this last group of youthful marijuana users, the real danger is not that they will fill our prisons or psychiatric facilities, not that they will become addicted to more dangerous drugs, and not that they will do harm to anyone but themselves. A small number of them will, with a tragic lack of necessity, do some of these, but the real danger is that they will lose a sense of their real capacity for experience and that they will abandon, and in many cases have already abandoned, claims for an influential role in the collective enterprise of the society. Their future will become a progressive drift toward a totally privatized existence. In a sense, while they appear to be in revolt against suburban values—an appearance reinforced by their easy appropriation of the language of adult commentators—when at all specified, their values appear to be precisely the values of suburban life, the values of suburban life stripped of ritualistic references to larger social purposes.

In essence, they merely want to be left alone to "do their thing," with as little unenjoyed or alienating labor as possible. While many of them strongly identified with the hero of *The Graduate,* few of them could describe what it could possibly be that he wanted that was different from what his parents had or were, except perhaps the desire to remain the child of affluent parents. There is in this development a profound feeling of loss, but one is equally uncertain about realistic alternatives. For these young people marijuana use ranges from a temporary easing of the pains of boredom to a protected illusion of their own existence and importance, as a way of protecting themselves from the illusion they have learned from us—that something significant ought to happen.

Throughout this essay we have leaned in the direction of a necessary redefinition of the legal status of marijuana, a redefinition in the direction of liberalization of access. *In no way, however, do we think that marijuana should be freely available to adolescents.* Adolescents should no more be encouraged to use marijuana than they should be encouraged to use alcohol. But, by the same token, we don't feel that experimentation with marijuana is in itself an immediate indication of impending personal or social disaster. Indeed, many of the young people we have talked to who previously were pot smokers are now turning on to alcohol. Possibly they sense that it is even easier to get, involves less of a hassle with parents and community, and that—if properly defined by group values—can provide them with the same important illusions that marijuana previously provided.

How, then, does a community respond to this issue? Clearly, law reform, if ultimately possible, appears nowhere on the immediate horizon. More important, the underlying crisis of our young people would not be substantially altered by that occurrence. One could not help but be struck by how many of the youthful supporters of Senator McCarthy abandoned pot along with their beards in the situation of what appeared to be a direct encounter with social life. One was also struck by the number who continued to "turn on" with marijuana, but how much less important it became. One was further struck by how many were unmoved by the entire campaign because of a deep-seated pessimism about the possibilities of genuine participation in social affairs and how confirmed they must now feel in their dark view. This begins to suggest something of the style of solutions: that we begin to take both young people and ourselves more seriously—in terms both of our commitment to social life and of our capacities for personal pleasure.

As we have said, it is not that the young do not listen; they appear to listen all too well. Nor is it that they don't talk; they talk too much. The problem is that adults rarely listen and that our talk, when it occurs, often doesn't make sense. At least not to the young. It is perhaps understandable that this is the way things happen in the midst of the complexities of family life. The failure of this kind of effective communication is equally evident in the schools of the country. This too can be explained. The question remains: Where do we go from here? It might begin with the admission to ourselves and to the young that they are not necessarily what we expected them to be; indeed, no more like we expected them to be than the present social world is what many of us expected it to be. That we are prepared to begin talking in terms that allow the young to recognize themselves as well as recognize our expectations, and the reasons for these expectations. That our talk be honest—honest about them, about ourselves, and about our communities. And, of crucial significance, that we will not surrender them to the forces of hysteria, bigotry, ignorance, and dishonesty in our communities.

THE DANGERS OF MARIHUANA—
FACTS YOU SHOULD KNOW

Federal Bureau of Narcotics

Recently, within the United States, we have witnessed an increasing abuse of marihuana as well as other hallucinogenic or "mind-changing" drugs. Regrettably this trend has been encouraged by a small number of misguided but highly articulate spokesmen, who have attempted either to justify or to excuse the use of such drugs. As a consequence of promotional activities by these spokesmen, many impressionable young persons have been led to experiment with marihuana. It is therefore wise for every citizen to acquaint himself with the basic medical and sociological facts concerning marihuana.

WHAT IS MARIHUANA?

The technical name of the plant from which all marihuana preparations are derived is *cannabis sativa* (L.), sometimes called cannabis indica, Indian hemp, or simply hemp. The cannabis plant is native to large areas of the world and its fibers have been used for the manufacture

---

Reprint of undated pamphlet issued by the Federal Bureau of Narcotics.

of twine, rope, bags, clothing, and paper. The sterilized seeds are occasionally used in various feed mixtures and particularly for bird seed. Marihuana has also been used in the treatment of a variety of clinical disorders as an analgesic, a poultice for corns and in other ways. All of these medical uses were found to be either unsound, inefficient, or without predictable effect. Hence, the drug has been removed from the U.S. Pharmacopeia as well as the official drug lists of nearly all other countries. However, legitimate medical research into marihuana's possible utilization in a range of useful therapeutic functions continues. Such research has never been prohibited by Federal laws.

Under the Federal law, "marihuana" is defined to mean all parts of the cannabis plant except for the stalks and sterilized seeds. All other preparations of the plant, whether of leaves, flowers, resins, or chemical extracts, are various forms of marihuana. The best known of these is hashish, a concentrated preparation of marihuana. In this country, the term "marihuana" usually refers to a preparation of pulverized leaves, resins, flowers, or combination of these, also called "pot," or "grass," for smoking in pipes or homemade cigarettes (called "reefers," "sticks," or "joints"). We now know that marihuana contains a number of potent compounds called tetrahydrocannabinols which affect the mind and body in various ways.

The strength of any given preparation of marihuana depends upon the amount of tetrahydrocannabinol which is contained in it. The strongest preparations, such as hashish, are made in certain areas of the world, particularly India and the Near East. A substantial quantity of hashish finds its way into this country's illicit traffic; however, most marihuana users customarily must settle for more adulterated forms. This is primarily due to state and Federal policing activity plus the general air of social condemnation, all of which results in making it difficult, expensive, and dangerous to acquire and possess marihuana. Thus, American users accept whatever grade of marihuana they can get at whatever price it is offered and whenever it is available.

EFFECTS ON THE MIND AND BODY

The consumption of marihuana produces a variety of immediate mental and physical effects which become more pronounced with chronic use. The 1965 report on Drug Dependence for the World Health Organization describes the nature of the intoxication as follows:

> "Among the more prominent subjective effects of cannabis ... are: hilarity ... carelessness; loquacious euphoria ... distortion of sensation

and perception . . . impairment of judgement and memory; distortion of emotional responsiveness; irritability; and confusion. Other effects, which appear after repeated administration . . . include: lowering of the sensory threshold, especially for optical and acoustical stimuli . . . illusions, and delusions that predispose to antisocial behavior; anxiety and aggressiveness as a possible result of various intellectual and sensory derangements; and sleep disturbances." [1]

The effects of the drug on the nervous system and brain are undoubtedly the most profound and constitute the greatest problem for the user and the persons around him. These include the precipitation of psychotic episodes during which the user becomes mentally unbalanced for varying periods of time. A recent study which described the effect of the most active of the tetrahydrocannabinols (abbreviated as THC) reports the following:

"It has long been known that marihuana and hashish can cause psychotic reactions, but usually such reactions are ascribed to individual idiosyncrasies rather than being usual or common reactions to the drug. The data in these experiments, however, definitely indicate that the psychotomimetic effects of $\triangle^1$—THC are dependent on dosage and that sufficiently high doses can cause psychotic reactions in almost any individual. Psychotic reactions after smoking marihuana under the usual conditions in the United States appear to be rare but the low incidence of such psychotic breaks may reflect nothing more than the low tetrahydrocannabinol content of most of the marihuana available in the United States." [2]

Those who have studied users of marihuana have found that:

"Excessive indulgence in cannabis is apt to produce in healthy individuals and more so in susceptible individuals, mental confusion which may lead to delusions with restlessness and disordered movements. Intellectual impairment as well as disorientation may show itself in various ways." [3]

Prior to the studies showing that tetrahydrocannabinols in appropriate concentration cause psychotic reactions, there had been considerable controversy over the connections between marihuana use and criminality.

---

[1] Eddy, N. B.; Halbach, H.; Isbell, H., and Seevers, M. H.: Drug Dependence: Its Significance and Characteristics, Bull. World Health Organ. 32:721, 1965.
[2] Isbell, H.; Jasinski, D.; Gorodetzky, C. W.; Korte, F.; Claussen, V.; Hoage, M.; Sieper, H.; and von Spulak, F.: Method of Assay in Human Subjects and Results with Crude Extracts, Purified Tetrahydrocannabinols and Synthetic Compounds, National Academy of Science—National Research Council, Committee on Problems of Drug Dependence, Minutes, p. 4844, 1967.
[3] Chopra, I. C., and Chopra, R. N.: The Use of the Cannabis Drug in India, Bull. Narcotics, p. 23, Jan.–Mar., 1957.

A recent report of the New York County Medical Society noted that habitual use of hashish is definitely associated with criminality, violence, and insanity.[4]

A sufficient dose of marihuana is capable of producing all of the effects of hashish and even of LSD,[5] which is conceded to be one of the most powerful drugs known to man. To resolve the dispute, it is enough to say that for certain individuals, a small dose, and for all individuals, a large dose of marihuana's active ingredients causes temporary insanity. What each individual does while in a psychotic state will vary with the individual and his circumstances at the time of the psychosis. The important question for society is no longer in what manner marihuana use causes crime, but rather how many crimes would not be committed but for the addition of this drug to the social environment.

MARIHUANA VS. ALCOHOL

Some marihuana users have tried to excuse their indulgence by claiming that it is no worse than consuming alcohol. While alcoholism constitutes a major social problem, surely it is not valid to justify the adoption of a new abuse by trying to show that it is no worse than a presently existing one. The result could only be *added* social damage from a new source. Moreover, marihuana, unlike alcohol, is nearly always consumed by its users for the express purpose of attaining a "high," a disorientating intoxication. Evidence of studies of chronic marihuana users also indicates that a more dangerous psychosis may result.

Another significant difference between alcohol and marihuana which has been given considerable attention is that alcohol more rapidly impairs motor coordination, thus disabling the inebriate. Marihuana intoxication, on the other hand, does not result in such rapid motor incoordination. This difference becomes very important when the marihuana user operates a car, for cannabinol distorts time and space concepts very radically.[6]

MARIHUANA AND ADDICTION

The question regarding the addiction liability of marihuana has been the subject of considerable debate among scientists, and research in the

---

[4] Report of the Subcommittee on Narcotic Addiction, The Dangerous Drug Problem, New York Med., Vol. 22, No. 9, p. 3, 1966.

[5] Louria, D.: *Nightmare Drugs,* p. 32, 1966.

[6] Maurer, D. W., and Vogel, V. H.: *Narcotics and Narcotic Addiction,* p. 243, 1962.

area still continues. Chopra found that, "Repetition of the dose developed into craving for the drug, and gradually there developed in such individuals habitual use and increasing tolerance which led to increase of dosage." However, he pointed out that this was in no way as significant as in the case of morphine-type drugs. Recent studies in England also uncovered a suggestion of tolerance and progressive dosage. Nevertheless, all agree that marihuana does not produce a dependence of the morphine type, and abstention does not result in the classic withdrawal symptoms which invariably accompany abstention from narcotic drugs. The World Health Organization has recently chosen to discontinue the use of the terms "addiction" and "habituation" and substitute the single term "dependence." Thus, one may speak of "marihuana dependence" or "morphine-type dependence" without confusion.

From a medical standpoint, this distinction cannot be overlooked, but it assumes less importance when considering the practical social dangers of the drug. Dr. David P. Ausubel, in his book, *Drug Addiction,* noted that chronic users of marihuana will go to great lengths to insure that they will not be without the drug. Deprivation, he says, may result in "anxiety, restlessness, irritability, or even a state of depression with suicidal fantasies, sometimes self-mutilating actions, or actual suicidal attempts." Other researchers have also observed that, from a psychiatric point of view, marihuana dependence is but little different from narcotic addiction.[7]

Another dangerous aspect of habitual marihuana use is the pattern of graduation to narcotic addiction. Of course, not all persons who use marihuana go on to use heroin, but actual experience leaves little doubt that a large majority of narcotic addicts began their drug-taking with marihuana. Intensive research conducted at the Public Health Service Hospital in Lexington, reported in 1967 by Dr. John C. Ball, disclosed that of 2,213 addicts examined, 70.4 percent had used marihuana prior to their addiction. This sample included addicts from all classes and professions, representing 46 states. Moreover, in those states classified as areas in which marihuana is often available, it was found that of 1,759 addicts, 80 percent had first used marihuana.

As a result of intensive psychiatric evaluation of 80 subjects, Dr. P. A. L. Chapple concluded that the connection between marihuana abuse and heroin addiction could not be accounted for simply on the basis that both drugs are often available from the same illicit source. The evidence is strong that the use of marihuana develops a taste for

---

[7] Chapple, P. A. L.: Cannabis, a Toxic and Dangerous Substance—A Study of 80 Takers, Brit. J. of Addiction 61:269, 1966.

drug intoxication which, in turn, leads many people to the use of more potent drugs—even heroin.

CONTROL AND ABUSE IN THE UNITED STATES TODAY

Marihuana is the subject of worldwide prohibition as expressed in the 1961 Single Convention on Narcotic Drugs. On the advice of the Expert Committee on Dependence-Producing Drugs of the World Health Organization, it was placed in a special category with heroin as being a drug "particularly liable to abuse and to produce ill effects." The United States, which acceded to the Single Convention in the spring of 1967, has controlled marihuana since the passage of the Marihuana Tax Act of 1937. Under this Act, the use of marihuana preparations is confined to bona fide medical research and industrial needs and all other uses are prohibited. A person found guilty of the illegal sale or transfer of marihuana may be sentenced to not less than 5 nor more than 20 years imprisonment for the first offense. A person found guilty of illegal possession of marihuana may be sentenced to a probationary term or not less than 2 nor more than 10 years imprisonment for the first offense.

The efficiency of Federal, state and local law enforcement agencies in coping with the illicit marihuana traffic has succeeded in preventing this abuse from becoming the major problem it is in some other countries.

This success has also, unfortunately, resulted in concealing from many observers the full dangers involved. The low potency of the marihuana which is available and the arrest of those who traffic in it have resulted in partially disguising its consumption as a causative factor in crime and psychosis; a connection which is more apparent in those countries where use has been widespread and has been effectively deterred.

In contrast to the social and scientific realities, the prophets of the drug experience make fantastic claims for the virtues of marihuana. They would have it regarded as a "benevolent herb" which may lead its users to profound philosophic truths, greater social intimacy and keener artistic expression. These claims are often accompanied by otherwise valid criticisms of society's ills and hypocrisies. Such observations are designed to enlist the individual's sympathies and thus to convince him that the claims are as justified as the criticisms. However, it takes little philosophic sophistication to recognize that such virtues do not reside in drugs but in men. They are the products of conscious labor, and cannot be attained on the peddler's prescription. At best, drugs provide only mechanisms to escape from problems and hence to escape from the character development which would ultimately permit their solution.

The spread of marihuana abuse can only add to the difficulties which already plague our society, not solve them.

The Committee on Alcoholism and Drug Dependence of the Council on Mental Health of the American Medical Association in a recent article on dependence on cannabis stated: "Only an aroused and concerned public can create, mobilize and implement resources to deal adequately with as serious a problem as drug dependence in all its forms. . . . Frank and forceful public discussions, focusing on the futility and inherent dangers in experimentation with drugs such as marihuana and the consequences of any subsequent psychological dependence, can act as deterrents," and finally: "Marihuana is centuries old, but it represents a constant danger. The responsibilities of the citizen, including the physician, are clearly defined. The time to begin is now." [8]

---

[8] J.A.M.A. 201: 368, August 7, 1967.

DEPENDENCE ON
CANNABIS (MARIHUANA)

American Medical Association

Unlike narcotics, barbiturates and other sedatives, and amphetamines and other stimulants,[1-3] cannabis (marihuana) *has no known use in medical practice in most countries* of the world, including the United States. Despite this fact, the practicing physician should understand the nature of cannabis and psychological dependence on it, as well as the treatment of persons involved who may become his patients.

Reprinted from *Journal of American Medical Association* 201 (August 7, 1967): 368–71, with the permission of the publisher. This statement was prepared by the American Medical Association's Committee on Alcoholism and Drug Dependence and approved by the Council on Mental Health.

[1] American Medical Association's Council on Mental Health and National Academy of Sciences—National Research Council's Committee on Drug Addiction and Narcotics: Narcotics and Medical Practice: The Use of Narcotic Drugs in Medical Practice and the Medical Management of Narcotic Addicts, *JAMA* 185:976–982 (Sept 21) 1963.

[2] *Dependence on Barbiturates and Other Sedative Drugs,* Committee on Alcoholism and Addiction and Council on Mental Health, *JAMA* 193:673–677 (Aug 23) 1965.

[3] *Dependence on Amphetamines and Other Stimulant Drugs,* Committee on Alcoholism and Addiction and Council on Mental Health, *JAMA* 197:1023–1027 (Sept 19) 1966.

While there is no accurate measure of the prevalence of nonmedical use of cannabis and its preparations, it is clear that they are widely used in many parts of the world, including the United States. Those who utilize cannabis in one form or another include various personality types in diverse socioeconomic and cultural circumstances. In the United States, attitudes of rebellion against authority and thrill seeking are not uncommonly found among marihuana smokers.

HISTORY AND GENERAL BACKGROUND

As early as 1200 BC the hemp plant, *Cannabis sativa,* was described as a source of long textile fibers, and its "narcotic" properties were documented in Chinese writings by 200 AD. Its numerous derivatives, which can be smoked, eaten, or drunk, have become known throughout the world by a variety of names, including hashish, bhang, ganja, dagga, and marihuana. Traffic in and use of cannabis derivatives now is restricted in practically every civilized country in the world, including those where custom has allowed its introduction into religious rites.

India, where the intoxicating properties of ganja were generally recognized by about the tenth century, has undertaken a phased program for the reduction of the use of cannabis in the various forms of indigenous medicine, which will hopefully lead to the eventual elimination of such use.

Despite almost universal prohibition, cannabis use is still socially acceptable in certain parts of the world, though there is a trend away from such acceptance. The principal areas of the world involved in the nonmedical use of cannabis preparations are the Middle East, the African nations, and the Americas, including the United States.

The migratory course of marihuana to the New World is an interesting historical development. Apparently originating in Asia and the Eastern Mediterranean basin, the drug spread via Africa and South America to Mexico. Only within the past 60 years has marihuana been used in the United States. In spite of the proximity of Europe to the Mediterranean, its use there had little significance until recently, when it was imported to England and France as the American "vice."

Wide differences in the volume and form of use are evident despite the absence of hard data on the amount by country. Some authors believe that marihuana smoking is on the increase in the United States. Again, there are no data to prove or disprove this belief because there is no base line from which to make a judgment. Increasing or not, use is substantial and represents a problem with medical, social, and legal implications.

The term "cannabis" is used in international language according to these definitions:

"Cannabis" means the flowering or fruiting tops of the cannabis plant (excluding the seeds and leaves when not accompanied by the tops) from which the resin has not been extracted, by whatever name these parts may be designated.

"Cannabis plant" means any plant of the genus *Cannabis.*

"Cannabis resin" means the separated resin, whether crude or purified, obtained from the cannabis plant.

The term "marihuana," used primarily in the Americas and in England, refers almost exclusively to the preparations of the leaves and flowering tops of the cannabis plant, which are dried, sometimes mixed with tobacco, and then typically smoked in cigarettes. In the vernacular of the street, they are called "reefers," "joints," or "sticks" containing "hay," "grass," "pot," "weed," or "tea." The inhaled smoke has increased effect when the cigarette is reduced to a short "butt," because the active ingredients concentrate there during smoking.

Legally, the preparations of cannabis are dealt with in international treaties and in the western countries, including the United States, in the same general manner as the narcotics. In the United States, they are controlled under the Marihuana Tax Act, administered by the Federal Bureau of Narcotics.

PHARMACOLOGY AND BIOCHEMISTRY

The female cannabis plant develops a resinous material which incorporates the active pharmacological principles. This resin can be extracted from the base of cannabis confections, beverages, and medicaments, or from the dried tops of the plant, leaves, and flowers, and may be pulverized and smoked with or without admixture with tobacco. The inhaled smoke is irritating, and long continued exposure to it induces chronic respiratory disorders.

The principal active ingredients of cannabis resin are cannabinols, especially tetrahydrocannabinols, which are now known to exist in several isomeric forms. Many cannabinols have been isolated, but it is not yet known what their exact state or proportion is in the resin which brings about the typical effects of the drug as a whole in man.

A tetrahydrocannabinol has been synthesized recently, and its identity with a product of a natural origin established. In addition, many cannabinol derivatives have been prepared, utilizing, for the most part, starting materials of natural origin. Extensive animal and clinical trials of these substances are adding much to our knowledge of cannabis action.

The actions of cannabis are exerted primarily on the central nervous system, but their modes of action are poorly understood. Their effects, through smoking, are felt in a very few minutes and may persist for as long as 12 hours.

CANNABIS DEPENDENCE AND ITS CONSEQUENCES

No physical dependence or tolerance has been demonstrated. Neither has it been demonstrated that cannabis causes any lasting mental or physical changes; comments by physicians who have recently visited colleagues in Africa suggest a need for more intensive study of this possibility.

Persons who use marihuana continually and as the symptomatic expression of a psychological conflict, a means of gaining social acceptance, or a way of escaping painful experiences of anxiety or depression may be said to be psychologically dependent on the substance. Continuous use may be associated with the development of psychiatric illness, although few chronic users are admitted to psychiatric inpatient facilities. Chronic marihuana users often are lethargic, neglect their personal appearance, and occasionally may experience a deep sense of failure after believing they are capable of accomplishing great things. The extent of psychological dependence on marihuana in the United States is not known, but such dependence may reasonably be presumed to be less than that to narcotic drugs on the grounds that the satisfactions obtained from marihuana by drug dependence-prone individuals are insufficient to meet their psychological needs.

Of greater interest than psychological dependence on marihuana is the casual, episodic, noncontinuous use of the substance by adolescents and young adults in and around urban centers and college towns, and indications that its use among high school students may be spreading. Such experimental use, if it does not lead to intoxication or frequent use and dependence, may not be medically dangerous. However, it is of concern as a medicolegal problem because marihuana is a drug, because its possession and distribution violates federal and many state laws, and finally, because its use is probably disproportionately higher among young persons with developing psychiatric problems than among those without them.

It is in the nature of adolescence to seek new and exciting experiences, to question self, family, and society, to try on and discard new guises of behavior, to reconcile opposing pulls and strains, and to act like child and adult. Such experiences contribute to personal growth and ultimately to intellectual development and social progress, though in some instances the behavior may appear to some viewers as thoughtless, irresponsible, or rebellious. The kaleidoscopic activity of adolescence assumes forms and patterns unique to each generation of adolescents, each having its own values, totems, and taboos. The content of an adolescent's experiments depends on many variables related to the cultural patterns and mores of his area, his own psychological development, and if marihuana is involved, on its availability.

Urban areas, with their concentrated population, and college towns within a two- or three-hour driving range of cities attract those who participate in drug traffic; although in college towns, marihuana suppliers are most often students who purchase the drug from a city "pusher" and then bring it into the college community. The number of young persons who become psychologically dependent on marihuana or progress from marihuana to drugs that produce physical as well as psychological dependence is not known. It is likely that those who do become dependent on marihuana or other drugs are psychiatrically disturbed and that drug use is but one of a complex of psychological and behavioral symptoms manifested by them.

Most experimenters either give up the drug quickly or continue to use it on a casual basis similar to the social use of alcohol. Those experimenters who find the effects of the drug unpleasurable, or at least not worthwhile for them, are the ones who immediately forego further use.

Most persons who experiment with and many who become dependent on marihuana do not go on to stimulants, narcotics, or hallucinogens, such as lysergic acid diethylamide (LSD). It is a fact, however, that persons physically dependent on other substances, such as heroin, almost always have had experience with marihuana, although not necessarily prior to experiences with so-called hard drugs.

Another area of society in which marihuana use has been observed for many years is the urban ghettos where feelings of hopelessness, powerlessness, oppression, and futile dissatisfaction provide fertile soil for cultivating the growth of such use. The use of marihuana among Puerto Ricans and both southern and northern Negroes is reputed to be high. In all likelihood, marihuana use among the poverty-stricken urbanite is concomitant with use of other dependence-inducing substances and a broad range of asocial and antisocial activity.

CHARACTERISTICS OF CANNABIS INTOXICATION

Subjectively, the user experiences one or more of the following effects: a feeling of well-being, hilarity, euphoria, distortion of time and space perception, impaired judgment and memory, irritability, and confusion.

After repeated administration and high dosage, other effects are noted such as:

> lowering of the sensory threshold, especially for optical and acoustical stimuli, thereby resulting in [a feeling of] intensified appreciation of works of art . . .; hallucinations, illusions and delusions that predispose to antisocial behavior; anxiety and aggressiveness as a possible result of the various intellectual and sensory derangements; and sleep disturbances.
>
> In the psychomotor sphere, hypermotility occurs without impairment of coordination. Among somatic effects, often persistent, are injection of the ciliary vessels and oropharyngitis, chronic bronchitis and asthma. These conditions and hypoglycaemia, with ensuing bulimia, are symptoms of intoxication, not of withdrawal.[4]

While some persons assert that marihuana improves artistic and other creative endeavor, there is no evidence that this is so.

There is little difficulty in recognizing the intoxication of a person who has smoked a significant amount of marihuana in the preceding few hours. If the physician has an opportunity to smell the smoke of a "reefer," a characteristic acrid odor will be noted. Federal, state, and local narcotic enforcement officers and certain clinical laboratories may be helpful in identifying the odor or the dried marihuana preparation, should the latter come into the physician's hands.

The problem of recognizing a nonintoxicated marihuana-dependent person or experimenter is quite difficult. As indicated earlier, there is no physical dependence, and hence, no withdrawal syndrome. A *careful* longitudinal history from the patient and from his close friends and relatives regarding his behavior and associates may be productive. This history should be obtained in a nonjudgmental manner. Such a history, even when marihuana use has not been admitted, coupled with a careful mental-status examination may indicate the possibility of such drug use. If the patient demonstrates a psychopathological condition of such nature which could make him vulnerable to experimentation with drugs or to their abuse, positive confirmation of marihuana or other drug abuse should not be considered a prerequisite for treatment of his condition. Such treatment is indicated whether or not he experiments with or has become psychologically dependent on marihuana.

TREATMENT

Drug dependence is a multifaceted problem, embracing not only medical issues but almost every aspect of our culture and socioeconomic

---

[4] Eddy, N. B., et al.: Drug Dependence: Its Significance and Characteristics, *Bull WHO* 32:728–729 (No. 5) 1965.

system. Obviously, there is no simple solution. The treatment and re-habilitation of the person with psychological dependence on marihuana ordinarily will require the attention not only of the physician but also of many others concerned with the problem. There will be complicating legal, emotional, social, moral, or religious issues which require special skills not ordinarily possessed by the physician, and he may well find it necessary to enlist the services of those who do possess them.

Because marihuana abuse does not result in physical dependence, the physician need not apply himself to physical complications of with-drawal. He must, however, determine at the onset of treatment whether other drugs are being taken simultaneously whose withdrawal requires careful management. This is frequently the case.

Ordinarily, minimal protection during the period of acute intoxication is all that is required, beyond providing appropriate measures for cor-recting any concurrent physical illnesses, including malnutrition. Dur-ing the initial phase, ambulatory treatment of the person with psycho-logical dependence (as contrasted with the experimenter) is generally not satisfactory because of the tendency to relapse. At least brief hos-pitalization is usually recommended to separate the patient from his supply, establish relations, and initiate treatment. Complete cessation of the use of the drug is necessary, and circumstances may require the family or others to seek legal means by which the patient can be brought to treatment, in those states where this is possible.

The major focus of effective treatment cannot be on the repeated drug abuse alone, because psychological dependence is almost universally symptomatic of serious underlying personality problems, severe neurotic conflicts, or psychotic reactions. The task of the physician is to learn from the patient *what* really bothers him at both conscious and uncon-scious levels, and what needs are being spuriously met at both these levels by taking marihuana.

It is also the physician's task to help the patient come to such a full comprehension of his intrapsychic and interpersonal problems that they can be eliminated. Short of this, the physician may have to give long-term supportive therapy that will enable the patient to live as productive and satisfying a life as possible with his psychic handicaps and in a drug-free state. The physician, of course, cannot change real vocational, family, social, and other environmental problems contributing to the patient's difficulty merely by treating his intrapsychic disorder. For this, as noted above, collaboration with others possessing additional pertinent skills is essential.

The physician who does not have sufficient professional training to equip him to handle these difficulties may wish to make early psychiatric referral. When psychiatric resources are not available, the physician may be called upon to provide limited individual, group, or family therapy over an extended period of time. In such cases, it is particularly important to seek additional help in the community from the appropriate agencies, interested lay organizations, or concerned professionals who can add substance to the treatment program.

The physician's attitude will influence his approach to the patient. It is important for the physician to remember that a person who has a psychological dependence on marihuana is sick and deserving of understanding and treatment, even though he may have been involved in unlawful activity.

A concomitant consideration is that, through the use of marihuana, a behavioral pattern often has been established in which the patient has experienced rejection by the wider society and acceptance perhaps only by those with similar problems. He may therefore have alienated himself from more desirable associates and family, or perhaps never have achieved a period of reasonably satisfactory adjustment to which he may return. Rehabilitation may require concerted community support, with simultaneous efforts to provide housing, employment, spiritual assistance, and other aids.

Each patient represents a unique therapeutic problem calling for ingenuity on the part of all who endeavor to help. The prognosis for persons psychologically dependent on marihuana, and particularly for experimenters, is good in most cases.

LEGAL CONTROL

Legal control is one of the most important and effective aspects of prevention. Federal control of marihuana is the responsibility of the Federal Bureau of Narcotics under the Marihuana Tax Act of 1937 (US Code Title 26, sections 4,741–4,776).

The basic features of federal control are to make marihuana dealings visible to public scrutiny, and to render difficult the acquisition of marihuana for nonmedical and noncommercial purposes.

The act requires all persons with legitimate need to handle marihuana to register and pay an occupational tax, requires that all marihuana transactions be recorded on official forms provided for that purpose, makes transfers to a registered person subject to a tax of $1 an ounce, and makes transfers to an unregistered person subject to a prohibitive tax of $100 an ounce.

The controls over marihuana under the federal and state laws are dissimilar. Under the federal law, marihuana is not considered a narcotic drug. On the other hand, many states have covered marihuana by including it within the definition of "narcotic drug" since adoption of the Uniform Narcotic Drug Act in 1932. Marihuana is equated in many state laws with the narcotic drugs because the abuse characteristics of the two types of drugs, the methods of illicit trafficking, and the types of traffickers have a great deal in common.

THE PHYSICIAN-CITIZEN'S ROLE

Only an aroused and concerned public can create, mobilize, and implement resources to deal adequately with as serious a problem as drug dependence in all its forms. The proper stimulus must come from citizens who are community leaders aware of these needs and from professionals who apply themselves to these needs.

Frank and forceful public discussions, focusing on the futility and inherent dangers in experimentation with drugs such as marihuana and the consequences of any subsequent psychological dependence, can act as deterrents.

Expanded counseling services in schools could present more effective and more suitable alternatives to young people for dealing with their problems.

Continuing emphasis on the incompatabilities between a primarily punitive approach toward those who experiment with or become psychologically dependent on marihuana and modern concepts of treatment and rehabilitation could lead to further improvement of legislation and enhance the opportunities for the drug-dependent person to obtain treatment. The Narcotic Addict Rehabilitation Act of 1966, which went into effect Feb 6, 1967, was a substantial step in this direction at the federal level.

Persistent vigilance by law-enforcement agencies in eliminating illegal sources of the drugs needs public support and sufficient means with which to do the job. Real crusading may be required before adequate amounts of public funds are devoted to creating and operating affective treatment facilities and programs for the afflicted and for the control of illicit drug use.

Finally, only community understanding, compassion, interest, and active aid will enable the rehabilitated drug-dependent person to find a satisfactory place in society.

Marihuana is centuries old, but it represents a constant danger. The responsibilities of the citizen, including the physician, are clearly defined. The time to begin is now.

MARIHUANA AND SOCIETY

Council on Mental Health

After careful appraisal of available information concerning marihuana (cannabis) and its components, and their derivatives, analogues and isomers, the Council on Mental Health and the Committee on Alcoholism and Drug Dependence of the American Medical Association and the Committee on Problems of Drug Dependence of the National Research Council, National Academy of Sciences, have reached the following conclusions:

Cannabis is a dangerous drug and as such is a public health concern.

For centuries, the hemp plant (cannabis) has been used extensively and in various forms as an intoxicant in Asia, Africa, South America, and elsewhere. With few exceptions, organized societies consider such use undesirable and therefore a drug problem, and have imposed legal and social sanctions on the user and the distributor.

Reprinted from *Journal of American Medical Association* 204 (June 24, 1968): 1181–82, with the permission of the publisher.

Some of the components of the natural resins obtained from the hemp plant are powerful psychoactive agents; hence the resins themselves may be. In dogs and monkeys, they have produced complete anesthesia of several days' duration with quantities of less than 10 mg/kg.

Although dose-response curves are not so accurately defined in man, the orders of potency on a weight (milligram) basis are greater than those for many other powerful psychoactive agents, such as the barbiturates. They are markedly greater than those for alcohol. In India, where weak decoctions are used as a beverage, the government prohibits charas, the potent resin, even for use in folk medicine. In many countries where chronic heavy use of cannabis occurs, such as Egypt, Morocco, and Algeria, it has a marked effect of reducing the social productivity of a significant number of persons.

The fact that no physical dependence develops with cannabis does not mean it is an innocuous drug. Many stimulants are dangerous psychoactive substances although they do not cause physical dependence.

*Legalization of marihuana would create a serious
abuse problem in the United States.*

The current use of cannabis in the United States contrasts sharply with its use in other parts of the world. In this country, the pattern of use is primarily intermittent and of the "spree" type, and much of it consists of experimentation by teenagers and young adults. Further, hemp grown in the United States is not commonly of high potency and "street" samples sometimes are heavily adulterated with inert materials.

With intermittent and casual use of comparatively weak preparations, the medical hazard is not so great, although even such use when it produces intoxication can give rise to disorders of behavior with serious consequences to the individual and to society.

And, while it is true that now only a small proportion of marihuana users in the United States are chronic users and can be said to be strongly psychologically dependent on the drug, their numbers, both actual and potential, are large enough to be of public health concern.

If all controls on marihuana were eliminated, potent preparations probably would dominate the legal market, even as they are now beginning to appear on the illicit market. If the potency of the drug were legally controlled, predictably there would be a market for the more powerful illegal forms.

When advocates of legalizing marihuana claim that it is *less harmful* than alcohol, they are actually comparing the relatively insignificant effects of marihuana at the lower end of the dose-response curve with the effects of alcohol at the toxicity end of the curve—i.e., the "spree" use of marihuana vs. acute or chronic "poisoning" with alcohol. If they compared both drugs at the upper end of the curve, they would see that the effects on the individual and society are highly deleterious in both cases.

Admittedly, if alcohol could be removed from the reach of alcoholics, one of the larger medical and social problems could be solved. But to make the active preparations of cannabis generally available would solve nothing. Instead, it would create a comparable problem of major proportions.

That some marihuana users are now psychologically dependent, that nearly all users become intoxicated, and that more potent forms of cannabis could lead to even more serious medical and social consequences— these facts argue for the retention of legal sanctions.

Penalties for violations of the marihuana laws
are often harsh and unrealistic.

Persons violating federal law with respect to possession of marihuana are subject to penalties of from 2 to 10 years imprisonment for the first offense, 5 to 20 years for the second offense, and 10 to 40 years for additional offenses. Suspension of sentence, probation, and parole are allowed only for the first offense. Many of the state laws provide for comparable penalties. With respect to sale, penalties are even more severe.

Laws should provide for penalties in such a fashion that the courts would have sufficient discretion to enable them to deal flexibly with violators. There are various degrees of both possession and sale. Possession ranges from the youngster who has one or two marihuana cigarettes to an individual who has a substantial quantity. Sale may range from the transfer of a single cigarette to the disposition of several kilograms of the drug.

While persons should not be allowed to become involved with marihuana with impunity, legislators, law enforcement officials, and the courts should differentiate in the handling of the occasional user, the frequent user, the chronic user, the person sharing his drug with another, and the dealer who sells for a profit.

Of particular concern is the youthful experimenter who, by incurring a criminal record through a single thoughtless act, places his future career in jeopardy. The lives of many young people are being needlessly damaged.

For those persons who are chronic users of the drug, and are psychologically dependent on it, general medical and psychiatric treatment, plus social rehabilitative services, should be made readily available. Such persons should not be treated punitively for their drug abuse alone any more than are persons dependent on other drugs, such as narcotics or alcohol.

Furthermore, if the purpose of imposing penalties is to deter acts which might injure the individual and disrupt society, then equitable penalties, insofar as they enhance respect for the law, can contribute to effective prevention.

Additional research on marihuana should be encouraged.

Only recently has an active hallucinogenic principle of cannabis been exactly identified and synthesized. Sufficient time has not elapsed to obtain a substantial body of pharmacologic and clinical evidence concerning its effects. There are no carefully controlled clinical studies of long-time effects of cannabis on the central nervous or other organ systems. These and other considerations point to the importance of ongoing research in this area.

It must be emphasized, however, that the issue which faces the United States today is not whether we know all there is to know about marihuana scientifically. Obviously every effort should be made to correct the deficiencies in our knowledge. The issue is whether we can ignore the experiences and observations established over centuries of heavy use of hemp preparations in various societies. A current solution to the problem does not relate to what is not known, but to those facts which are known about cannabis and its preparations. There is extensive experience in its use in all of its forms, including the effects of the potent natural resins which contain the active biological principles.

Educational programs with respect to marihuana should be directed to all segments of the population.

Educational material, based on scientific knowledge, should point out the nature of marihuana and the effects of its use. Such material should be an integral part of a total educational program on drug abuse.

Primary and secondary schools, as well as colleges and universities, should establish such programs.

The communications media should disseminate authoritative information to the general public.

Physicians, as professional practitioners and concerned members of the community, should call attention frequently and forcibly to the problems of drug abuse and drug dependence.

An informed citizenry, in the final analysis, is the most effective deterrent of all.

THE GREAT MARIJUANA HOAX

Allen Ginsberg

How much there is to be revealed about marijuana in this decade in America for the general public! The actual experience of the smoked herb has been clouded by a fog of dirty language perpetrated by a crowd of fakers who have not had the experience and yet insist on downgrading it. The paradoxical key to this bizarre impasse of awareness is precisely that the marijuana consciousness is one that, ever so gently, shifts the center of attention *from* habitual shallow, purely verbal guidelines and repetitive secondhand ideological interpretations of experience to *more direct, slower, absorbing, occasionally microscopically minute engagement with sensing phenomena.*

A few people don't *like* the experience and report back to the language world that it's a drag. But the vast majority all over the world who have smoked the several breaths necessary to feel the effect, adjust to the strangely familiar sensation of Time slowdown, and explore this new space thru natural curiosity, report that it's a useful area of mind-

Reprinted from *The Atlantic Monthly* 218 (November 1966): 104 and 107–12, Copyright © 1966, by Allen Ginsberg, with the permission of the publisher and the author.

consciousness to be familiar with. Marijuana is a metaphysical herb less habituating than tobacco, whose smoke is no more disruptive than Insight.

This essay, conceived by a mature middle-aged gentleman, the holder at present of a Guggenheim Fellowship for creative writing, a traveler on many continents with experience of customs and modes of different cultures, is dedicated to those who have *not* smoked marijuana, who don't know exactly what it is but have been influenced by sloppy, or secondhand, or unscientific, or (as in the case of drug-control bureaucracies) definitely self-interested language used to describe the marijuana high pejoratively. I offer the pleasant suggestion that a negative approach to the whole issue (as presently obtains in what are aptly called square circles in the USA) is not necessarily the best, and that it is time to shift to a more positive attitude toward this specific experience.[1] If one is not inclined to have the experience oneself, this is a free country and no one is obliged to have an experience merely because friends, family, or business acquaintances have had it and report themselves pleased. On the other hand, an equal respect and courtesy are required for the sensibilities of one's familiars for whom the experience has not been closed off by the door of Choice.

The black cloud of negative propaganda on marijuana emanates from one particular source: the US Treas. Dept. Narcotics Bureau.[2] If the tendency (a return to common sense) to leave the opiate problem with qualified M.D.'s prevails, the main function of this large Bureau will shift to the persecution of marijuana. Otherwise, the Bureau will have no function except as a minor tax office, for which it was originally purposed, under aegis of Secty. of Treasury. Following Parkinson's Law that a bureaucracy will attempt to find work for itself, or following a simpler line of thought, that the agents of this Bureau have a business interest in perpetuating the idea of a marijuana "menace" lest they lose their employment, it is not unreasonable to suppose that a great deal of violence, hysteria & energy of the anti-marijuana language propaganda emanating from this source has as its motive a rather obnoxious self-interest, all the more objectionable for its tone of moralistic evangelism. This hypocrisy is recognizable to anybody who has firsthand experience of the so-called narcotic; which, as the reader may have noticed, I have termed an herb, which it is—a leaf or blossom—in order to switch from negative terminology and inaccurate language.

A marvelous project for a sociologist, and one which I am sure will be in preparation before my generation grows old, will be a close examination of the actual history and tactics of the Narcotics Bureau and its former chief Power, Harry J. Anslinger, in planting the seed of the marijuana "menace" in the public mind and carefully nurturing its growth over the last few decades until the unsuspecting public was forced to accept an outright lie.[3]

I must begin by explaining something that I have already said in public for many years: that I occasionally use marijuana in preference to alcohol, and have for several decades. I say occasionally and mean it quite literally; I have spent about as many hours high as I have spent in movie theaters—sometimes three hours a week, sometimes twelve or twenty or more, as at a film festival—with about the same degree of alteration of my normal awareness.

I therefore do know the subjective possibilities of marijuana and therein take evidence of my own senses between by own awareness of the mysterious ghastly universe of joy, pain, discovery, birth & death, the emptiness & awesomeness of its forms and consciousness described in the Prajnaparamita Sutra central to a Buddhist or even Christian or Hindu view of Kosmos which I sometimes experience while high, as for the last two paragraphs, and the cheap abstract inexperienced version of exactly the same thing one may have read in the newspapers, written by reporters (who smoke pot themselves occasionally nowadays) taking the main part of their poorly written squibs of misinformation from the texts & mouths of Chiefs of Narcotics Bureaus, Municipal or Federal— or an occasional doctor notorious in the profession for his ungracious stupidity & insulting manners.

What was this criminal vision of marijuana presented by the Narcotics Department for years in cheap sex magazines and government reports? Who invented the myths of base paranoia close to murder, frothing at the mouth of Egyptian dogs, sex orgies in cheap dives, debilitation and terror and physiological or mysterious psychic addiction? An essentially grotesque Image, a thought-hallucination magnified myriad thru mass media, a by-product of Fear—something quite fiendish—"Dope Fiend," the old language, a language abandoned in the early sixties when enough of the general public had sufficient personal experience to reject such palpable poppycock [4] & the bureaucratic line shifted to defense of its own existence with the following reason: necessary to control marijuana because smoking leads to search for thrill kicks; this leads to next step, the monster Heroin. And a terrible fate.

In historical context this recent excuse for repression of marijuana seems to the author so irrational that it is impossible to disprove. Yet public confusion may warrant some precise analysis: A) There are no legitimate sociological/medical study documents warranting the Narcotics Department's assertion of causal relation between use of marijuana and graduation to opiates. B) There never had been any hint of such association before the two classes of drugs were forcibly juxtaposed in black market by said department; Anslinger testified to that in 1937. C) A greater percent of opiate users started with bananas, cigarette & alcohol than started with marijuana—no causal relationship is indicated in any case. D) The number of millions of respectable Americans who smoke marijuana have obviously not proceeded on to opiates. E) In test sociological cases, i.e., societies such as Morocco and India where marijuana use is universal, there is very small use of opiates, and no social association or juxtaposition between the two classes of drugs. What juxtaposition there is in America has been created and encouraged by the propaganda and police repression tactics of the Narcotics Bureau. (*Pharmacological Basis of Therapeutics* 1965, and 1965 California Atty. General's Report both characterize the claimed causal relationship as "unproved.")

In sound good health I smoked legal ganja (as marijuana is termed in India, where it is traditionally used in preference to alcohol), bought from government tax shops in Calcutta, in a circle of devotees, yogis, and hymn-singing pious Shaivite worshipers in the burning ground at Nimtallah Ghat in Calcutta, where it was the custom of these respected gentlemen to meet on Tues. and Saturday nights, smoke before an improvised altar of blossoms, sacramental milk-candy & perhaps a fire taken from the burning wooden bed on which lay a newly dead body, of some friend perhaps, likely a stranger if a corpse is a stranger, pass out the candy as God's gift to friend and stranger, and sing holy songs all night, with great strength and emotion, addressed to different images of the Divine Spirit. Ganja was there considered a beginning of sadhana (Yogic path or discipline) by some; others consider the Ascetic Yogi Shiva Himself to have smoked marijuana; on His birthday marijuana is mixed as a paste with almond milk by the grandmothers of pious families and imbibed as a sacrament by this polytheistic nation, considered by some a holy society. The professors of English at Benares University brought me a bottle for the traditional night of Shivaratri, birthday of the Creator & Destroyer who is the patron god of this oldest continuously inhabited city on Earth. "BOM BOM MAHADEV!" (Boom Boom Great God!) is the Mantra Yogis' cry as they raise the ganja pipe to their brows before inhaling.

All India is familiar with ganja, and so is all Africa, and so is all the Arab world; and so were Paris and London in smaller measure in high-minded but respectable nineteenth-century circles; and so on a larger scale is America even now. Young and old, millions perhaps, smoke marijuana and see no harm. And we have not measured the Latin-American world, Mexico particularly, which gave the local herb its familiar name. In some respects we may then see its prohibition as an arbitrary cultural taboo.

There has been a tendency toward its suppression in the Arab world with the too hasty adoption of Western rationality & the enlarged activity of the American fanatic Mr. Anslinger, retired from the Narcotics Bureau but now US representative to the UN World Health Organization Narcotic Drugs Commission, a position from which he circulates hysterical notices and warnings manufactured in Washington's Treas. Dept. to the police forces of the cities of the world—so I was told by a police official in Tel Aviv, an old school chum who laughed about the latest release, a grim warning against the dangers of Khat, a traditional energizing leaf chewed by Bedouins of Arabia & businessmen & princes in Ethiopia, as well as a few traditional Yemenite Jews.

Professor Alfred R. Lindesmith in *The Addict and the Law* (Indiana University Press) has already objected in public print to the Department's manipulation and attempted quashing of various medical-juridic reports; the impartial LaGuardia Report of 1944 was rudely attacked by Anslinger; a President's Judicial Advisory Council Policy Statement (1964) has characterized the activities of the Bureau as exceeding legal rightfulness in "criminalizing" by executive fiat & administrative dictum those addicted to addicting drugs who for decades have been prevented from going to a doctor for treatment unless it was under the aegis of Lexington Jail, and thru police channels. Memory of the British East India Hemp Commission report, the largest in history, done in the 1890s, which concluded that marijuana was *not* a problem, has been ignored; [5] memories of our own Panama Canal military reports giving marijuana a clean bill of health have been unavailing in consideration of the Bureau; [6] thousands of intelligent citizens have been put in prison for uncounted years for possession or sale of marijuana, even if they grew it themselves and only smoked in private; youths have been entrapped into selling small or large quantities of the grass to police agents and consequently found themselves faced with all the venomous bullshit that an arbitrary law can create, from the terrors of arrest to the horror of years in jail; the author receives letters of complaint and appeals for help, from many US cities, from acquaintances, fellow litterateurs, even scholarly investigators of the subject writing books about it, as well as from one energetic poet founding a fine project for an Artist's Workshop (John Sinclair in Detroit, sentenced to six months for letting an agent buy marijuana for the second time); Ken Kesey, the novelist, is now in exile; 21,931 arrests for marijuana from 1963 to 1965 reported from

California alone, according to Prof. Alfred R. Lindesmith. The whole scene is so shrouded in bureaucratic mystery that there are no national figures available anywhere.

One becomes awed by the enormity of the imposition. It is not a healthy activity for the State to be annoying so many of its citizens thusly; it creates a climate of topsy-turvy law and begets disrespect for the law and the society that tolerates execution of such barbarous law,[7] and a climate of fear and hatred for the administrators of the law. Such a law is a threat to the existence of the State itself, for it sickens and debilitates its most adventurous and sensitive citizens. Such a law, in fact, can drive people mad.

It is no wonder then that most people who have smoked marijuana in America often experience a state of anxiety, of threat, of paranoia, in fact, which may lead to trembling or hysteria, at the microscopic awareness that they are breaking a Law, that thousands of Investigators are trained and paid to smoke them out and jail them, that thousands of their community are in jail, that inevitably a few friends are "busted" with all the hypocrisy and expense and anxiety of that trial & perhaps punishment —jail and victimage by the bureaucracy that made, propagandized, administers, and profits from such a monstrous law.

From my own experience and the experience of others I have concluded that most of the horrific effects and disorders described as characteristic of marijuana "intoxication" by the US Federal Treasury Department's Bureau of Narcotics are, quite the reverse, precisely traceable back to the effects on consciousness not of the narcotic but of the law and the threatening activities of the US Federal Treasury Department Bureau of Narcotics itself. Thus, as the Buddha said to a lady who offered him a curse, the gift is returned to the giver when it is not accepted.

I myself experience this form of paranoia when I smoke marijuana, and for that reason smoke it in America more rarely than I did in countries where it is legal. I noticed a profound difference of effect. The anxiety was directly traceable to fear of being apprehended and treated as a deviant criminal & put thru the hassle of social disapproval, ignominious Kafkian tremblings in vast court buildings coming to be judged, the helplessness of being overwhelmed by force or threat of deadly force and put in brick & iron cell.

This apprehension deepened when on returning this year from Europe, I was stopped, stripped, and searched at customs. The dust of my pockets was examined with magnifying glass for traces of weed. I had publicly spoken in defense of marijuana and attacked the conduct of the Bureau, and now my name was down on a letter/dossier at which I secretly peeked, on the Customs search-room desk. I quote the first sentence, referring to myself and Orlovsky: "These persons are reported to be smuggling (or importing) narcotics. . . ."

On a later occasion, when I was advised by several friends and near acquaintances that Federal Narcotics personnel in NYC had asked them to "set me up" for an arrest, I became incensed enough to write a letter of complaint to my congressman. He replied that he thought I was being humorless about the reason for my being on a list for Customs investigation, since it was natural (I had talked about the dread subject so much in public); anyway, not Kafkian as I characterized it. As for my complaint about being set up—that, with my letter, was forwarded to the Treasury Dept. in Washington for consideration and reply. Thus, the reply received December 22, 1965: "I would advise you that I have been in touch with the Bureau of Narcotics and am of the opinion that nothing has been done in your case that is illegal or inconsistent with law enforcement practices designed to enforce the narcotics laws." In this case it was police request to arrested friends that they carry marijuana to *my* apartment and to that of the novelist William S. Burroughs.

Rather than radically alter the preceding composition written in 1965 —let it remain for the reader who has not smoked marijuana a manifestation of marijuana-high thought structure in a mode which intersects our mutual consciousness, namely language—I wish to add here a few thoughts.

I have spent half a year in Morocco, smoking kif often: old gentlemen & peaceable youths sit amiably, in cafés or under shade trees in outdoor gardens, drinking mint tea, passing the tiny kif pipe, and looking quietly at the sea. This is the true picture of the use of kif in North Africa, exactly the opposite of the lurid stereotype of mad-dog human beings deliberately spread by our Treasury Department police branch. And I set this model of tranquil sensibility beside the tableau of aggravated New York executives sipping whiskey before a 1965 TV set's imagery of drunken American violence covering the world from the highways to Berkeley all the way to the dirt roads of Vietnam.

No one has yet remarked that the suppression of Negro rights, culture, and sensibility in America has been complicated by the marijuana laws. African sects have used pot for divine worship (much as I have described its sacred use in India). And to the extent that jazz has been an adaptation of an African religious form to American context, marijuana has been closely associated with the development of this indigenous American form of chant & prayer. Use of marijuana has always been widespread among the Negro population in this country, and suppression of its use, with constant friction and bludgeoning of the Law, has been a major unconscious, or unmentionable, method of assault on negro Person.

Although most scientific authors who present their reputable evidence for the harmlessness of marijuana make no claim for its surprising *usefulness,* I do make that claim:

Marijuana is a useful catalyst for specific optical and aural aesthetic perceptions. I apprehended the structure of certain pieces of jazz & classical music in a new manner under the influence of marijuana, and these apprehensions have remained valid in years of normal consciousness. I first discovered how to see Klee's Magic Squares as the painter intended them (as optically three-dimensional space structures) while high on marijuana. I perceived ("dug") for the first time Cézanne's "petit sensation" of space achieved on a two-dimensional canvas (by means of advancing & receding colors, organization of triangles, cubes, etc. as the painter describes in his letters) while looking at *The Bathers* high on marijuana. And I saw anew many of nature's panoramas & landscapes that I'd stared at blindly without even noticing before; thru the use of marijuana, awe & detail were made conscious. These perceptions are permanent—any deep aesthetic experience leaves a trace, & an idea of what to look for that can be checked back later. I developed a taste for Crivelli's symmetry; and saw Rembrandt's *Polish Rider* as a sublime Youth on a Deathly horse for the first time—saw myself in the rider's face, one might say—while walking around the Frick Museum high on pot. These are not "hallucinations"; these are deepened perceptions that one might have catalyzed not by pot but by some *other* natural event (as natural as pot) that changes the mind, such as an intense Love, a death in the family, a sudden clear dusk after rain, or the sight of the neon spectral reality of Times Square one sometimes has after leaving a strange movie. So it's all *natural.*

At this point it should be revealed for those unaware that most of the major (best and most famous, too) poets, painters, musicians, cineasts, sculptors, actors, singers & publishers in America and England have been smoking marijuana for years and years. I have gotten high with the majority of the dozens of contributors to the Don Allen *Anthology of New American Poetry 1945–1960;* and in years subsequent to its publication have sat down to coffee and a marijuana cigarette with not a few of the more academic poets of the rival Hall-Pack-Simpson anthology. No art opening in Paris, London, New York, or Wichita at which one may not sniff the incense fumes of marijuana issuing from the ladies' room. Up and down Madison Avenue it is charming old inside knowledge; and in the clacketing vast city rooms of newspapers on both coasts, copyboys and reporters smoke somewhat less marijuana than they take tranquilizers or Benzedrine, but pot begins to rival liquor as a non-medicinal delight in conversation. Already eight years ago I smoked marijuana with a couple of Narcotics Department plainclothesmen who were trustworthy enough to invite to a literary reception. A full-page paid advertisement in the New York *Times,* quoting authoritative medical evidence of the harmlessness of marijuana, and signed by a thousand of its most famous smokers, would once and for all break the cultural ice and end once and for all the tyranny of the Treasury Department Narcotics Bureau. For it would only manifest in public what everybody sane in the centers of communication in America knows anyway, an enormous open secret—that it is time to end Prohibition again. And with it put an end to the gangsterism, police mania, hypocrisy, anxiety, and national stupidity generated by administrative abuse of the Marijuana Tax Act of 1937.

It should be understood, I believe, that *in this area* we have been undergoing police-state conditions in America, with characteristic mass brainwashing of the public, persecution & jail, elaborate systems of plainclothes police and police spies and stool pigeons, abuse of constitutional guarantees of privacy of home and person from improper search and seizure. The police prohibition of marijuana (accompanied with the even more obnoxious persecution of sick heroin addicts who all along should have been seeing the doctor) has directly created vast black markets, crime syndicates, crime waves in the cities, and a breakdown of law and order in the State itself. For the courts of large cities are clogged with so-called narcotic crimes and behind schedule, and new laws (such as the recent NY Rockefeller Stop & Frisk & No-Knock) spring up against the citizen to cope with the massive unpopularity of prohibition.

Not only do I propose end of prohibition of marijuana but I propose a total dismantling of the whole cancerous bureaucracy that has perpetrated this historic screw-up on the United States. And not only is it necessary that the Bureau of Narcotics be dismantled & consigned to the wax museum of history, where it belongs, but it is also about time that a full-scale congressional investigation with all the resources of the embattled medical, legal & sociological authorities, who for years have been complaining in vain, should be undertaken to fix the precise responsibility for this vast swindle on the administrative & mass-media shoulders where it belongs. What was the motive & method in perpetrating this insane hoax on public consciousness? Have any laws of malfeasance in public office been violated?

Not only an investigation of how it all happened but some positive remuneration is required for those poor citizens who have been defenseless against beatings, arrest, and anxiety for years—a minority directly & physically persecuted by the police of cities and states and by agents of the nation; a minority often railroaded to jail by uncomprehending judges for months, for years, for decades; a minority battling idiotic laws, and even then without adequate legal representation for the slim trickery available to the rich to evade such laws. For the inoffensive charming smokers of marijuana who have undergone disgraceful jail-ings, money is due as compensation. This goes back decades for thou-sands of people, who, I claim, are among the most sensitive citizens of the nation; and their social place and special honor of character should be rewarded by a society which urgently needs this kind of sensibility where it can be seen in public.

I have long felt that there were political implications to the suppres-sion of marijuana, beyond the obvious revelation (which Burroughs pointed out in *Naked Lunch*) of the cancerous nature of the marijuana-suppression bureaucracy. When the citizens of this country see that such an old-time, taken-for-granted, flag-waving, reactionary truism of police, press, and law as the "reefer menace" is in fact a creepy hoax, a scare-crow, what will they begin to think of the whole of taken-for-granted public REALITY?

What of other issues filled with the same threatening hysteria? The specter of Communism? Respect for the police and courts? Respect for the Treasury Department? If marijuana is a hoax, what is Money? What is the War in Vietnam? What are the Mass Media?

As I declared at the beginning of this essay, marijuana consciousness shifts attention from stereotyped verbal symbols to "more direct, slower, absorbing, occasionally microscopically minute engagement with sens-ing phenomena" during the high. Already millions of people have gotten high and looked at the images of their Presidents and governors and representatives on television and seen that all were betraying signs of false character. Or heard the impersonal robot tones of radio news-casters announcing mass deaths in Asia.

It is no wonder that for years the great centers of puritanism of con-sciousness, blackout & persecution of the subtle vibrations of personal consciousness catalyzed by marijuana have been precisely Moscow and Washington, the centers of the human power war. Fanatical rigid men-tality pursuing abstract ideological obsessions make decisions in the right-wing mind of America, pursuing a hateful war against a mirror-image of the same "sectarian, dogmatic" ideological mentality in the Communist camp. It is part of the same pattern that both centers of power have the most rigid laws against marijuana. And that marijuana and versions of the African ritual music (folk-rock) are slowly catalyzing anti-ideological consciousness of the new generations on both sides of the Iron Time curtain.

I believe that future generations will have to rely on new faculties of awareness, rather than on new versions of old idea-systems, to cope with the increasing godlike complexity of our planetary civilization, with its overpopulation, its threat of atomic annihilation, its centralized network of abstract word-image communication, its power to leave the earth. A new consciousness, or new awareness, will evolve to meet a changed ecological environment. It has already begun evolving in younger generations from Prague to Calcutta; part of the process is a re-examination of certain heretofore discarded "primitive" devices of communication with Self and Selves. Negro worship rituals have invaded the West via New Orleans and Liverpool, in altered but still recognizably functional form. The odd perceptions of Zen, Tibetan Yoga, Mantra Yoga, & indigenous American peyotism and shamanism affect the consciousness of a universal generation, children who can recognize each other by hairstyle, tone of voice, attitude to nature, and attitude to Civilization. The air-waves are filled with songs of hitherto unheard-of frankness and beauty.

These then are some of the political or social implications of the public legitimization of marijuana as a catalyst to self-awareness.

A LITTLE ANTHOLOGY OF MARIJUANA FOOTNOTES

Footnote 1:

The English Journal of Medicine, *The Lancet,* Editorial, November 9, 1963. "At most of the recent references the question was raised whether the marijuana problem might be abolished by removing the substance from the list of dangerous drugs where it was placed in 1951, and giving it the same social status as alcohol by legalizing its import and consumption.

"This suggestion is worth considering. Besides the undoubted attraction of reducing, for once, the number of crimes that a member of our society can commit, and of allowing the wider spread of something that can give pleasure, a greater revenue would certainly come to the State from taxation than from fines. Additional gains might be the reduction of interracial tension, as well as that between generations; for 'pot' spread from South America to Britain via the United States and the West Indies. Here it has been taken up by the younger members of a society in which alcohol is the inheritance of the more elderly."

Footnote 2:

Anslinger, Harry J., and Oursler, W. C.: *The Murderers* (New York: Farrar, Straus & Cudahy, 1961), p. 38.

"As the Marijuana situation grew worse, I knew action had to be taken to get proper control legislation passed. By 1937, under my direction, the Bureau launched two important steps: First, a legislative plan to seek from congress a new law that would place Marijuana and its distribution directly under federal control. Second, on radio and at major forums, such as that presented annually by the New York Herald Tribune, I told the story of this evil weed of the fields and river beds and roadsides. I wrote articles for magazines; our agents gave hundreds of lectures to parents, educators, social and civic leaders. In network broadcasts I reported on the growing list of crimes, including murder and rape. I described the nature of Marijuana and its close kinship to hashish. I continued to hammer at the facts.

"I believe we did a thorough job, for the public was alerted, and the laws to protect them were passed, both nationally and at the state level."

Footnote 3:

"Traffic in Opium and Other Dangerous Drugs," Report by the Government of the United States of America for the Year Ended December 31st, 1938, by Hon. H. J. Anslinger, Commissioner of Narcotics, p. 7.

"The Narcotics Section recognizes the great danger of marihuana due to its definite impairment of the mentality and the fact that its continuous use leads direct to the insane asylum."

Footnote 4:

The Pharmacological Basis of Therapeutics, Goodman and Gillman, 1956 ed., pp. 170–177: "There are no lasting ill effects from the acute use of marihuana, and fatalities have not been known to occur. . . . Careful and complete medical and neuropsychiatric examinations of habitues reveal no pathological conditions or disorders of cerebral functions attributable to the drug. . . . Although habituation occurs, psychic dependence is not as prominent or compelling as in the case of morphine, alcohol, or perhaps even tobacco habituation."

Footnote 5:

Report of the British East India Hemp Commission, 1893–94, Ch. XIII, pp. 263–264 (Summary of Conclusions regarding effects).

"The Commission has now examined all the evidence before them regarding the effects attributed to hemp drugs. . . . In regard to the physical effects, the Commission have come to the conclusion that the moderate use of hemp drugs is practically attended by no evil results at all. There may be exceptional cases in which, owing to idiosyncracies of constitution, the drugs in even moderate use may be injurious. There is probably nothing the use of which may not possibly be injurious in cases of exceptional intolerance. . . .

"In respect to the alleged mental effects of the drugs, the Commission have come to the conclusion that the moderate use of hemp drugs produces no injurious effects on the mind. . . .

"In regard to the moral effects of the drugs, the Commission are of the opinion that their moderate use produces no moral injury whatever . . . for all practical purposes it may be laid down that there is little or no connection between the use of hemp drugs and crime.

"Viewing the subject generally, it may be added that the moderate use of these drugs is the rule, and that the excessive use is comparatively exceptional."

Footnote 6:

Panama Canal Zone Governor's Committee, April–December, 1925 (*The Military Surgeon,* Journal of the Association of Military Surgeons of the United States, November, 1933, p. 274).

"After an investigation extending from April 1 to December 1925, the Committee reached the following conclusions: There is no evidence that marihuana as grown here is a 'habit-forming' drug in the sense in which the term is applied to alcohol, opium, cocaine, etc., or that it has any appreciably deleterious influence on the individual using it."

Footnote 7:

Proceedings, White House Conference on Narcotic and Drug Abuse, September, 1962, State Department Auditorium, Washington, D.C., p. 266: "It is the opinion of the Panel that the hazards of Marijuana per se have been exaggerated and that long criminal sentences imposed on an occasional user or possessor of the drug are in poor social perspective. Although Marijuana has long held the reputation of inciting individuals to commit sexual offenses and other antisocial acts, the evidence is inadequate to substantiate this. Tolerance and physical dependence do not develop and withdrawal does not produce an abstinence syndrome."

James H. Fox, Ph.D., Director, Bureau of Drug Abuse Control, Food and Drug Administration: Statement August 24, 1966, before National Student Association Subcommittee on Drugs and the Campus. NSA Convention, Urbana, Illinois; Quoted Champaign *News-Gazette* August 25, 1966.

"My studies have led me to essentially the same conclusion as Mr. Ginsberg's. I think we can now say that marijuana does not lead to degeneration, does not affect the brain cells, is not habit-forming, and does not lead to heroin addiction. I would say that there may very well be some modification in government attitudes towards marijuana."

The Marihuana Problem in the City of New York, by the Mayor's Committee on Marihuana: The Sociological Study, Intro. by Dudley D. Schoenfeld, M.D. Reprinted in *The Marihuana Papers.* Bobbs-Merrill, New York, 1966.

"Conclusions:

7. The practice of smoking marihuana does not lead to addiction in the medical sense of the word.

9. The use of marihuana does not lead to morphine or heroin or cocaine addiction, and no effort is made to create a market for these narcotics by stimulating the practice of marihuana smoking.

10. Marihuana is not the determining factor in the commission of major crimes.

13. The publicity concerning the catastrophic effects of marihuana smoking in New York City is unfounded."

Ibid.: Intellectual Functioning, Florence Halpern, MA
"Conclusions:

6. Indulgence in marihuana does not appear to result in mental deterioration."

Ibid.: Addiction and Tolerance

"The evidence available then—the absence of any compelling urge to use the drug, the absence of any distressing abstinence symptoms, the statements that no increase in dosage is required to repeat the desired effect in users— justifies the conclusion that neither true addiction nor tolerance is found in marihuana users. The continuation and the frequency of usage of marihuana, as in the case of many other habit-forming substances, depend on the easily controlled desires for its pleasurable effects."

Ibid. Summary by George B. Wallace, M.D., Chairman

"From the study as a whole, it is concluded that marihuana is not a drug of addiction, comparable to morphine, and that if tolerance is acquired, this is of very limited degree. Furthermore those who have been smoking marihuana for a period of years showed no mental or physical deterioration which may be attributed to the drug.

No evidence was found of an acquired tolerance for the drug.

The sensations desired are pleasurable ones—a feeling of contentment, inner satisfaction, free play of imagination. Once this stage is reached, the experienced user realizes that with further smoking the pleasurable sensations will be changed to unpleasant ones, and so takes care to avoid this."

MARIJUANA: THE REAL PROBLEMS AND THE RESPONSIBILITIES OF THE PROFESSIONS IN SOLVING THEM

Joel Fort

What opportunities have you had of obtaining information regarding the matters connected with hemp drugs in regard to which your answers are framed? What classes and what proportion of the people eat, drink, or smoke hemp drugs, and in what localities? Is the use of these drugs on the increase, or decrease? What proportion of the consumers are: (a) habitual moderate; (b) habitual excessive; (c) occasional moderate; (d) occasional excessive consumers? To what extent is the consumption of each of these drugs practiced in solitude or in company? Is there a tendency for the moderate habit to develop into the excessive? If not beneficial, do you consider the moderate use to be harmless? Give reasons for your answer. Does the habitual moderate use produce any noxious effects— physical, mental, or moral? Do you think the cultivation of the hemp plant should be in any way controlled; would this be feasible; if so, indicate the method by which such control could be exercised? Would it be feasible to prohibit the use of these drugs; would the drug be consumed illicitly; how could the prohibition be

Reprinted from *Psychiatric Opinion* 5 (October 1968): 9–15, with the permission of the publisher.

enforced; would the prohibitions be followed by recourse to alcohol or other drugs?

Thus began the inquiry of the Indian Hemp Drugs Commission carried out by the British in 1893–94 to determine whether there was a cannabis problem and how it could best be dealt with. In 1968 we need to ask ourselves why passion, extremism, ignorance, and irrationality have come to be substituted in regard to marijuana (and other matters) for the above objectivity and reason. Why have many physicians and other professionals allied themselves with drug policemen and politicians in criminalizing our youth and in talking about marijuana as though it were more dangerous than any other phenomenon in our society including cancer, guns, or the hydrogen bomb?

To understand the use of any drug, whether aspirin, penicillin, or alcohol, one must look at the full context of drugs, including the full range of psychoactive or mind-altering drugs (alcohol, nicotine, barbiturates, amphetamines, LSD, narcotics, tranquilizers, and many others, in addition to marijuana). Even more important is to recognize drug usage as a symptom or barometer of a society which is in many ways sick, hypocritical, primitive, and underdeveloped; a society which is drug-ridden, crime-ridden, and myth-ridden.

The "problem" of marijuana is taken for granted by most laymen and professionals and consists of a vague conglomerate of fear-inducing impressions, or paranoia, including the concepts of "dope fiend" (with marijuana at the least being a stepping-stone to this evil state), "sexual excesses," assassination, psychosis, crime, dropping out, and general immorality. As with most things the truth is far more complex. What is deviant, abnormal, sick, or criminal is not handed down by God but rather is arbitrarily and subjectively defined for each culture and society by certain moral entrepreneurs or rule makers, in this case, narcotic police (especially the Federal Bureau of Narcotics), medical bureaucrats, politicians, and the mass media.

With marijuana, alcohol, or any other drug, it is important to differentiate short-term effects and long-term effects, average doses and large doses, use and abuse, and other dimensions which are customarily glossed over. Abuse of drugs involves excessive use to an extent that it impairs an individual's health or social or vocational adjustment. Documented cases of drug abuse involving marijuana are few and short-lived, but the situation can best be put in perspective by discussing a concept dear to the hearts of drug extremists, "hard" drugs.

Although the American Medical Association and the National Research Council recently saw fit to issue a special statement to the effect that marijuana is a "dangerous drug," the committee members (who for the most part have had no research or clinical experience with marijuana in either natural or pathological settings) would have been more accurate and honest if they had said that marijuana, like all drugs including aspirin and alcohol, can be dangerous depending on how it is used, for what purposes, and by whom. Even those who have been rescued from well-deserved obscurity (and who make a good living from the marijuana demonology) now admit that it is not a narcotic despite the false classification of the laws and that it does not produce addiction (physical dependency). However, the latest one-dimensional oversimplification is the stress on psychological dependence or habituation. Under this concept, a person becomes so accustomed to something from regular use that he feels restless or uncomfortable when the agent is no longer available. Psychological dependence can occur with marijuana just as it can and often does with caffeine, nicotine, alcohol, and with such things as television or one's spouse. Habituation to anything will divert a certain amount of time, energy, and money, but fortunately it does not always impair an individual's functioning. The real significance of habituation must always be determined for each person within the full context of his life.

The major definitions of "hardness" would certainly include death, damage to body organs, mental illness, addiction, and accidents. Thus, without minimizing in any way the seriousness of a bad LSD trip, amphetamine psychosis, or heroin addiction, the doctor, policeman, and politician should be giving the highest priority to reducing and eliminating the use and abuse of alcohol and tobacco. Most people reluctantly acknowledge the millions of deaths and disabilities resulting from cigarette smoking, but few seem aware of America's 6,000,000 alcoholics with their cirrhosis of the liver (the 6th leading cause of death in America), addiction, job loss, family disruption, and mental illness (including chronic brain damage which accounts for 20 percent of those in state mental hospitals). Fifty percent of those in prison for murder, robbery, theft and rape committed these crimes after taking alcohol and 50–70 percent of the 53,000 deaths and 2,500,000 serious injuries on the highways each year are associated with alcohol consumption. To say the least, physicians and other professionals who have preoccupied themselves with marijuana, LSD, or narcotics have been hypocritical and have helped the drug policemen in their systematic efforts to delude the public and aggrandize their agencies. As a final example, heroin— which has been made the foundation of the drug demonology—is "hard" in the sense of liability to induce physical dependency, but it is "softer" than alcohol or tobacco in that it produces no irreversible physical damage to body organs, even with many years of heavy daily use.

No drug is harmless, and no drug is inherently desirable, necessary or life-enhancing.

Surely marijuana is the most remarkable chemical substance ever known if it has even a fraction of the properties attributed to it by various self-appointed experts. It is said to produce both sexual "excesses" and decreased interest in sex; violence and passivity; radicalism and dropping-out; heroin addiction and LSD use; psychosis and consciousness-expansion. Actually, the effects of any mind-altering drug (assuming a moderate or average dose) depend mainly on the personality and character structure of the user, including their moods, attitudes and expectations, all interacting with the pharmacological properties of the drug and the socio-cultural setting in which the drug is consumed. This principle is best illustrated by the most common mind-altering drug experience in our society, the cocktail party or other group "turn-on" with alcohol. People of similar ages and backgrounds consume the same quantities of the drug and behave in markedly different ways, ranging through passivity or drowsiness, aggressiveness or violence, amorousness or overt sexual behavior, euphoria or gloominess. Happily, there is no drug, including marijuana, which will magically transform an otherwise conforming, well-adjusted normal person into a licentious, violent psychotic; and, unhappily, there is no drug, including marijuana, which will transform mediocrity and ignorance into productive genius.

Pharmacologically, tetrahydrocannabinol, the active principle of the (female) cannabis sativa plant variously referred to as marijuana, ganja, kif, hashish, charas, bhang, etc., now appears to have a mixed sedative-stimulant effect on the central nervous system and mind. Some prefer to refer to it by nonspecific and often emotional terms—intoxicant, psychedelic, hallucinogen, etc.—which help to confuse rather than to illuminate. Some of its properties (keeping in mind the broad principle of mind-altering drug effects enunciated above) are similar to depressant drugs such as alcohol, barbiturates, and morphine, while others are similar to stimulants such as caffeine and amphetamines.

Historically, cannabis derivatives or products have been used for at least 5,000 years, and it is presently used by an estimated 250,000,000 people in North America, South America, the West Indies, Europe, Africa, and Asia, second in popularity only to alcohol, a drug which has been aggressively manufactured, distributed, advertised and "pushed" by those liking and profiting from that drug.

Conservatively it seems likely that at least 5,000,000 Americans are users of marijuana, often referred to as pot, grass or weed. The tens of thousands of arrests and the seizures of large quantities of the plant are only the top of the iceberg, since it is estimated that in the United States 15–20 percent of college students and 20–40 percent of urban high school students use or have used it. Many more have experimented with it in the past, including 10 percent of a recent representative sample of adults surveyed in the San Francisco metropolitan area. As significant as the numbers involved is the spread to all socio-economic classes and occupational groups. Surveys I have conducted over the past year show that in one large urban school district 18 percent of 7th grade boys and 12 percent of the girls have used marijuana. In the 12th grade, 41 percent of the boys and 43 percent of the girls have used the drug, the majority with some regularity.

Obviously, pot is *now,* just as alcohol and tobacco are now, for a large proportion of the young and for increasing numbers of the older generations.

Many types of bias have contributed to the ignorance, confusion and hysteria about marijuana. Generalizing from laboratory or pathological experience to the natural situation; from the results or consequences of another drug such as heroin; or from the pronouncements of the Federal Bureau of Narcotics (recently re-organized and renamed the Bureau of Narcotics and Dangerous Drugs) are the most common sources of error. There is a notable absence of logic, rationality and statistical reasoning.

Why are so many people, young and old, seeking out old and new drugs, legally and illegally? Certainly it reflects widespread alienation, with growing numbers of individuals finding school, jobs, and leisure-time pursuits lacking in meaning and significance. There is reaction and over-reaction to decades of lies and distortions about drugs and about other important subjects, and there are communication and credibility gaps which accompany the generation gap. The role models of the young—their parents and other "mature" adults—consistently utilize mind-altering drugs whenever they socialize, relax, or seek pleasure. The alcoholic beverage, tobacco, and over-the-counter "sedative" industries spend millions of dollars every single day in advertising and promoting drug usage, stressing such lures as youthfulness, sexual pleasure and happiness. Our society has been taught, and has gullibly accepted, that it is natural, harmless and beneficial to place a dried plant leaf (tobacco) in one's mouth, ignite it, and inhale and exhale the resulting smoke. It should not be surprising that this practice has carried over to marijuana smoking, but it *should* emphasize the interdependency of the different drug problems and the necessity for a combined approach. Peer group and conformist pressures constitute another contributing cause, along with the absence of drug education and of more constructive alternatives to drug use. Then there is the crimino-genic effect of the extreme drug laws. Sociologists have long recognized that to label "vice" illegal, deviant, or abnormal actually makes it far more interesting and attractive to many people, particularly those who see themselves as being disaffiliated from, or in revolt against, the estab-lishment, as do most of our youth.

When we discuss and react to marijuana, we respond to a symbol of the chasm between young and old, between open and closed minds, be-tween libertarian and authoritarian mentalities. Politicians have loved the subject; the more one succeeds in foisting the marijuana menace on the public, the less one needs to talk about alcohol, racism, poverty, war and other far more serious matters, the discussion of which in any depth might result in loss of votes, decreased income, or worst of all, unpopu-larity. The drug laws have an important scapegoating and anti-intel-lectual function in our society, being used to attack youth and other minorities, dissent, and nonconformity.

Early in this century we had widespread (but much less than now) use of alcohol and of tonics containing opium and/or alcohol. The con-cept of addiction was not yet delineated, and no survey or statistical data exists to substantiate the claims of drug policemen and their medi-cal allies that "1 in 400" Americans were "addicts." Whatever the for-mer prevalence of use, despite increasingly severe criminal penalties for users and distributors, more people are using more drugs (including more potentially-dangerous ones) than ever before. We see, then, that the present system is "soft on drugs," an appellation frequently mis-directed against modern reformers in much the same way that political dissenters are often labeled as traitors or Communists. What the current laws are "hard on" is not marijuana, but rather human beings, and the time is long overdue for us to redirect our focus and our priorities despite intimidation and harassment by those benefiting from the status quo.

Those who have been influenced by the 12th century tale of a group of assassins (actually religious fanatics seeking to free their country) who were said to have used marijuana (hashish, etymologically derived from the Arabic for assassin) should take comfort from the fact that mind-altering drugs don't work that way, and that from the findings of schol-ars, these men actually were influenced by wine and beautiful women.

There is another sacred cow of the marijuana demonology which I call the stepping-stone theory. Like the domino theory of foreign policy, this rests upon a very insubstantial foundation. Basically it states that even if marijuana isn't actually a combination of arsenic and the H-bomb, it is necessary to devote vast resources to spying upon, entrapping and jailing the young who use it, so that we can save them from stepping up to heroin (sometimes in recent years shifted to LSD). Even if there were some causal relationship, which there clearly is not, between smoking or eating marijuana and becoming a heroin addict, the proper approach would be education and rehabilitation, not expulsion from school, a criminal record, and training in real crime and homosexuality in one of our prisons. In any case there is an inverse relationship, for as marijuana use has increased astronomically, the use of and addiction to heroin has declined. Even Anslinger, the author of most of our current stereotypes and policies, in presenting his anecdotal and hysterical accounts of marijuana's dangers to a respectful Congress in 1937, stated in response to a question that there was no relationship between marijuana and heroin. The philosopher David Hume and others have pointed out that just because one thing follows another in sequence does not show causality. If one asks about mind-altering drug usage in its full and proper context in talking with heroin addicts, one finds that the first drugs used (and illegally in the early teens) were alcohol and tobacco. Some of these individuals then later used marijuana, and some, a small minority even a decade ago, later used heroin. The bare statement that 50–70 percent of heroin addicts used marijuana may impress the untrained and uncritical, but in reality it is meaningless and a non sequitur. The limited association between the two drugs was a direct consequence of misguided laws which, as another of their criminogenic effects, drove the two together in the black market traffic as they were made profitable to the purveyors of vice.

The real marijuana problem is the law and its fanatical enforcement. Police, bureaucrats, politicians, and the mass media define the drug for society as being far more interesting, important, and desirable than it actually is. Since most discussions are polarized in terms of the criminalization of anyone even remotely associated with marijuana (including in many states anyone in a room or building where any amount of the drug is present), few individuals ever get around to talking about specific and constructive alternatives. Legalization of pot, for most people, seems to mean something analagous to what we have done with tobacco and alcohol, i.e., making them essentially uncontrolled and overavailable, while many individuals and many governments profit from their widespread use and abuse.

The first major responsibility of the professional should be to help communicate to the public and its "leaders" that the present system has been notably unsuccessful and dangerously harmful and that we can be much more selective and sophisticated in our policies by concentrating the criminal law on antisocial behavior, on real crime (increasing dramatically in our cities), and on large-scale trafficking in disapproved drugs.

The major reform in which I have been involved nationally is to take the drug user and possessor (whether of alcohol, tobacco, marijuana, LSD, or heroin) entirely out of the criminal law, recognizing such use and possession as a public health and sociological matter. It is as barbaric and inhumane to manufacture criminals out of drug users as it was to put the mentally ill in dungeons and burn witches at the stake. It is also unsuccessful and expensive. If we were to consistently and completely enforce our present drug laws, schools would be depopulated and our unjailed youth decimated overnight, particularly in regard to the illegal use of alcohol and tobacco with marijuana a distant third in extent of use. Unfortunately, there are those in our society who would like to do just that with marijuana, while hypocritically ignoring the other drugs despite the real health and social problems stemming from their use.

The issue is not how harmful or harmless marijuana is, or may be found to be (if the blocking of research by the narcotics agencies can be overcome by professional outcry); rather it is how to deal with the situation in a constructive and humane manner. No amount of research will show the drug to be as dangerous as a number of agents already widely disseminated in our society.

Truth, rationality, and concern for human welfare are ideally qualities to be provided by the professions, particularly medicine, even when something or somebody considered to be evil is involved. I would hope that most of the readers of this article will subscribe to the following statement, first circulated at the 1967 meeting of the American Sociological Association, and signed among others by Professors Alfred Lindesmith, Howard Becker, and the writer:

> We, the undersigned medical and social scientists having national and international experience with the problems and challenges of marijuana use, wish to indicate our agreement that the present extreme laws imposing criminal penalties on users of marijuana require drastic and immediate reform through judicial and legislative action. Social and legal policies in the United States regarding this substance should recognize possession or use as a sociological and public health matter, removing this from the criminal law and reserving such criminal penalites solely for antisocial behavior and if necessary, illicit manufacture and distribution. Present marijuana laws were based almost entirely on self-serving, hearsay testimony presented in an artificially created climate of emotionalism and failed to reflect or consider scientific knowledge or thinking. Such legislative action in the 1930's has defeated the purposes

for which it was supposedly intended and has brought about far more extensive drug use, and has done far more social and individual harm than marijuana itself. Clinical and social research, which is practically nonexistent at the present time due to current repressive policies of narcotics agencies, should be urgently accelerated and broadened. State and national conferences of true experts in the pharmacological, psychological, sociological, and other aspects of marijuana use, should be convened in the near future to provide guidelines to government for future policies of regulation and control.

An ideal program for reducing the use of mind-altering drugs should deal with all of them and should involve physicians and all other professionals. Such a program should include the law reforms mentioned above.

> A total ban on advertising and/or promotion of any of these drugs. Higher taxation.
> Prominent, unequivocal labeling of alcohol and tobacco as to their multiple dangers and higher taxation of the sale and purchase of these substances.
> Treatment by private practitioners and special clinics of the drug abuser (alcoholic, chronic tobacco smoker, heroin addict, amphetamine psychotic, LSD bad tripper, barbiturate addict, etc.).
> Full-scale educational programs beginning in elementary school, and extending on to adults, to present facts about all of the drugs in one context and to demythologize and desensationalize them.
> Developing better role models for the young.
> Attacking the roots of the multiple drug problems—i.e., bureaucratization, poverty, racism, disease, boredom, inadequate family associations, and in general, the low quality of American life.

To do nothing or to uphold the status quo is to be part of the problem, and perhaps to authenticate the words of T. S. Eliot, "The line down the middle of the road is yellow."

Let us remember, as doctors and as men, other words from the Book of Job:

> *From out of the city the dying groan, and the soul of the wounded cries for help.*

PART **3**

RESEARCH REPORTS

ADVERSE REACTION TO MARIHUANA

Martin H. Keeler

Eleven individuals who reported adverse reactions associated with the use of marihuana were interviewed. Their difficulties included one report of panic and fear, one report of depersonalization, one report of gross confusion and disorientation, two reports of depression, and four reports of paranoid phenomena during the drug reaction. The individual who reported confusion during the reaction also experienced recurrence of confusion and hallucinations intermittently afterwards. One of the individuals who experienced depression during the reaction had similar experiences thereafter.

Two other individuals reported major changes in behavior and style of life after the use of marihuana. Four others were interviewed who had become schizophrenic subsequent to the combined use of marihuana, lysergic acid diethylamide, and amphetamine. All 17 of these individuals were of superior intelligence and all were or had been uni-

Reprinted from *American Journal of Psychiatry* 124 (November 1967): 674–77, copyright 1967, the American Psychiatric Association with the permission of the publisher and author.

versity students. None was a delinquent in the usual sense; none had ever been arrested. All but two came from middle-class backgrounds two came from upper lower-class families.

More detailed presentation of the clinical data will be preceded by description of the marihuana reaction and followed by presentation of other reports of adverse reaction and consideration of the problems involved in the evaluation of such data.

DESCRIPTION OF THE MARIHUANA REACTION

Knowledge of usual reaction is required to interpret reports of unusual drug reaction. Bouquet summarized the effects of marihuana in terms that are consistent with the statements made by marihuana users interviewed in the clinic from which this study derives. Euphoria, a feeling of well-being, increase of self-confidence, and decreased self-criticism occur.

The user feels that he is unusually aware of the function of his limbs and that he could perform feats of physical agility or grace but that he is too tranquil to do so. The power to focus concentration is lost or relinquished. Associations are rapid and disorganized. Concepts of time and space are altered. Illusions, visual and auditory hallucinations, and sensitivity to sound occur.

Allentuck described the effects of the administration of marihuana to 78 subjects. He stated that euphoria and difficulties in concentration and sustaining attention were frequent. Excitement, anxiety, and/or dysphoric reactions occurred in some subjects.

Physiologic responses to marihuana include tachycardia, mydriasis, and suffusion of the conjunctiva. Subjective sensations often include feelings of rightness, heaviness or pressure in the head, dryness of the mouth, and a "floating sensation."

CASE REPORTS

Case 1. A 21-year-old man stated that after smoking more than his usual amount he became disoriented to time and place, could not think, and had difficulty in controlling his limbs. For some weeks thereafter he intermittently experienced hallucinations resembling those he had had during the reaction. These sensations were accompanied by a degree of anxiety approaching panic.

Case 2. A 19-year-old woman stated that during a marihuana reaction she had become intensely anxious and apprehensive without any idea of what she was afraid of. She said that she had been agitated and in a state of panic.

Case 3. A 20-year-old woman stated that while smoking marihuana she would become convinced that she did not exist in a spatial sense. She would think that she was merged with the universe, or, alternatively, a point in space without dimensions. Such ideation, accompanied by anxiety, would persist for some hours after the use of the drug.

Case 4. A 19-year-old man reported that during a marihuana reaction he became convinced that his internal organs were rotting and that he would die. This was related to a conviction that he had done evil things.

Case 5. A 23-year-old woman stated that during the marihuana reaction and for some hours afterwards she would have the "horrors." She described this as a feeling that indescribably evil things would happen to her because of the kind of person she was.

Case 6. A 20-year-old woman reported that during a marihuana reaction she became convinced that her friends had informed the police that there would be a marihuana party so that they might raid the house and catch her using the drug.

Case 7. A 22-year-old man stated that during the drug reaction he would become convinced that his taking the drug was part of some gigantic plot but that he did not know what the plot was.

Case 8. A 20-year-old man stated that during the marihuana reaction he would become preoccupied with whether his friends thought he was a homosexual. There was no reality testing of this conviction during the drug reaction.

Case 9. A 23-year-old man stated that during the marihuana reaction he would become preoccupied with the possibility of a police raid and would interpret every noise he heard as caused by approaching police.

Case 10. A 20-year-old man stated that after taking marihuana he recognized that his previous goals, including what he called conventional ambition, conformity, and fear, were not as important as the need to express himself and achieve independent identity. His interest and achievement in academic areas deteriorated and his dress became nonconventional.

Case 11. A 22-year-old woman stated that after taking marihuana she recognized that her graduate school work did not permit adequate self-expression. She did not drop out of school and her intelligence was such that she continued to do passable work. She stated that her academic work had once been a source of pleasure but that she now recognized that she had been "brainwashed" by the system.

Four individuals who demonstrated sufficient thinking disorders and inappropriate affect to justify the diagnosis of schizophrenia were interviewed, and they admitted to the almost daily use of amphetamine and marihuana and the regular use of LSD.

OTHER REPORTS OF ADVERSE REACTION

Allentuck administered the equivalent of between 30 and 330 mg. of tetrahydrocannabinol orally to 72 subjects. Six subjects had acute brain syndromes during the reaction. Three others became psychotic within the next few weeks. It was Allentuck's opinion that these latter psychoses would have occurred even if the drug had not been administered.

Ames administered between .24 and .46 gm. of a cannabis extract orally to each of ten subjects. One subject experienced intense anxiety and five subjects exhibited some degree of delusional thinking.

De Farias observed nine subjects smoking 2.82 gm. and seven of the same subjects smoking 1.56 gm. of cannabis. Delirium and confusion with apprehension of impending death occurred in one subject.

Chopra and associates implicated marihuana in the difficulties of 600 patients admitted to mental hospitals in India. They classified these reactions as acute mania, chronic mania, and dementia. Hallucinations, a dare-devil attitude with unresistable impulses to do willful damage, and amnesia for the attack upon remission characterized acute mania. The patients with chronic mania were cheerful, boastful, and had a sense of well-being. Data such as these have been questioned by many on several accounts. Such a large proportion of the population in the area involved uses cannabis that a high proportion of hospitalized patients would give such a history even if the drug were harmless. The criteria whereby psychoses caused by marihuana differ from other psychoses is not explicit.

Benabud reported evidences of acute or subacute cannabis effect in 49 percent of the 1,252 patients admitted to a Moroccan mental hospital in 1956. He considered certain types of excitation, impulsivity, oneiric, and visual hallucinatory states to be cannabis-induced. One or more of these phenomena were present in such disorders or were superimposed on other psychopathological conditions.

Benabud defined six percent of the admissions in the year studied as "cannabis-mobilized psychoses." This is defined as a psychosis of a functional type precipitated by cannabis intoxication. He defined 11 percent of the admissions in the year studied as "cannabis-aggravated psychoses." This is defined as a preexistent psychotic condition made worse by the use of cannabis.

Benabud's report, like that of Chopra and associates, has been subjected to some criticism. So many people in the area use cannabis that many hospital patients would have done so by chance alone. Many difficulties ascribed to cannabis could have resulted from other causes.

The reports of Allentuck, Ames, and De Farias, previously noted, do not have the weaknesses of the Chopra and associates and the Benabud reports. Specific psychotic syndromes were observed to occur during the marihuana reaction.

DISCUSSION

There is good reason for controversy as to the prevalence of adverse reaction to marihuana. For proper evaluation of adverse drug effect, information is required as to number of untoward reactions, the size of the population using the drug, dosage, and the nature of the population using the drug. As will be discussed below, none of this information is available for marihuana.

In the case of marihuana a definition of adverse reaction is also required. The evaluation of adverse reaction is, in addition, dependent on the interpretation of such a statement as, "Marihuana in itself does not produce functional psychopathology but may precipitate such in individuals who are so predisposed."

There is no accurate or reasonably accurate way of determining how many acute difficulties occur during or immediately after marihuana use. Most of these reactions do not come to medical attention. There are great differences in the potency of different preparations. The populations from which the reports of adverse reactions in this study are derived might be defined as university nonconformist. These individuals are of superior intelligence, more than average education, and not delinquent in the usual sense. It is not justified to assume that adverse reactions would be the same in this group, a delinquent group in a large city of the United States, and the urban poor of Morocco.

There is some difficulty in the evaluation of changes in style of life subsequent to marihuana use. Many individuals so change direction without drug use; many begin to use drugs only after they have so changed direction. No one has the right to define a change in style of life and goals of life as psychopathology. Nevertheless, when this occurs immediately after drug use it may be permissible to consider such a change to be an adverse drug reaction.

Perhaps all investigators would agree that marihuana cannot produce functional psychopathology but can only precipitate it in individuals so predisposed. Many would interpret this as an exoneration of the drug. Others would hold that the occurrence of psychopathology in an individual at a given time requires many factors and that more people have predisposition to mental illness than develop it. In this sense marihuana usage might precipitate trouble that would not have otherwise occurred or would have otherwise occurred at a later time.

It is the author's opinion that the literature does indicate that marihuana, depending on dose and subject, can precipitate acute brain syndromes, panic, and delusional thinking during the reaction. The use of the drug can initiate changes in style of life. It is left to others to decide whether this constitutes psychopathology.

It is the clinical impression of the author that this dissolution of ordinary adaptive and defensive psychological structure that occurs during the marihuana reaction is potentially dangerous for individuals with a predisposition to schizophrenia.

The evaluation of the harm a drug does requires some consideration of its benefits. Users of marihuana state that it is a source of positive pleasure, that it enhances creativity, that it provides insight, and that it enriches their lives. These are hardly minor claims. All but two of the 11 individuals reporting adverse reactions considered the benefits to far outweigh the unfortunate aspects and planned to continue use of the drug.

BECOMING A MARIHUANA USER

Howard S. Becker

The use of marihuana is and has been the focus of a good deal of attention on the part of both scientists and laymen. One of the major problems students of the practice have addressed themselves to has been the identification of those individual psychological traits which differentiate marihuana users from nonusers and which are assumed to account for the use of the drug. That approach, common in the study of behavior categorized as deviant, is based on the premise that the presence of a given kind of behavior in an individual can best be explained as the result of some trait which predisposes or motivates him to engage in the behavior.[1]

---

[1] See, as examples of this approach, the following: Eli Marcovitz and Henry J. Meyers, "The Marihuana Addict in the Army," *War Medicine,* VI (December, 1944), 382–91; Herbert S. Gaskill, "Marihuana, an Intoxicant," *American Journal of Psychiatry,* CII (September, 1945), 202–4; Sol Charen and Luis Perelman, "Personality Studies of Marihuana Addicts," *American Journal of Psychiatry,* CII (March, 1946), 674–82.

Reprinted from *The American Journal of Sociology* 59 (November 1953): 235–42, with the permission of the publisher, The University of Chicago Press, and the author. Paper read at the meetings of the Midwest Sociological Society in

This study is likewise concerned with accounting for the presence or absence of marihuana use in an individual's behavior. It starts, however, from a different premise: that the presence of a given kind of behavior is the result of a sequence of social experiences during which the person acquires a conception of the meaning of the behavior, and perceptions and judgments of objects and situations, all of which make the activity possible and desirable. Thus, the motivation or disposition to engage in the activity is built up in the course of learning to engage in it and does not antedate this learning process. For such a view it is not necessary to identify those "traits" which "cause" the behavior. Instead, the problem becomes one of describing the set of changes in the person's conception of the activity and of the experience it provides for him.[2]

This paper seeks to describe the sequence of changes in attitude and experience which lead to *the use of marihuana for pleasure.* Marihuana does not produce addiction, as do alcohol and the opiate drugs; there is no withdrawal sickness and no ineradicable craving for the drug.[3] The most frequent pattern of use might be termed "recreational." The drug is used occasionally for the pleasure the user finds in it, a relatively casual kind of behavior in comparison with that connected with the use of addicting drugs. The term "use for pleasure" is meant to emphasize the noncompulsive and casual character of the behavior. It is also meant to eliminate from consideration here those few cases in which marihuana is used for its prestige value only, as a symbol that one is a certain kind of person, with no pleasure at all being derived from its use.

The analysis presented here is conceived of as demonstrating the greater explanatory usefulness of the kind of theory outlined above as opposed to the predispositional theories now current. This may be seen in two ways: (1) predispositional theories cannot account for that group of users (whose existence is admitted)[4] who do not exhibit the trait or traits considered to cause the behavior and (2) such theories cannot account for the great variability over time of a given individual's behavior with reference to the drug. The same person will at one stage

---

Omaha, Nebraska, April 25, 1953. The research on which this paper is based was done while I was a member of the staff of the Chicago Narcotics Survey, a study done by the Chicago Area Project, Inc., under a grant from the National Mental Health Institute.

[2] This approach stems from George Herbert Mead's discussion of objects in *Mind, Self, and Society* (Chicago: University of Chicago Press, 1934), pp. 277–80.

[3] Cf. Roger Adams, "Marihuana," *Bulletin of the New York Academy of Medicine,* XVIII (November, 1942), 705–30.

[4] Cf. Lawrence Kolb, "Marihuana," *Federal Probation,* II (July, 1938), 22–25; and Walter Bromberg, "Marihuana: A Psychiatric Study," *Journal of the American Medical Association,* CXIII (July 1, 1939), 11.

be unable to use the drug for pleasure, at a later stage be able and willing to do so, and, still later, again be unable to use it in this way. These changes, difficult to explain from a predispositional or motivational theory, are readily understandable in terms of changes in the individual's conception of the drug as is the existence of "normal" users.

The study attempted to arrive at a general statement of the sequence of changes in individual attitude and experience which have always occurred when the individual has become willing and able to use marihuana for pleasure and which have not occurred or not been permanently maintained when this is not the case. This generalization is stated in universal terms in order that negative cases may be discovered and used to revise the explanatory hypothesis.[5]

Fifty interviews with marihuana users from a variety of social backgrounds and present positions in society constitute the data from which the generalization was constructed and against which it was tested.[6] The interviews focused on the history of the person's experience with the drug, seeking major changes in his attitude toward it and in his actual use of it and the reasons for these changes. The final generalization is a statement of that sequence of changes in attitude which occurred in every case known to me in which the person came to use marihuana for pleasure. Until a negative case is found, it may be considered as an explanation of all cases of marihuana use for pleasure. In addition, changes from use to nonuse are shown to be related to similar changes in conception, and in each case it is possible to explain variations in the individual's behavior in these terms.

This paper covers only a portion of the natural history of an individual's use of marihuana,[7] starting with the person having arrived at the point of willingness to try marihuana. He knows that others use it to "get high," but he does not know what this means in concrete terms. He is curious about the experience, ignorant of what it may turn out to be, and afraid that it may be more than he has bargained for. The steps outlined below, if he undergoes them all and maintains the attitudes developed in them, leave him willing and able to use the drug for pleasure when the opportunity presents itself.

---

[5] The method used is that described by Alfred R. Lindesmith in his *Opiate Addiction* (Bloomington: Principia Press, 1947), chap. i. I would like also to acknowledge the important role Lindesmith's work played in shaping my thinking about the genesis of marihuana use.

[6] Most of the interviews were done by the author. I am grateful to Solomon Kobrin and Harold Finestone for allowing me to make use of interviews done by them.

[7] I hope to discuss elsewhere other stages in this natural history.

I

The novice does not ordinarily get high the first time he smokes marihuana, and several attempts are usually necessary to induce this state. One explanation of this may be that the drug is not smoked "properly," that is, in a way that insures sufficient dosage to produce real symptoms of intoxication. Most users agree that it cannot be smoked like tobacco if one is to get high:

> Take in a lot of air, you know, and . . . I don't know how to describe it, you don't smoke it like a cigarette, you draw in a lot of air and get it deep down in your system and then keep it there. Keep it there as long as you can.

Without the use of some such technique[8] the drug will produce no effects, and the user will be unable to get high:

> The trouble with people like that [who are not able to get high] is that they're just not smoking it right, that's all there is to it. Either they're not holding it down long enough, or they're getting too much air and not enough smoke, or the other way around or something like that. A lot of people just don't smoke it right, so naturally nothing's gonna happen.

If nothing happens, it is manifestly impossible for the user to develop a conception of the drug as an object which can be used for pleasure, and use will therefore not continue. The first step in the sequence of events that must occur if the person is to become a user is that he must learn to use the proper smoking technique in order that his use of the drug will produce some effects in terms of which his conception of it can change.

Such a change is, as might be expected, a result of the individual's participation in groups in which marihuana is used. In them the individual learns the proper way to smoke the drug. This may occur through direct teaching:

> I was smoking like I did an ordinary cigarette. He said, "No, don't do it like that." He said, "Suck it, you know, draw in and hold it in your lungs till you . . . for a period of time."
>
> I said, "Is there any limit of time to hold it?"
>
> He said, "No, just till you feel that you want to let it out, let it out." So I did that three or four times.

---

[8] A pharmacologist notes that this ritual is in fact an extremely efficient way of getting the drug into the blood stream (R. P. Walton, *Marihuana: America's New Drug Problem* [Philadelphia: J. B. Lippincott, 1938], p. 48).

Many new users are ashamed to admit ignorance and, pretending to know already, must learn through the more indirect means of observation and imitation:

> I came on like I had turned on [smoked marihuana] many times before, you know. I didn't want to seem like a punk to this cat. See, like I didn't know the first thing about it—how to smoke it, or what was going to happen, or what. I just watched him like a hawk—I didn't take my eyes off him for a second, because I wanted to do everything just as he did it. I watched how he held it, how he smoked it, and everything. Then when he gave it to me I just came on cool, as though I knew exactly what the score was. I held it like he did and took a poke just the way he did.

No person continued marihuana use for pleasure without learning a technique that supplied sufficient dosage for the effects of the drug to appear. Only when this was learned was it possible for a conception of the drug as an object which could be used for pleasure to emerge. Without such a conception marihuana use was considered meaningless and did not continue.

II

Even after he learns the proper smoking technique, the new user may not get high and thus not form a conception of the drug as something which can be used for pleasure. A remark made by a user suggested the reason for this difficulty in getting high and pointed to the next necessary step on the road to being a user:

> I was told during an interview, "As a matter of fact, I've seen a guy who was high out of his mind and didn't know it."
> I expressed disbelief: "How can that be, man?"
> The interviewee said, "Well, it's pretty strange, I'll grant you that, but I've seen it. This guy got on with me, claiming that he'd never got high, one of those guys, and he got completely stoned. And he kept insisting that he wasn't high. So I had to prove to him that he was."

What does this mean? It suggests that being high consists of two elements: the presence of symptoms caused by marihuana use and the recognition of these symptoms and their connection by the user with his use of the drug. It is not enough, that is, that the effects be present; they alone do not automatically provide the experience of being high. The user must be able to point them out to himself and consciously connect them with his having smoked marihuana before he can have this experience. Otherwise, regardless of the actual effects produced, he considers that the drug has had no effect on him: "I figured it either had no effect on me or other people were exaggerating its effect on them, you know. I thought it was probably psychological, see." Such persons believe that the whole thing is an illusion and that the wish to be high leads the user to deceive himself into believing that something is happening when, in fact, nothing is. They do not continue marihuana use, feeling that "it does nothing" for them.

Typically, however, the novice has faith (developed from his observation of users who do get high) that the drug actually will produce some new experience and continues to experiment with it until it does. His failure to get high worries him, and he is likely to ask more experienced users or provoke comments from them about it. In such conversations he is made aware of specific details of his experience which he may not have noticed or may have noticed but failed to identify as symptoms of being high:

> I didn't get high the first time. . . . I don't think I held it in long enough. I probably let it out, you know, you're a little afraid. The second time I wasn't sure, and he [smoking companion] told me, like I asked him for some of the symptoms or something, how would I know, you know. . . . So he told me to sit on a stool. I sat on—I think I sat on a bar stool—and he said, "Let your feet hang," and then when I got down my feet were real cold, you know.
>
> And I started feeling it, you know. That was the first time. And then about a week after that, sometime pretty close to it, I really got on. That was the first time I got on a big laughing kick, you know. Then I really knew I was on.

One symptom of being high is an intense hunger. In the next case the novice becomes aware of this and gets high for the first time:

> They were just laughing the hell out of me because like I was eating so much. I just scoffed [ate] so much food, and they were just laughing at me, you know. Sometimes I'd be looking at them, you know, wondering why they're laughing, you know, not knowing what I was doing. [Well, did they tell you why they were laughing eventually?] Yeah, yeah, I come back, "Hey, man, what's happening?" Like, you know, like I'd ask, "What's happening?" and all of a sudden I feel weird, you know. "Man, you're on, you know. You're on pot [high on marihuana]." I said, "No, am I?" Like I don't know what's happening.

The learning may occur in more indirect ways:

> I heard little remarks that were made by other people. Somebody said, "My legs are rubbery," and I can't remember all the remarks that were made because I was very attentively listening for all these cues for what I was supposed to feel like.

The novice, then, eager to have this feeling, picks up from other users some concrete referents of the term "high" and applies these notions to his own experience. The new concepts make it possible for him to locate these symptoms among his own sensations and to point out to himself a "something different" in his experience that he connects with drug use. It is only when he can do this that he is high. In the next case, the contrast between two successive experiences of a user makes clear the crucial importance of the awareness of the symptoms in being high and re-emphasizes the important role of interaction with other users in acquiring the concepts that make this awareness possible:

> [Did you get high the first time you turned on?] Yeah, sure. Although, come to think of it, I guess I really didn't. I mean, like that first time it was more or less of a mild drunk. I was happy, I guess, you know what I mean. But I didn't really know I was high, you know what I mean. It was only after the second time I got high that I realized I was high the first time. Then I knew that something different was happening.
>
> [How did you know that?] How did I know? If what happened to me that night would of happened to you, you would've known, believe me. We played the first tune for almost two hours—one tune! Imagine, man! We got on the stand and played this one tune, we started at nine o'clock. When we got finished I looked at my watch, it's a quarter to eleven. Almost two hours on one tune. And it didn't seem like anything.
>
> I mean, you know, it does that to you. It's like you have much more time or something. Anyway, when I saw that, man, it was too much. I knew I must really be high or something if anything like that could happen. See, and then they explained to me that that's what it did to you, you had a different sense of time and everything. So I realized that that's what it was. I knew then. Like the first time, I probably felt that way, you know, but I didn't know what's happening.

It is only when the novice becomes able to get high in this sense that he will continue to use marihuana for pleasure. In every case in which use continued, the user had acquired the necessary concepts with which to express to himself the fact that he was experiencing new sensations caused by the drug. That is, for use to continue, it is necessary not only to use the drug so as to produce effects but also to learn to perceive these effects when they occur. In this way marihuana acquires meaning for the user as an object which can be used for pleasure.

With increasing experience the user develops a greater appreciation of the drug's effects; he continues to learn to get high. He examines succeeding experiences closely, looking for new effects, making sure the old ones are still there. Out of this there grows a stable set of categories for experiencing the drug's effects whose presence enables the user to get high with ease.

The ability to perceive the drug's effects must be maintained if use is to continue; if it is lost, marihuana use ceases. Two kinds of evidence support this statement. First, people who become heavy users of alcohol, barbiturates, or opiates do not continue to smoke marihuana, largely because they lose the ability to distinguish between its effects and those of the other drugs.[9] They no longer know whether the marihuana gets them high. Second, in those few cases in which an individual uses marihuana in such quantities that he is always high, he is apt to get this same feeling that the drug has no effect on him, since the essential element of a noticeable difference between feeling high and feeling normal is missing. In such a situation, use is likely to be given up completely, but temporarily, in order that the user may once again be able to perceive the difference.

III

One more step is necessary if the user who has now learned to get high is to continue use. He must learn to enjoy the effects he has just learned to experience. Marihuana-produced sensations are not automatically or necessarily pleasurable. The taste for such experience is a socially acquired one, not different in kind from acquired tastes for oysters or dry martinis. The user feels dizzy, thirsty; his scalp tingles; he misjudges time and distances; and so on. Are these things pleasurable? He isn't sure. If he is to continue marihuana use, he must decide that they are. Otherwise, getting high, while a real enough experience, will be an unpleasant one he would rather avoid.

The effects of the drug, when first perceived, may be physically unpleasant or at least ambiguous:

> It started taking effect, and I didn't know what was happening, you know, what it was, and I was very sick. I walked around the room, walking around the room trying to get off, you know; it just scared me at first, you know. I wasn't used to that kind of feeling.

In addition, the novice's naïve interpretation of what is happening to him may further confuse and frighten him, particularly if he decides, as many do, that he is going insane:

---

[9] "Smokers have repeatedly stated that the consumption of whiskey while smoking negates the potency of the drug. They find it very difficult to get 'high' while drinking whiskey and because of that smokers will not drink while using the 'weed'" (cf. New York City Mayor's Committee on Marihuana, *The Marihuana Problem in the City of New York* [Lancaster, Pa.: Jaques Cattell Press, 1944], p. 13).

I felt I was insane, you know. Everything people done to me just wigged me. I couldn't hold a conversation, and my mind would be wandering, and I was always thinking, oh, I don't know, weird things, like hearing music different.... I get the feeling that I can't talk to anyone. I'll goof completely.

Given these typically frightening and unpleasant first experiences, the beginner will not continue use unless he learns to redefine the sensations as pleasurable:

It was offered to me, and I tried it. I'll tell you one thing. I never did enjoy it at all. I mean it was just nothing that I could enjoy. [Well, did you get high when you turned on?] Oh, yeah, I got definite feelings from it. But I didn't enjoy them. I mean I got plenty of reactions, but they were mostly reactions of fear. [You were frightened?] Yes. I didn't enjoy it. I couldn't seem to relax with it, you know. If you can't relax with a thing, you can't enjoy it, I don't think.

In other cases the first experiences were also definitely unpleasant, but the person did become a marihuana user. This occurred, however, only after a later experience enabled him to redefine the sensations as pleasurable:

[This man's first experience was extremely unpleasant, involving distortion of spatial relationships and sounds, violent thirst, and panic produced by these symptoms.] After the first time I didn't turn on for about, I'd say, ten months to a year.... It wasn't a moral thing; it was because I'd gotten so frightened, bein' so high. An' I didn't want to go through that again, I mean, my reaction was, "Well, if this is what they call bein' high, I don't dig [like] it."... So I didn't turn on for a year almost, accounta that....

Well, my friends started, an' consequently I started again. But I didn't have any more, I didn't have that same initial reaction, after I started turning on again.

[In interaction with his friends he became able to find pleasure in the effects of the drug and eventually became a regular user.]

In no case will use continue without such a redefinition of the effects as enjoyable.

This redefinition occurs, typically, in interaction with more experienced users who, in a number of ways, teach the novice to find pleasure in this experience which is at first so frightening.[10] They may reassure him as to the temporary character of the unpleasant sensations and minimize their seriousness, at the same time calling attention to the

---

[10] Charen and Perelman, *op. cit.,* p. 679.

more enjoyable aspects. An experienced user describes how he handles newcomers to marihuana use:

> Well, they get pretty high sometimes. The average person isn't ready for that, and it is a little frightening to them sometimes. I mean, they've been high on lush [alcohol], and they get higher that way than they've ever been before, and they don't know what's happening to them. Because they think they're going to keep going up, up, up till they lose their minds or begin doing weird things or something. You have to like reassure them, explain to them that they're not really flipping or anything, that they're gonna be all right. You have to just talk them out of being afraid. Keep talking to them, reassuring, telling them it's all right. And come on with your own story, you know: "The same thing happened to me. You'll get to like that after a while." Keep coming on like that; pretty soon you talk them out of being scared. And besides they see you doing it and nothing horrible is happening to you, so that gives them more confidence.

The more experienced user may also teach the novice to regulate the amount he smokes more carefully, so as to avoid any severely uncomfortable symptoms while retaining the pleasant ones. Finally, he teaches the new user that he can "get to like it after awhile." He teaches him to regard those ambiguous experiences formerly defined as unpleasant as enjoyable. The older user in the following incident is a person whose tastes have shifted in this way, and his remarks have the effect of helping others to make a similar redefinition:

> A new user had her first experience of the effects of marihuana and became frightened and hysterical. She "felt like she was half in and half out of the room" and experienced a number of alarming physical symptoms. One of the more experienced users present said, "She's dragged because she's high like that. I'd give anything to get that high myself. I haven't been that high in years."

In short, what was once frightening and distasteful becomes, after a taste for it is built up, pleasant, desired, and sought after. Enjoyment is introduced by the favorable definition of the experience that one acquires from others. Without this, use will not continue, for marihuana will not be for the user an object he can use for pleasure.

In addition to being a necessary step in becoming a user, this represents an important condition for continued use. It is quite common for experienced users suddenly to have an unpleasant or frightening experience, which they cannot define as pleasurable, either because they have used a larger amount of marihuana than usual or because it turns out to be a higher-quality marihuana than they expected. The user has sensations which go beyond any conception he has of what being high is and is in much the same situation as the novice, uncomfortable and frightened. He may blame it on an overdose and simply be more careful in the future. But he may make this the occasion for a rethinking of his attitude toward the drug and decide that it no longer can give him pleasure. When this occurs and is not followed by a redefinition of the drug as capable of producing pleasure, use will cease.

The likelihood of such a redefinition occurring depends on the degree of the individual's participation with other users. Where this participation is intensive, the individual is quickly talked out of his feeling against marihuana use. In the next case, on the other hand, the experience was very disturbing, and the aftermath of the incident cut the person's participation with other users to almost zero. Use stopped for three years and began again only when a combination of circumstances, important among which was a resumption of ties with users, made possible a redefinition of the nature of the drug:

> It was too much, like I only made about four pokes, and I couldn't even get it out of my mouth, I was so high, and I got real flipped. In the basement, you know, I just couldn't stay in there anymore. My heart was pounding real hard, you know, and I was going out of my mind; I thought I was losing my mind completely. So I cut out of this basement, and this other guy, he's out of his mind, told me, "Don't, don't leave me, man. Stay here." And I couldn't.

> I walked outside, and it was five below zero, and I thought I was dying, and I had my coat open; I was sweating, I was perspiring. My whole insides were all ..., and I walked about two blocks away, and I fainted behind a bush. I don't know how long I laid there. I woke up, and I was feeling the worst, I can't describe it at all, so I made it to a bowling alley, man, and I was trying to act normal, I was trying to shoot pool, you know, trying to act real normal, and I couldn't lay and I couldn't stand up and I couldn't sit down, and I went up and laid down where some guys that spot pins lay down, and that didn't help me, and I went down to a doctor's office. I was going to go in there and tell the doctor to put me out of my misery ... because my heart was pounding so hard, you know. ... So then all week end I started flipping, seeing things there and going through hell, you know, all kinds of abnormal things. ... I just quit for a long time then.

> [He went to a doctor who defined the symptoms for him as those of a nervous breakdown caused by "nerves" and "worries." Although he was no longer using marihuana, he had some recurrences of the symptoms which led him to suspect that "it was all his nerves."] So I just stopped worrying, you know; so it was about thirty-six months later I started making it again. I'd just take a few pokes, you know. [He first resumed use in the company of the same user-friend with whom he had been involved in the original incident.]

A person, then, cannot begin to use marihuana for pleasure, or continue its use for pleasure, unless he learns to define its effects as enjoyable, unless it becomes and remains an object which he conceives of as capable of producing pleasure.

IV

In summary, an individual will be able to use marihuana for pleasure only when he goes through a process of learning to conceive of it as an object which can be used in this way. No one becomes a user without (1) learning to smoke the drug in a way which will produce real effects; (2) learning to recognize the effects and connect them with drug use (learning, in other words, to get high); and (3) learning to enjoy the sensation he perceives. In the course of this process he develops a disposition or motivation to use marihuana which was not and could not have been present when he began use, for it involves and depends on conceptions of the drug which could only grow out of the kind of actual experience detailed above. On completion of this process he is willing and able to use marihuana for pleasure.

He has learned, in short, to answer "Yes" to the question: "Is it fun?" The direction his further use of the drug takes depends on his being able to continue to answer "Yes" to this question and, in addition, on his being able to answer "Yes" to other questions which arise as he becomes aware of the implications of the fact that the society as a whole disapproves of the practice: "Is it expedient?" "Is it moral?" [11] Once he has acquired the ability to get enjoyment out of the drug, use will continue to be possible for him. Considerations of morality and expediency, occasioned by the reactions of society, may interfere and inhibit use, but use continues to be a possibility in terms of his conception of the drug. The act becomes impossible only when the ability to enjoy the experience of being high is lost, through a change in the user's conception of the drug occasioned by certain kinds of experience with it.

In comparing this theory with those which ascribe marihuana use to motives or predispositions rooted deep in individual behavior, the evidence makes it clear that marihuana use for pleasure can occur only when the process described above is undergone and cannot occur without it. This is apparently so without reference to the nature of the individual's personal makeup or psychic problems. Such theories assume that people have stable modes of response which predetermine the way

---

[11] Another paper will discuss the series of developments in attitude that occurs as the individual begins to take account of these matters and adjust his use to them.

they will act in relation to any particular situation or object and that, when they come in contact with the given object or situation, they act in the way in which their makeup predisposes them.

This analysis of the genesis of marihuana use shows that the individuals who come in contact with a given object may respond to it at first in a great variety of ways. If a stable form of new behavior toward the object is to emerge, a transformation of meanings must occur, in which the person develops a new conception of the nature of the object.[12] This happens in a series of communicative acts in which others point out new aspects of his experience to him, present him with new interpretations of events, and help him achieve a new conceptual organization of his world, without which the new behavior is not possible. Persons who do not achieve the proper kind of conceptualization are unable to engage in the given behavior and turn off in the direction of some other relationship to the object or activity.

This suggests that behavior of any kind might fruitfully be studied developmentally, in terms of changes in meanings and concepts, their organization and reorganization, and the way they channel behavior, making some acts possible while excluding others.

---

[12] Cf. Anselm Strauss, "The Development and Transformation of Monetary Meanings in the Child," *American Sociological Review,* XVII (June, 1952), 275–86.

CLINICAL AND PSYCHOLOGICAL
EFFECTS OF MARIHUANA IN MAN

Andrew T. Weil, Norman E. Zinberg,
Judith M. Nelsen

In the spring of 1968 we conducted a series of pilot experiments on acute marihuana intoxication in human subjects. The study was not undertaken to prove or disprove popularly held convictions about marihuana as an intoxicant, to compare it with other drugs, or to introduce our own opinions. Our concern was simply to collect some long overdue pharmacological data. In this article we describe the primitive state of knowledge of the drug, the research problems encountered in designing a replicable study, and the results of our investigations.

Marihuana is a crude preparation of flowering tops, leaves, seeds, and stems of female plants of Indian hemp *Cannabis sativa* L.; it is usually smoked. The intoxicating constituents of hemp are found in the sticky resin exuded by the tops of the plants, particularly the females. Male plants produce some resin but are grown mainly for hemp fiber, not for

Reprinted from *Science* 162 (December 13, 1968): 1235–42, copyright 1968 by the American Association for the Advancement of Science with the permission of the publisher and Andrew T. Weil. This work was conducted in the Behavioral Pharmacology Laboratory of the Boston University School of Medicine, sponsored and supported by its division of psychiatry, and at the Boston University Medical Center, Boston, Massachusetts.

marihuana. The resin itself, when prepared for smoking or eating, is known as "hashish." Various *Cannabis* preparations are used as intoxicants throughout the world; their potency varies directly with the amount of resin present (*1*). Samples of American marihuana differ greatly in pharmacological activity, depending on their composition (tops contain most resin; stems, seeds, and lower leaves least) and on the conditions under which the plants were grown. In addition, different varieties of *Cannabis* probably produce resins with different proportions of constituents (*2*). Botanists feel that only one species of hemp exists, but work on the phytochemistry of the varieties of this species is incomplete (*3*). Chronic users claim that samples of marihuana differ in quality of effects as well as in potency; that some types cause a preponderance of physical symptoms, and that other types tend to cause greater distortions of perception or of thought.

Pharmacological studies of *Cannabis* indicate that the tetrahydrocannabinol fraction of the resin is the active portion. In 1965, Mechoulam and Gaoni (*4*) reported the first total synthesis of $(—)-\triangle^1$-*trans*-tetrahydrocannabinol (THC), which they called "the psychotomimetically active constituent of hashish (marihuana)." Synthetic THC is now available for research in very limited supply.

In the United States, the use of *Cannabis* extracts as therapeutics goes back to the 19th century, but it was not until the 1920's that use of marihuana as an intoxicant by migrant Mexican laborers, urban Negroes, and certain Bohemian groups caused public concern (*3*). Despite increasingly severe legal penalties imposed during the 1930's, use of marihuana continued in these relatively small populations without great public uproar or apparent changes in numbers or types of users until the last few years. The fact that almost none of the studies devoted to the physiological and psychological effects of *Cannabis* in man was based on controlled laboratory experimentation escaped general notice. But with the explosion of use in the 1960's, at first on college campuses followed by a spread downward to secondary schools and upward to a portion of the established middle class, controversy over the dangers of marihuana generated a desire for more objective information about the drug.

Of the three known studies on human subjects performed by Amer-

---

[1] R. J. Bouquet, *Bull. Narcotics* 2, 14 (1950).

[2] F. Korte and H. Sieper, in *Hashish: Its Chemistry and Pharmacology*, G. E. W. Wolstenholme and J. Knight, Eds. (Little, Brown, Boston, 1965), pp. 15–30.

[3] Task Force on Narcotics and Drug Abuse, the President's Commission on Law Enforcement and the Administration of Justice, *Task Force Report: Narcotics and Drug Abuse* (1967), p. 14.

[4] R. Mechoulam, and Y. Gaoni, *J. Amer. Chem. Soc.* 67, 3273 (1965).

icans, the first (see 5) was done in the Canal Zone with 34 soldiers; the consequences reported were hunger and hyperphagia, loss of inhibitions, increased pulse rate with unchanged blood pressure, a tendency to sleep, and unchanged performance of psychological and neurological tests. Doses and type of marihuana were not specified.

The second study, known as the 1944 LaGuardia Report (6), noted that 72 prisoners, 48 of whom were previous *Cannabis* users, showed minimum physiological responses, but suffered impaired intellectual functioning and decreased body steadiness, especially well demonstrated by nonusers after high doses. Basic personality structures remained unchanged as subjects reported feelings of relaxation, disinhibition, and self-confidence. In that study, the drug was administered orally as an extract. No controls were described, and doses and quality of marihuana were unspecified.

Williams *et al.* in 1946 (7) studied a small number of prisoners who were chronic users; they were chiefly interested in effects of long-term smoking on psychological functioning. They found an initial exhilaration and euphoria which gave way after a few days of smoking to indifference and lassitude that somewhat impaired performance requiring concentration and manual dexterity. Again, no controls were provided.

Predictably, these studies, each deficient in design for obtaining reliable physiological and psychological data, contributed no dramatic or conclusive results. The 1967 President's Commission on Law Enforcement and the Administration of Justice described the present state of knowledge by concluding (3): ". . . no careful and detailed analysis of the American experience [with marihuana] seems to have been attempted. Basic research has been almost nonexistent. . . ." Since then, no other studies with marihuana itself have been reported, but in 1967 Isbell (8) administered synthetic THC to chronic users. At doses of 120 $\mu g/kg$ orally or 50 $\mu g/kg$ by smoking, subjects reported this drug to be similar to marihuana. At higher doses (300 to 400 $\mu g/kg$ orally or 200 to 250 $\mu g/kg$ by smoking), psychotomimetic effects occurred in most subjects. This synthetic has not yet been compared with marihuana in nonusers or given to any subjects along with marihuana in double-blind fashion.

---

[5] J. F. Siler, W. L. Sheep, L. B. Bates, G. F. Clark, G. W. Cook, W. A. Smith, *Mil. Surg.* (November 1933), pp. 269–280.

[6] Mayor's Committee on Marihuana, *The Marihuana Problem in the City of New York*, 1944.

[7] E. G. Williams, C. K. Himmelsbach, A. Winkler, D. C. Ruble, B. J. Lloyd, *Public Health Rep.* 61, 1059 (1946).

[8] H. Isbell, *Psychopharmacologia* 11, 184 (1967).

Investigations outside the United States have been scientifically deficient, and for the most part have been limited to anecdotal and sociological approaches (*9–12*). So far as we know, our study is the first attempt to investigate marihuana in a formal double-blind experiment with the appropriate controls. It is also the first attempt to collect basic clinical and psychological information on the drug by observing its effects on marihuana-naive human subjects in a neutral laboratory setting.

RESEARCH PROBLEMS

That valid basic research on marihuana is almost nonexistent is not entirely accounted for by legislation which restricts even legitimate laboratory investigations or by public reaction sometimes verging on hysteria. A number of obstacles are intrinsic to the study of this drug. We now present a detailed description of our specific experimental approach, but must comment separately on six general problems confronting the investigator who contemplates marihuana research.

1) Concerning the route of administration, many pharmacologists dismiss the possibility of giving marihuana by smoking because, they say, the dose cannot be standardized (*13*). We consider it not only possible, but important to administer the drug to humans by smoking rather than by the oral route for the following reasons. (i) Smoking is the way nearly all Americans use marihuana. (ii) It is possible to have subjects smoke marihuana cigarettes in such a way that drug dosage is reasonably uniform for all subjects. (iii) Standardization of dose is not assured by giving the drug orally because little is known about gastrointestinal absorption of the highly water-insoluble cannabinols in man. (iv) There is considerable indirect evidence from users that the quality of the intoxication is different when marihuana or preparations of it are ingested rather than smoked. In particular, ingestion seems to cause more powerful effects, more "LSD-like" effects, longer-lasting effects, and more hangovers (*12, 14*). Further, marihuana smokers are accustomed to a very rapid onset of action due to efficient absorption through the lungs, whereas the latency for onset of effects may be 45 or 60 minutes after

[9] I. C. Chopra and R. N. Chopra, *Bull. Narcotics* 9, 4 (1957).

[10] F. Ames, *J. Ment. Sci.* 104, 972 (1958).

[11] C. J. Miras, in *Hashish: Its Chemistry and Pharmacology,* G. E. W. Wolstenholme and J. Knight, Eds. (Little, Brown, Boston, 1965), pp. 37–47.

[12] J. M. Watt, in *Hashish: Its Chemistry and Pharmacology,* G. E. W. Wolstenholme and J. Knight, Eds. (Little, Brown, Boston, 1965), pp. 54–66.

[13] AMA Council on Mental Health, *J. Amer. Med. Ass.* 204, 1181 (1968).

[14] G. Joachimoglu, in *Hashish: Its Chemistry and Pharmacology,* G. E. W. Wolstenholme and J. Knight, Eds. (Little, Brown, Boston, 1965), pp. 2–10.

ingestion. (v) There is reported evidence from experiments with rats and mice that the pharmacological activities of natural hashish (not subjected to combustion) and hashish sublimate (the combustion products) are different (*14*).

2) Until quite recently, it was extremely difficult to estimate the relative potencies of different samples of marihuana by the techniques of analytical chemistry. For this study, we were able to have the marihuana samples assayed spectrophotometrically (*15*) for THC content. However, since THC has not been established as the sole determinant of marihuana's activity, we still feel it is important to have chronic users sample and rate marihuana used in research. Therefore, we assayed our material by this method as well.

3) One of the major deficiencies in previous studies has been the absence of negative control or placebo treatments, which we consider essential to the design of this kind of investigation. Because marihuana smoke has a distinctive odor and taste, it is difficult to find an effective placebo for use with chronic users. The problem is much less difficult with nonusers. Our solution to this dilemma was the use of portions of male hemp stalks (*16*), devoid of THC, in the placebo cigarettes.

4) In view of the primitive state of knowledge about marihuana, it is difficult to predict which psychological tests will be sensitive to the effects of the drug. The tests we chose were selected because, in addition to being likely to demonstrate effects, they have been used to evaluate many other psychoactive drugs. Of the various physiological parameters available, we chose to measure (i) heart rate, because previous studies have consistently reported increases in heart rate after administration of marihuana (for example, *5*); (ii) respiratory rate, because it is an easily measured vital sign, and depression has been reported (*11, 17*); (iii) pupil size, because folklore on effects of marihuana consistently includes reports of pupillary dilatation, although objective experimental evidence of an effect of the drug on pupils has not been sought; (iv) conjunctival appearance, because both marihuana smokers and eaters are said to develop red eyes (*11*); and (v) blood sugar, because hypoglycemia has been invoked as a cause of the hunger and hyperphagia commonly reported by marihuana users, but animal and human evidence of this

---

[15] We thank M. Lerner and A. Bober of the U.S. Customs Laboratory, Baltimore, for performing this assay.

[16] We thank R. H. Pace and E. H. Hall of the Peter J. Schweitzer Division of the Kimberly-Clark Corp. for supplying placebo material.

[17] S. Garattini, in *Hashish: Its Chemistry and Pharmacology*, G. E. W. Wolstenholme and J. Knight, Eds. (Little, Brown, Boston, 1965), pp. 70–78.

effect is contradictory (*6, 10, 11*). [The LaGuardia Report, quoted by Jaffe in Goodman and Gilman (*18*) described hyperglycemia as an effect of acute intoxication.] We did not measure blood pressure because previous studies have failed to demonstrate any consistent effect on blood pressure in man, and we were unwilling to subject our volunteers to a nonessential annoyance.

5) It is necessary to control set and setting. "Set" refers to the subject's psychological expectations of what a drug will do to him in relation to his general personality structure. The total environment in which the drug is taken is the setting. All indications are that the form of marihuana intoxication is particularly dependent on the interaction of drug, set, and setting. Because of recent increases in the extent of use and in attention given this use by the mass media, it is difficult to find subjects with a neutral set toward marihuana. Our method of selecting subjects (described below), at the least, enabled us to identify the subjects' attitudes. Unfortunately, too many researchers have succumbed to the temptation to have subjects take drugs in "psychedelic" environments or have influenced the response to the drug by asking questions that disturb the setting. Even a question as simple as, "How do you feel?" contains an element of suggestion that alters the drug-set-setting interaction. We took great pains to keep our laboratory setting neutral by strict adherence to an experimental timetable and to a prearranged set of conventions governing interactions between subjects and experimenters.

6) Medical, social, ethical, and legal concerns about the welfare of subjects are a major problem in a project of this kind. Is it ethical to introduce people to marihuana? When can subjects safely be sent home from the laboratory? What kind of follow-up care, if any, should be given? These are only a few specific questions with which the investigator must wrestle. Examples of some of the precautions we took are as follows. (i) All subjects were volunteers. All were given psychiatric screening interviews and were clearly informed that they might be asked to smoke marihuana. All nonusers tested were persons who had reported that they had been planning to try marihuana. (ii) All subjects were driven home by an experimenter; they agreed not to engage in unusual activity or operate machinery until the next morning and to report any unusual, delayed effects. (iii) All subjects agreed to report for follow-up interviews 6 months after the experiment. Among other things, the check at 6 months should answer the question whether participation in the

---

[18] J. H. Jaffee, in *The Pharmacological Basis of Therapeutics*, L. S. Goodman and A. Gilman, Eds. (Macmillan, New York, ed. 3, 1965), pp. 299–301.

experiment encouraged further drug use. (iv) All subjects were protected from possible legal repercussions of their participation in these experiments by specific agreements with the Federal Bureau of Narcotics, the Office of the Attorney General of Massachusetts, and the Massachusetts Bureau of Drug Abuse and Drug Control (*19*).

SUBJECTS

The central group of subjects consisted of nine healthy, male volunteers, 21 to 26 years of age, all of whom smoked tobacco cigarettes regularly but had never tried marihuana previously. Eight chronic users of marihuana also participated, both to "assay" the quality of marihuana received from the Federal Bureau of Narcotics and to enable the experimenters to standardize the protocol, using subjects familiar with their responses to the drug. The age range for users was also 21 to 26 years. They all smoked marihuana regularly, most of them every day or every other day.

The nine "naive" subjects were selected after a careful screening process. An initial pool of prospective subjects was obtained by placing advertisements in the student newspapers of a number of universities in the Boston area. These advertisements sought "male volunteers, at least 21 years old, for psychological experiments." After nonsmokers were eliminated from this pool, the remaining volunteers were interviewed individually by a psychiatrist who determined their histories of use of alcohol and other intoxicants as well as their general personality types. In addition to serving as a potential screening technique to eliminate volunteers with evidence of psychosis, or of serious mental or personality disorder, these interviews served as the basis for the psychiatrist's prediction of the type of response an individual subject might have after smoking marihuana. (It should be noted that no marihuana-naive volunteer had to be disqualified on psychiatric grounds.) Only after a prospective subject passed the interview was he informed that the "psychological experiment" for which he had volunteered was a marihuana study. If he consented to participate, he was asked to sign a release, informing him that he would be "expected to smoke cigarettes containing marihuana or an inert substance." He was also required to agree to a number of conditions, among them that he would "during the course

---

19 We thank E. L. Richardson, Attorney General of the Commonwealth of Massachusetts for permitting these experiments to proceed and N. L. Chayet for legal assistance. We do not consider it appropriate to describe here the opposition we encountered from governmental agents and agencies and from university bureaucracies.

of the experiment take no psychoactive drugs, including alcohol, other than those drugs administered in the course of the experiment."

It proved extremely difficult to find marihuana-naive persons in the student population of Boston, and nearly 2 months of interviewing were required to obtain nine men. All those interviewed who had already tried marihuana volunteered this information quite freely and were delighted to discuss their use of drugs with the psychiatrist. Nearly all persons encountered who had not tried marihuana admitted this somewhat apologetically. Several said they had been meaning to try the drug but had not got around to it. A few said they had no access to it. Only one person cited the current laws as his reason for not having experimented with marihuana. It seemed clear in the interviews that many of these persons were actually afraid of how they might react to marihuana; they therefore welcomed a chance to smoke it under medical supervision. Only one person (an Indian exchange student) who passed the screening interview refused to participate after learning the nature of the experiment.

The eight heavy users of marihuana were obtained with much less difficulty. They were interviewed in the same manner as the other subjects and were instructed not to smoke any marihuana on the day of their appointment in the laboratory.

Subjects were questioned during screening interviews and at the conclusion of the experiments to determine their knowledge of marihuana effects. None of the nine naive subjects had ever watched anyone smoke marihuana or observed anyone high on marihuana. Most of them knew of the effects of the drug only through reports in the popular press. Two subjects had friends who used marihuana frequently; one of these (No. 4) announced his intention to "prove" in the experiments that marihuana really did not do anything; the other (No. 3) was extremely eager to get high because "everyone I know is always talking about it very positively."

SETTING

Greatest effort was made to create a neutral setting. That is, subjects were made comfortable and secure in a pleasant suite of laboratories and offices, but the experimental staff carefully avoided encouraging any person to have an enjoyable experience. Subjects were never asked how they felt, and no subject was permitted to discuss the experiment with the staff until he had completed all four sessions. Verbal interactions between staff and subjects were minimum and formal. At the end of each session, subjects were asked to complete a brief form asking whether they thought they had smoked marihuana that night; if so, whether a high dose or a low dose; and how confident they were of their answers. The experimenters completed similar forms on each subject.

MARIHUANA

Marihuana used in these experiments was of Mexican origin, supplied by the Federal Bureau of Narcotics (*20*). It consisted of finely chopped leaves of *Cannabis,* largely free of seeds and stems. An initial batch, which was judged to be of low potency by the experimenters on the basis of the doses needed to produce symptoms of intoxication in the chronic users, was subsequently found to contain only 0.3 percent of THC by weight. A second batch, assayed at 0.9 percent THC, was rated by the chronic users to be "good, average" marihuana, neither exceptionally strong nor exceptionally weak compared to their usual supplies. Users consistently reported symptoms of intoxication after smoking about 0.5 gram of the material with a variation of only a few puffs from subject to subject. This second batch of marihuana was used in the experiments described below; the low dose was 0.5 gram, and the high dose was 2.0 grams.

All marihuana was administered in the form of cigarettes of standard size made with a hand-operated rolling machine. In any given experimental session, each person was required to smoke two cigarettes in succession (Table 1).

TABLE 1.

Composition of the dose. The placebo cigarette consisted of placebo material, tobacco filler, and mint leaves for masking flavor. The low dose was made up of marihuana, tobacco filler, and mint leaves. The high dose consisted of marihuana and mint leaves.

Dose	Marihuana in each cigarette (g)	Total dose marihuana (2 cigarettes) (g)	Approximate dose THC
Placebo	—		—
Low	0.25	0.5	4.5 mg
High	1.0	2.0	1.8 mg

Placebo material consisted of the chopped outer covering of mature stalks of male hemp plants; it contained no THC. All cigarettes had a

---

[20] We thank D. Miller and M. Seifer of the Federal Bureau of Narcotics (now part of the Bureau of Narcotics and Dangerous Drugs, under the Department of Justice) for help in obtaining marihuana for this research.

tiny plug of tobacco at one end and a plug of paper at the other end so that the contents were not visible. The length to which each cigarette was to be smoked was indicated by an ink line. Marihuana and placebos were administered to the naive subjects in double-blind fashion. Scented aerosols were sprayed in the laboratory before smoking, to mask the odor of marihuana. The protocol during an experimental session was as follows. The sessions began at approximately 5.30 p.m.

Time	Procedure
0:00	Physiological measurements; blood sample drawn
0:05	Psychological test battery No. 1 (base line)
0:35	Verbal sample No. 1
0:40	Cigarette smoking
1:00	Rest period
1:15	Physiological measurements; blood sample drawn
1:20	Psychological test battery No. 2
1:50	Verbal sample No. 2
1:55	Rest period (supper)
2:30	Physiological measurements
2:35	Psychological test battery No. 3
3:05	End of testing

EXPERIMENTAL SESSIONS

Chronic users were tested only on high doses of marihuana with no practice sessions. Each naive subject was required to come to four sessions, spaced about a week apart. The first was always a practice session, in which the subject learned the proper smoking technique and during which he became thoroughly acquainted with the tests and the protocol. In the practice session, each subject completed the entire protocol, smoking two hand-rolled tobacco cigarettes. He was instructed to take a long puff, to inhale deeply, and to maintain inspiration for 20 seconds, as timed by an experimenter with a stopwatch. Subjects were allowed 8 to 12 seconds to smoke each of the two cigarettes. One purpose of this practice smoking was to identify and eliminate individuals who were not tolerant to high doses of nicotine, thus reducing the effect of nicotine on the variables measured during subsequent drug sessions (*21*). A surprising number (five) of volunteers who had described themselves in screening interviews as heavy cigarette smokers, "inhaling" up to two packs of cigarettes a day, developed acute nicotine reactions when they smoked two tobacco cigarettes by the required method. Occurrence of such a reaction disqualified a subject from participation in the experiments.

---

21 The doses of tobacco in placebo and low-dose cigarettes were too small to cause physiological changes in subjects who qualified in the practice session.

In subsequent sessions, when cigarettes contained either drug or placebo, all smoking was similarly supervised by an experimenter with a stopwatch. Subjects were not permitted to smoke tobacco cigarettes while the experiment was in progress. They were assigned to one of the three treatment groups listed in Table 2.

TABLE 2.

ORDER OF TREATMENT.

Group	Drug session		
	1	2	3
I	High	Placebo	Low
II	Low	High	Placebo
III	Placebo	Low	High

PHYSIOLOGICAL AND PSYCHOLOGICAL MEASURES

The physiological parameters measured were heart rate, respiratory rate, pupil size, blood glucose level, and conjunctival vascular state. Pupil size was measured with a millimeter rule under constant illumination with eyes focused on an object at constant distance. Conjunctival appearance was rated by an experienced experimenter for dilation of blood vessels on a 0 to 4 scale with ratings of 3 and 4 indicating "significant" vasodilatation. Blood samples were collected for immediate determinations of serum glucose and for the serum to be frozen and stored for possible future biochemical studies. Subjects were asked not to eat and not to imbibe a beverage containing sugar or caffeine during the 4 hours preceding a session. They were given supper after the second blood sample was drawn.

The psychological test battery consisted of (i) the Continuous Performance Test (CPT)—5 minutes; (ii) the Digit Symbol Substitution Test (DSST)—90 seconds; (iii) CPT with strobe light distraction—5 minutes; (iv) self-rating bipolar mood scale—3 minutes; and (v) pursuit rotor—10 minutes.

The Continuous Performance Test was designed to measure a subject's capacity for sustained attention (22). The subject was placed in a darkened room and directed to watch a small screen upon which six letters of the alphabet were flashed rapidly and in random order. The subject was instructed to press a button whenever a specified critical letter ap-

²² K. E. Rosvold, A. F. Mirsky, I. Sarason, E. D. Bransome, L. H. Beck, *J. Consult. Psychol.* 20, 343 (1956); A. F. Mirsky and P. V. Cardon, *Electroencephalogr. Clin. Neurophysiol.* 14, 1 (1962); C. Kornetsky and G. Bain, *Psychopharmacologia* 8, 277 (1965).

peared. The number of letters presented, correct responses, and errors of commission and omission were counted over the 5-minute period. The test was also done with a strobe light flickering at 50 cycles per second. Normal subjects make no or nearly no errors on this test either with or without strobe distraction; but sleep deprivation, organic brain disease, and certain drugs like chlorpromazine adversely affect performance. Presence or absence of previous exposure to the task has no effect on performance.

The Digit Symbol Substitution Test is a simple test of cognitive function (see Fig. 1). A subject's score was the number of correct answers

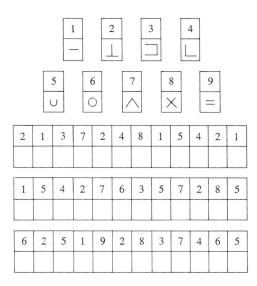

FIGURE 1.

This is a sample of the Digit Symbol Substitution Test as used in these studies. On a signal from the examiner the subject was required to fill as many of the empty spaces as possible with the appropriate symbols. The code was always available to the subject during the 90-second administration of the test. [This figure appeared originally in *Psychopharmacologia* 5, 164 (1964)]

in a 90-second period. As in the case of the CPT, practice should have little or no effect on performance.

The self-rating bipolar mood scale used in these experiments was one developed by Smith and Beecher (23) to evaluate subjective effects

---

23 G. M. Smith and H. K. Beecher, *J. Pharmacol.* 126, 50 (1959).

of morphine. By allowing subjects to rate themselves within a given category of moods, on an arbitrary scale from +3 to −3, it minimizes suggestion and is thus more neutral than the checklists often employed in drug testing.

The pursuit rotor measures muscular coordination and attention. The subject's task was to keep a stylus in contact with a small spot on a moving turntable. In these experiments, subjects were given ten 30-second trials in each battery. The score for each trial was total time in contact with the spot. There is a marked practice effect on this test, but naive subjects were brought to high levels of performance during their practice session, so that the changes due to practice were reduced during the actual drug sessions. In addition, since there was a different order of treatments for each of the three groups of naive subjects, any session-to-session practice effects were minimized in the statistical analysis of the pooled data.

At the end of the psychological test battery, a verbal sample was collected from each subject. The subject was left alone in a room with a tape recorder and instructions to describe "an interesting or dramatic experience" in his life until he was stopped. After exactly 5 minutes he was interrupted and asked how long he had been in the recording room. In this way, an estimate of the subject's ability to judge time was also obtained.

RESULTS

1) *Safety of marihuana in human volunteers.* In view of the apprehension expressed by many persons over the safety of administering marihuana to research subjects, we wish to emphasize that no adverse marihuana reactions occurred in any of our subjects. In fact, the five acute nicotine reactions mentioned earlier were far more spectacular than any effects produced by marihuana.

In these experiments, observable effects of marihuana were maximum at 15 minutes after smoking. They were diminished between 30 minutes and 1 hour, and they were largely dissipated 3 hours after the end of smoking. No delayed or persistent effects beyond 3 hours were observed or reported.

2) *Intoxicating properties of marihuana in a neutral setting.* With the high dose of marihuana (2.0 grams), all chronic users became "high" (*24*) by their own accounts and in the judgment of experimenters who

---

[24] We will attempt to define the complex nature of a marihuana high in a subsequent paper discussing the speech samples and interviews.

had observed many persons under the influence of marihuana. The effect was consistent even though prior to the session some of these subjects expressed anxiety about smoking marihuana and submitting to tests in a laboratory.

On the other hand, only one of the nine naive subjects (No. 3) had a definite "marihuana reaction" on the same high dose. He became markedly euphoric and laughed continuously during his first battery of tests after taking the drug. Interestingly, he was the one subject who had expressed his desire to get high.

3) *Comparison of naive and chronic user subjects.* Throughout the experiments it was apparent that the two groups of subjects reacted differently to identical doses of marihuana. We must caution, however, that our study was designed to allow rigorous statistical analysis of data from the naive group—it was not designed to permit formal comparison between chronic users and naive subjects. The conditions of the experiment were not the same for both groups: the chronic users were tested with the drug on their first visit to the laboratory with no practice and were informed that they were to receive high doses of marihuana. Therefore, differences between the chronic and naive groups reported below—although statistically valid—must be regarded as trends to be confirmed or rejected by additional experiments.

4) *Recognition of marihuana versus placebo.* All nine naive subjects reported that they had not been able to identify the taste or smell of marihuana in the experimental cigarettes. A few subjects remarked that they noticed differences in the taste of the three sets of cigarettes but could not interpret the differences. Most subjects found the pure marihuana cigarettes (high dose) more mild than the low dose or placebo cigarettes, both of which contained tobacco.

The subjects' guesses of the contents of cigarettes for their three sessions are presented in Table 3. It is noteworthy that one of the two subjects who called the high dose a placebo was the subject (No. 4) who had told us he wanted to prove that marihuana really did nothing. There were three outstanding findings: (i) most subjects receiving marihuana

TABLE 3.

SUBJECTS' APPRAISAL OF THE DOSE.

Actual dose	Guessed dose			Fraction correct
	Placebo	Low	High	
Placebo	8	1		8/9
Low	3	6		6/9
High	2	6	1	1/9

in either high or low dose recognized that they were getting a drug; (ii) most subjects receiving placebos recognized that they were receiving placebos; (iii) most subjects called their high dose a low dose, but none called his low dose a high dose, emphasizing the unimpressiveness of their subjective reactions.

5) *Effect of marihuana on heart rate.* The mean changes in heart rate from base-line rates before smoking the drug to rates at 15 and 90 minutes after smoking marihuana and placebo (Table 4) were tested for

TABLE 4.

Change in heart rate (beat/min) after smoking the best material. Results are recorded as a change from the base line 15 minutes and 90 minutes after the smoking session.

Subject	15 Minutes			90 Minutes		
	Placebo	Low	High	Placebo	Low	High
Naive subjects						
1	+ 16	+ 20	+ 16	+ 20	− 6	− 4
2	+ 12	+ 24	+ 12	− 6	+ 4	− 8
3	+ 8	+ 8	+ 26	− 4	+ 4	+ 8
4	+ 20	+ 8			+ 20	− 4
5	+ 8	+ 4	− 8		+ 22	− 8
6	+ 10	+ 20	+ 28	− 20	− 4	− 4
7	+ 4	+ 28	+ 24	+ 12	+ 8	+ 18
8	− 8	+ 20	+ 24	− 3	+ 8	− 24
9		+ 20	+ 24	+ 8	+ 12	
Mean	+ 7.8	+ 16.9	+ 16.2	+ 0.8	+ 7.6	− 2.9
S.E.	2.8	2.7	4.2	3.8	3.2	3.8
Chronic subjects						
10		+ 32			+ 4	
11		+ 36			+ 36	
12		+ 20			+ 12	
13		+ 8			+ 4	
14		+ 32			+ 12	
15		+ 54			+ 22	
16		+ 24				
17		+ 60				
Mean		+ 33.2			+ 15.0	
S.E.		6.0			5.0	

significance at the .05 level by an analysis of variance; Tukey's method was applied for all possible comparisons (Table 5). In the naive subjects, marihuana in low dose or high dose was followed by increased heart rate 15 minutes after smoking, but the effect was not demonstrated to be dose-dependent. The high dose caused a statistically greater increase in the heart rates of chronic users than in those of the naive subjects 15 minutes after smoking.

Two of the chronic users had unusually low resting pulse rates (56 and 42), but deletion of these two subjects (No. 11 and No. 15) still gave a significant difference in mean pulse rise of chronic users compared to naives. Because the conditions of the sessions and experimental design were not identical for the two groups, we prefer to report this difference as a trend that must be confirmed by further studies.

TABLE 5.

SIGNIFICANCE OF DIFFERENCES (AT THE .05 LEVEL) IN HEART RATE.
RESULTS OF TUKEY'S TEST FOR ALL POSSIBLE COMPARISONS.

Comparison	15 Minutes	90 Minutes
Low dose versus placebo	Significant	Significant
High dose versus placebo	Significant	Not significant
Low dose versus high dose	Not significant	Significant
Chronic users versus high dose	Significant	Significant

6) *Effect of marihuana on respiratory rate.* In the naive group, there was no change in respiratory rate before and after smoking marihuana. Chronic users showed a small but statistically significant increase in respiratory rate after smoking, but we do not regard the change as clinically significant.

7) *Effect of marihuana on pupil size.* There was no change in pupil size before and after smoking marihuana in either group.

8) *Effect of marihuana on conjunctival appearance.* Significant reddening of conjunctivae due to dilatation of blood vessels occurred in one of nine subjects receiving placebo, three of nine receiving the low dose of marihuana, and eight of nine receiving the high dose. It occurred in all eight of the chronic users receiving the high dose and was rated as more prominent in them. The effect was more pronounced 15 minutes after the smoking period than 90 minutes after it.

9) *Effect of marihuana on blood sugar.* There was no significant change in blood sugar levels after smoking marihuana in either group.

10) *Effect of marihuana on the Continuous Performance Test.* Performance on the CPT and on the CPT with strobe distraction was unaffected by marihuana for both groups of subjects.

11) *Effect of marihuana on the Digit Symbol Substitution Test.* The significance of the differences in mean changes of scores at the .05 level was determined by an analysis of variance by means of Tukey's method for all possible comparisons. Results of these tests are summarized in Tables 6 and 7.

The results indicate that: (i) Decrements in performance of naive subjects following low and high doses of marihuana were significant at

TABLE 6.

SIGNIFICANCE OF DIFFERENCES (AT THE .05 LEVEL) FOR THE DIGIT SYMBOL SUBSTITUTION TEST. RESULTS OF TUKEY'S TEST FOR ALL POSSIBLE COMPARISONS.

Comparison	15 Minutes	90 Minutes
Low dose versus placebo	Significant	Significant
High dose versus placebo	Significant	Significant
Low dose versus high dose	Significant	Not significant
Chronic users versus high dose	Significant	Significant

TABLE 7.

DIGIT SYMBOL SUBSTITUTION TEST. CHANGE IN SCORES FROM BASE LINE (NUMBER CORRECT) 15 AND 90 MINUTES AFTER THE SMOKING SESSION.

Subject	15 Minutes			90 Minutes		
	Placebo	Low	High	Placebo	Low	High
Naive subjects						
1	− 3	—	+ 5	− 7	+ 4	+ 8
2	+ 10	− 8	− 17	− 1	− 15	− 5
3	− 3	+ 6	− 7	− 10	+ 2	− 1
4	+ 3	− 4	− 3	− 7		
5	+ 4	+ 1	− 7	+ 6		− 8
6	− 3	− 1	− 9	+ 3	− 5	− 12
7	+ 2	− 4	− 6	+ 3	− 5	− 4
8	− 1	+ 3	+ 1	+ 4	+ 4	− 3
9	− 1	− 4	− 3	+ 6	− 1	− 10
Mean	+ 0.9	− 1.2	− 5.1	+ 0.4	− 2.6	− 3.9
S.E.	1.4	1.4	2.1	1.9	2.0	2.0
Chronic users						
10		− 4				− 16
11		+ 1				+ 6
12		+ 11				+ 18
13		+ 3				+ 4
14		− 2				− 3
15		− 6				+ 8
16		− 4				
17		+ 3				
Mean		+ 0.25				+ 2.8
S.E.		1.9				4.7

15 and 90 minutes after smoking. (ii) The decrement following marihuana was greater after high dose than after low dose at 15 minutes after taking the drug, giving preliminary evidence of a dose-response relationship. (iii) Chronic users started with good base-line performance and improved slightly on the DSST after smoking 2.0 grams of marihuana, whereas performance of the naive subjects was grossly impaired. Experience with the DSST suggests that absence of impairment in

chronic users cannot be accounted for solely by a practice effect. Still, because of the different procedures employed, we prefer to report this difference as a trend.

12) *Effect of marihuana on pursuit rotor performance.* This result is presented in Table 8. Again applying Tukey's method in an analysis of variance, we tested differences in mean changes in scores (Table 9).

TABLE 8.

PURSUIT ROTOR (NAIVE SUBJECTS). CHANGES IN SCORES (AVERAGES OF TEN TRIALS) FROM BASE LINE (SECONDS).

Subject	15 Minutes			90 Minutes		
	Placebo	Low	High	Placebo	Low	High
1	+ 1.20	− 1.04	− 4.01	+ 1.87	− 1.54	− 6.54
2	+ 0.89	− 1.43	− 0.12	+ 0.52	+ 0.44	− 0.68
3	+ 0.50	− 0.60	− 6.56	+ 0.84	− 0.96	− 4.34
4	+ 0.18	− 0.11	+ 0.11	+ 0.06	+ 1.95	− 1.37
5	+ 3.20	+ 0.39	+ 0.13	+ 2.64	+ 3.33	+ 0.34
6	+ 3.45	− 0.32	− 3.46	+ 2.93	+ 0.22	− 2.26
7	+ 0.81	+ 0.48	− 0.79	+ 0.63	+ 0.16	− 0.52
8	+ 1.75	− 0.39	− 0.92	+ 2.13	+ 0.40	+ 1.02
9	+ 3.90	− 1.94	− 2.60	+ 3.11	− 0.97	− 3.09
Mean	+ 1.8	− 0.6	− 2.0	+ 1.6	+ 0.3	− 1.9
S.E.	0.5	0.3	0.8	0.4	0.5	0.8

TABLE 9.

Significance of differences (at the .05 level) for the pursuit rotor. Results of Tukey's test for all possibe comparisons, 15 and 90 minutes after the smoking session.

Comparison	15 Minutes	90 Minutes
Low dose versus placebo	Significant	Significant
High dose versus placebo	Significant	Significant
Low dose versus high dose	Significant	Significant

Decrements in performance of naive subjects after both low and high doses of marihuana were significant at 15 and 90 minutes. This effect on performance followed a dose-response relation on testing batteries conducted at both 15 minutes and 90 minutes after the drug was smoked.

All chronic users started from good baselines and improved on the pursuit rotor after smoking marihuana. These data are not presented, however, because it is probable that the improvement was largely a practice effect.

13) *Effect of marihuana on time estimation.* Before smoking, all nine naive subjects estimated the 5-minute verbal sample to be 5 ± 2 min-

utes. After placebo, no subject changed his guess. After the low dose, three subjects raised their estimates to 10 ± 2 minutes, and after the high dose, four raised their estimates.

14) *Subjective effects of marihuana.* When questioned at the end of their participation in the experiment, persons who had never taken marihuana previously reported minimum subjective effects after smoking the drug, or, more precisely, few effects like those commonly reported by chronic users. Nonusers reported little euphoria, no distortion of visual or auditory perception, and no confusion. However, several subjects mentioned that "things seemed to take longer." Below are examples of comments by naive subjects after high doses.

> Subject 1: "It was stronger than the previous time (low dose) but I really didn't think it could be marihuana. Things seemed to go slower."
>
> Subject 2: "I think I realize why they took our watches. There was a sense of the past disappearing as happens when you're driving too long without sleeping. With a start you wake up to realize you were asleep for an instant; you discover yourself driving along the road. It was the same tonight with eating a sandwich. I'd look down to discover I'd just swallowed a bite but I hadn't noticed it at the time."
>
> Subject 6: "I felt a combination of being almost-drunk and tired, with occasional fits of silliness—not my normal reaction to smoking tobacco."
>
> Subject 8: "I felt faint briefly, but the dizziness went away, and I felt normal or slightly tired. I can't believe I had a high dose of marihuana."
>
> Subject 9: "Time seemed very drawn out. I would keep forgetting what I was doing, especially on the continuous performance test, but somehow every time an "X" (the critical letter) came up, I found myself pushing the button."

After smoking their high dose, chronic users were asked to rate themselves on a scale of 1 to 10, 10 representing "the highest you've ever been." All subjects placed themselves between 7 and 10, most at 8 or 9. Many of these subjects expressed anxiety at the start of their first battery of tests after smoking the drug when they were feeling very high. Then they expressed surprise during and after the test when they judged (correctly) that their performance was as good as or better than it had been before taking the drug.

15) The effect of marihuana on the self-rating mood scale, the effect of marihuana on a 5-minute verbal sample, and the correlation of personality type with subjective effects of marihuana will be reported separately.

DISCUSSION

Several results from this study raise important questions about the action of marihuana and suggest directions for future research. Our finding that subjects who were naive to marihuana did not become subjectively "high" after a high dose of marihuana in a neutral setting is interesting when contrasted with the response of regular users who consistently reported and exhibited highs. It agrees with the reports of chronic users that many, if not most, people do not become high on their first exposure to marihuana even if they smoke it correctly. This puzzling phenomenon can be discussed from either a physiological or psychosocial point of view. Neither interpretation is entirely satisfactory. The physiological hypothesis suggests that getting high on marihuana occurs only after some sort of pharmacological sensitization takes place. The psychosocial interpretation is that repeated exposure to marihuana reduces psychological inhibition, as part of, or as the result of a learning process.

Indirect evidence makes the psychological hypothesis attractive. Anxiety about drug use in this country is sufficiently great to make worthy of careful consideration the possibility of an unconscious psychological inhibition or block on the part of naive drug takers. The subjective responses of our subjects indicate that they had imagined a marihuana effect to be much more profoundly disorganizing than what they experienced. For example, subject No. 4, who started with a bias against the possibility of becoming high on marihuana, was able to control subjectively the effect of the drug and report that he had received a placebo when he had actually gotten a high dose. As anxiety about the drug is lessened with experience, the block may decrease, and the subject may permit himself to notice the drug's effects.

It is well known that marihuana users, in introducing friends to the drug, do actually "teach" them to notice subtle effects of the drug on consciousness (25). The apparently enormous influence of set and setting on the form of the marihuana response is consistent with this hypothesis, as is the testimony of users that, as use becomes more frequent, the amount of drug required to produce intoxication decreases—a unique example of "reverse tolerance." (Regular use of many intoxicants is accompanied by the need for increasing doses to achieve the same effects.)

On the other hand, the suggestion arising from this study that users and nonusers react differently to the drug, not only subjectively but also

---

25 H. S. Becker, *Outsiders: Studies in the Sociology of Deviance* (Macmillan, New York, 1963), chap. 3.

physiologically, increases the plausibility of the pharmacological-sensitization hypothesis. Of course, reverse tolerance could equally well be a manifestation of this sensitization.

It would be useful to confirm the suggested differences between users and nonusers and then to test in a systematic manner the hypothetical explanations of the phenomenon. One possible approach would be to continue to administer high doses of marihuana to the naive subjects according to the protocol described. If subjects begin reporting high responses to the drug only after several exposures in the absence of psychedelic settings, suggestions, or manipulations of mood, then the likelihood that marihuana induces a true physiological sensitization or that experience reduces psychological inhibitions, permitting real drug effects to appear, would be increased. If subjects fail to become high, we could conclude that learning to respond to marihuana requires some sort of teaching or suggestion.

An investigation of the literature of countries where anxieties over drug use are less prominent would be useful. If this difference between responses of users and nonusers is a uniquely American phenomenon, a psychological explanation would be indicated, although it would not account for greater effects with smaller doses after the initial, anxiety-reducing stage.

One impetus for reporting the finding of differences between chronic and naive subjects on some of the tests, despite the fact that the experimental designs were not the same, is that this finding agrees with the statements of many users. They say that the effects of marihuana are easily suppressed—much more so than those of alcohol. Our observation, that the chronic users after smoking marihuana performed on some tests as well as or better than they did before taking the drug, reinforced the argument advanced by chronic users that maintaining effective levels of performance for many tasks—driving, for example (26)—is much easier under the influence of marihuana than under that of other psychoactive drugs. Certainly the surprise that the chronic users expressed when they found they were performing more effectively on the CPT, DSST, and pursuit rotor tests than they thought they would is remarkable. It is quite the opposite of the false sense of improvement subjects have under some psychoactive drugs that actually impair performance.

What might be the basis of this suppressibility? Possibly, the actions of marihuana are confined to higher cortical functions without any gen-

---

26 Although the motor skills measured by the pursuit rotor are represented in driving ability, they are only components of that ability. The influence of marihuana on driving skill remains an open question of high medico-legal priority.

eral stimulatory or depressive effect on lower brain centers. The relative absence of neurological—as opposed to psychiatric—symptoms in marihuana intoxication suggests this possibility (7).

Our failure to detect any changes in blood sugar levels of subjects after they had smoked marihuana forces us to look elsewhere for an explanation of the hunger and hyperphagia commonly reported by users. A first step would be careful interviewing of users to determine whether they really become hungry after smoking marihuana or whether they simply find eating more pleasurable. Possibly, the basis of this effect is also central rather than due to some peripheral physiological change.

Lack of any change in pupil size of subjects after they had smoked marihuana is an enlightening finding especially because so many users and law-enforcement agents firmly believe that marihuana dilates pupils. (Since users generally observe each other in dim surroundings, it is not surprising that they see large pupils.) This negative finding emphasizes the need for data from carefully controlled investigations rather than from casual observation or anecdotal reports in the evaluation of marihuana. It also agrees with the findings of others that synthetic THC does not alter pupil size (8, 27).

Finally, we would like to comment on the fact that marihuana appears to be a relatively mild intoxicant in our studies. If these results seem to differ from those of earlier experiments, it must be remembered that other experimenters have given marihuana orally, have given doses much higher than those commonly smoked by users, have administered potent synthetics, and have not strictly controlled the laboratory setting. As noted in our introduction, more powerful effects are often reported by users who ingest preparations of marihuana. This may mean that some active constituents which enter the body when the drug is ingested are destroyed by combustion, a suggestion that must be investigated in man. Another priority consideration is the extent to which synthetic THC reproduces marihuana intoxication—a problem that must be resolved before marihuana research proceeds with THC instead of the natural resin of the whole plant.

The set, both of subjects and experimenters, and the setting must be recognized as critical variables in studies of marihuana. Drug, set, and setting interact to shape the form of a marihuana reaction. The researcher who sets out with prior conviction that hemp is psychotomimetic or a "mild hallucinogen" is likely to confirm his conviction experimentally (10), but he would probably confirm the opposite hypothesis if his bias were in the opposite direction. Precautions to insure neutrality

---

[27] L. E. Hollister, R. K. Richards, H. K. Gillespie, in preparation.

of set and setting, including use of a double-blind procedure as an absolute minimum, are vitally important if the object of investigation is to
measure real marihuana-induced responses.

CONCLUSIONS

1) It is feasible and safe to study the effects of marihuana on human
volunteers who smoke it in a laboratory.

2) In a neutral setting persons who are naive to marihuana do not
have strong subjective experiences after smoking low or high doses of
the drug, and the effects they do report are not the same as those described by regular users of marihuana who take the drug in the same
neutral setting.

3) Marihuana-naive persons do demonstrate impaired performance
on simple intellectual and psychomotor tests after smoking marihuana;
the impairment is dose-related in some cases.

4) Regular users of marihuana do get high after smoking marihuana
in a neutral setting but do not show the same degree of impairment of
performance on the tests as do naive subjects. In some cases, their performance even appears to improve slightly after smoking marihuana.

5) Marihuana increases heart rate moderately.

6) No change in respiratory rate follows administration of marihuana
by inhalation.

7) No change in pupil size occurs in short term exposure to marihuana.

8) Marihuana administration causes dilatation of conjunctival blood
vessels.

9) Marihuana treatment produces no change in blood sugar levels.

10) In a neutral setting the physiological and psychological effects of
a single, inhaled dose of marihuana appear to reach maximum intensity
within one-half hour of inhalation, to be diminished after 1 hour, and
to be completely dissipated by 3 hours (*28*).

[28] Sponsored and supported by Boston University's division of psychiatry, in part
through PHS grants MH12568, MH06795–06, MH7753–06, and MH33319, and
the Boston University Medical Center. The authors thank Dr. P. H. Knapp and Dr.
C. Kornetsky of the Boston University School of Medicine, Department of Psychiatry and Pharmacology, for consistent support and excellent advice, and J. Finkel-
stein of 650 Madison Avenue, New York City, for his support at a crucial time.

EXPERIENCES WITH MARIHUANA
IN A SAMPLE OF DRUG USERS

Stanley Grupp

Public attitudes and controversy regarding marihuana currently focus around two countervailing trends, one liberal and the other punitive. On the one hand, we find that knowledge about marihuana is relatively widespread and that an increasing number of persons have either smoked marihuana or know those who have. No less than *Time* magazine's 1966 Man of the Year was described as having this attribute.[1] The emergence of the "marihuana cult" and "let's legalize pot" movement is a parallel development. Simultaneously there has been a demand for reconsideration or elimination of criminal sanctions against users or sellers of marihuana.[2] In these several respects we have experienced a liberalization

---

[1] *Time,* Vol. 89, No. 1, January 6, 1967, 18.

[2] Note, for example, the activities of The Committee to Legalize Marihuana and the Ad Hoc Committee for Reform of Marihuana Laws. See Alfred R. Lindesmith, *The Addict and the Law* (Bloomington: Indiana University Press, 1965), Ch. 8, "The Marihuana Problem—Myth or Reality?" and The President's Commission on Law Enforcement and Administration of Justice, *Task Force Report: Narcotics and Drug Abuse* (Washington, D.C.: United States Government Printing Office, 1967).

Reprinted from *Sociological Focus* 1 (Winter 1967): 39–51, with the permission of the publisher.

of attitudes. On the other hand, we find that where reasonably reliable data is available, the rate of arrests for marihuana offenses is increasing at an unprecedented rate. This pattern has been accompanied by the view that criminal sanctions be retained.[3] Some may deplore one or the other of these trends, but trends they are.

While there is disagreement among professionals (Henry Giordano and James L. Goddard, for example) regarding the dangers of marihuana use, there is general agreement that more information and research is needed. The paucity of our knowledge has recently been emphasized by The President's Commission on Law Enforcement and Administration of Justice which observed, "with the possible exception of the 1944 La Guardia report, no careful and detailed analysis of the American experience [with marihuana] seems to have been attempted." [4] The Commission called for the National Institute of Mental Health to "execute a plan of research . . . covering all aspects of marihuana use." [5]

Much of the extant research and literature on marihuana is chemical or pharmacological in nature.[6] Research within a sociopsychological or sociological frame of reference is limited. Notable exceptions are the La Guardia Report and the work of Howard Becker.[7] Thus, current literature largely by necessity draws on early research and rather heavily on personal testimonials.[8] Only recently a few research studies with direct relevance to marihuana have started to be reported.[9] The above

---

[3] *Drug Arrests and Dispositions in California* . . . 1965 (Sacramento: California Bureau of Criminal Statistics, Department of Justice) and Donald E. Miller, "Narcotic Drug and Marihuana Controls," Paper presented at the National Association of Student Personnel Administrators Drug Education Conference, Washington, D.C., November 7–8, 1966.

[4] *Task Force Report: Narcotics and Drug Abuse, op. cit.,* note 2.

[5] *Ibid.*

[6] See, for example, United Nations, Economic and Social Council, Commission on Narcotic Drugs, *The Question of Cannabis: Cannabis Bibliography* (E/CN. 7/479, September 15, 1965).

[7] Mayor's Committee on Marihuana, *The Marihuana Problem in the City of New York* (Lancaster, Pennsylvania: Jaques Cattell Press, 1944) and Howard Becker, "Becoming a Marihuana User," *American Journal of Sociology,* Vol. 59, November, 1953 and "Marihuana Use and Social Control," *Social Problems,* Vol. 3, July, 1955. See also Howard Becker, *Outsiders: Studies in the Sociology of Deviance* (New York: The Free Press, 1963).

[8] See, for example, *The Marihuana Papers,* David Solomon (ed.) (Indianapolis: The Bobbs-Merrill Co., Inc., 1966), and *The New York Times,* "Is Marihuana Really Safe? Medical Scientists Differ," October 9, 1967, 1.

[9] John C. Ball, "Marihuana Smoking and the Onset of Heroin Use," Paper presented at the twenty-ninth meeting of the Committee on Problems of Drug Dependence, National Research Council, Lexington, Kentucky, February 13–15, 1967; John C. Ball, Carl D. Chambers, and Marion J. Ball, "The Association of Marihuana Smoking with Opiate Addiction in the United States," expanded version of a paper read at the Sixty-Second Annual Meeting of the American

citations are the most notable exceptions to the recency of most investigations in this area.

The assumption of the virtual inevitability of the marihuana-opiate-sequential-use pattern continues to dominate much of our thinking. Although informed persons recognize that marihuana use is not always a prelude to opiate consumption, such antecedent use of marihuana is commonly conjured up in defense of the continuation of penal sanctions which punish the possession and selling of marihuana. It would seem, however, that Ball *et al.* have laid this myth to rest. Conspicuous differences were reported as a matter of fact in the extent of experience with marihuana on the part of Northern metropolitan as compared to Southern addicts.[10] Similarly, Robins and Murphy have presented excellent documentation demonstrating that there are many marihuana users who have not moved on to the use of opiates.[11]

Relatively little, however, is known about the factors which sustain a marihuana-use pattern or about the transition process from the use of marihuana to the use of hard drugs. It seems apparent that increased knowledge about this transition will not only contribute to the store of information on the emergence of opiate-use patterns following marihuana use, but may also help to clarify our thinking with respect to the use of penal sanctions in dealing with marihuana users. Unless reliable data regarding this transition process can be collected, we will continue to strike in the dark and the level of exchange will remain on the impressionistic and, too often, emotional level. Ball and his associates feel that enough is known to characterize what they designate as the "dominant relationship" between marihuana use and the use of hard drugs. The relationship is summarized as follows:

> The incipient addict is predisposed to opiate addiction by his use of marihuana for the following reasons: marihuana is taken for its euphoric effects, it produces a "high"; both marihuana and heroin are only available from underworld sources of supply; both are initially taken within a peer-group recreational setting; both are illegal; the neighborhood friends with whom marihuana use begins are often the same friends who initiate the incipient addict to the use of opiates. A

Sociological Association, San Francisco, California, August 27–31, 1967; and Lee N. Robins and George E. Murphy, "Drug Use in a Normal Population of Young Negro Men," Paper presented at the American Public Health Association meetings, San Francisco, California, October 31–November 4, 1966.

[10] John C. Ball, Carl D. Chambers, and Marion J. Ball, *ibid.* See also, John C. Ball, "Two Patterns of Narcotic Drug Addiction in the United States," *The Journal of Criminal Law, Criminology and Police Science,* Vol. 56, No. 2, 1965, 203–211.

[11] Robins and Murphy, *op. cit.,* note 9.

principal effect, then, is one of differential association—becoming part of a drug-taking group.[12]

While the validity and general applicability of some of these statements may be open to some question, the fact is that they tell us little about the transition from marihuana to the use of opiates. Unfortunately, information about the factors related to the transition is at best difficult to obtain. It is necessary to rely on either the observations of: (1) marihuana smokers who have not used opiates or those who have used opiates and stopped, or (2) on the personal testimony of hard drug users describing their present and/or past experiences with marihuana. The remainder of this paper draws primarily on the last of these groups and is exploratory in nature. Selected experiences with marihuana of a sample of individuals with a history of drug use are described. Specific attention will be given to the perception of marihuana as a drug used for kicks and to experience with marihuana as related to different drug-use patterns. Unfortunately, the source of data (questionnaire responses) available for the present paper does not permit an examination of the transition process per se. It is felt, however, that further investigation along the lines projected may be helpful in illuminating the movement from experience with marihuana to the use of hard drugs.

DATA COLLECTION PROCEDURES

The primary data were collected by questionnaire in conjunction with a study concerned with anti-narcotic testing.[13] Subjects represent an availability sample of persons in the Nalline testing program in Chicago, Illinois and Oakland, California, as well as drug users incarcerated in the Santa Rita Rehabilitation Center, Pleasanton, California. The population represents drug users on probation, on parole, and/or incarcerated. All subjects in the above groups were reached during the months of May and June, 1963. In 1965 a group of research patients at the United States Public Health Service Hospital, now the National Institute of Mental Health Clinical Research Center, at Lexington, Kentucky completed the questionnaire.

Chicago and Oakland subjects were contacted at the time of their appearance at the Nalline Testing Center. All Chicago subjects were contacted by this investigator. The distribution of questionnaires in Oakland was made possible through the assistance of Captain Thorvald Brown of the Oakland Police Department and at the Santa Rita Reha-

---

[12] John C. Ball, Carl D. Chambers, and Marion J. Ball, *op. cit.,* note 9.
[13] Stanley E. Grupp, "The Nalline Test and Addict Attitudes" (Unpublished Ph.D. dissertation, Indiana University, 1967).

bilitation Center through the help of Dr. James Terry, Chief Medical Officer. The Lexington data were collected by permission of the Research Committee and through the help of Dr. Charles Haertzen. Only willing subjects were included in the study. No subjects were "forced" to participate. After the elimination of unusable questionnaires, 306 subjects remained. The subjects represented 100 from Oakland, 71 from Chicago, 45 from the Santa Rita Rehabilitation Center, and 90 from Lexington. In the discussion which follows, the numbers in several instances fall short of these totals because of non-response.

POPULATION CHARACTERISTICS [14]

The population was predominantly non-white (seventy percent) and male (eighty-five percent). There was nearly a balanced proportion among the single, the married, and the divorced-separated-widowed categories. The population was skewed toward an older age group with a mean age of 31.6 years. This is somewhat older than one would expect in an addict population. Viewed in terms of residential history the subjects were relatively stable. Approximately two-thirds had lived in their present community four years or longer. Those who were incarcerated were asked how long they had lived in the last community they lived in. The majority (sixty-four percent) had not graduated from high school while about one-fifth indicated they were high school graduates. A still smaller proportion (fifteen percent) claimed to have had some college.

Criminal involvement as measured by a relatively crude sentences-served index did not suggest an especially high degree of criminality. The maximum, medium, and minimum involvement groups represented forty-three, forty-three, and fourteen percent of the population respectively.[15]

---

[14] Characteristics of the population have been described in varying detail elsewhere. See Stanley E. Grupp, *ibid.;* "A Note on the Use of Lexington Subjects to Investigate Addict Mobility," *The International Journal of the Addictions,* Vol. 2, No. 2, Fall, 1967; "Addict Mobility and the Nalline Test," *The British Journal of Addiction,* forthcoming; and "The Effect of Age on Four Scales of the California Psychological Inventory," with Gary Ramseyer and Jay Richardson, *The Journal of General Psychology,* forthcoming.

[15] The assignment of individuals to the maximum, medium, and minimum categories was determined by the type of sentences served. The types of sentences and their respective weights were: federal prison—4, state prison—4, juvenile correctional institution—3, county jail—2, and city jail—1. For assignment purposes the responses on a given item were considered as one irrespective of the number of times a given type of sentence had been served. The point distribution dividing the three groups was: maximum—10–14, medium—5–9, and minimum—0–4.

Drug-use patterns were identified by an open-end question which asked the respondent to list all drugs he recalled using in the last five years. Marihuana was *not* included in the pattern forming process. Although drug-use patterns of the responding group (N = 247) were quite varied, a very high proportion (eighty-seven percent) reported the use of one or more opiates during the preceding five years. Approximately one-half (forty-nine percent) of the entire group reported a straight opiate consumption pattern exclusive of marihuana. Within the opiate group, straight heroin users were by far the most frequent. More than a third (thirty-six percent) were hard-core heroin users exclusive of marihuana. The second most frequent group (thirty percent) was the opiate-amphetamine pattern.

About one-half of the population started using drugs before they were twenty years of age. A sizeable minority (eighteen percent) indicated they were twenty-five years of age or older when they started to use drugs, while the remainder (thirty percent) initiated their experience between twenty and twenty-five years of age.

Two hundred and ninety-eight subjects responded to an independent question concerned with marihuana use. Of these, two hundred and sixty-five (eighty-nine percent) had experience with marihuana. Fifteen subjects claimed that marihuana was the only thing they used. Of those experienced with both marihuana and other drugs, one hundred and ninety-six (seventy-eight percent) had this experience prior to using other drugs, while fifty-four (twenty-two percent) estimated that this use occurred about the same time they started using other drugs. Thirty-three persons indicated they had never smoked marihuana. With respect to this sample, it is clear that experience with marihuana at one time or another is widespread among drug users. It is apparent, however, that marihuana use is not always antecedent to the use of other drugs. It is noted specifically that in one hundred and two instances (thirty-four percent) the experience or non-experience with marihuana fails to support the claim that marihuana use precedes the use of other drugs.

PERCEPTION OF MARIHUANA

The one hundred and ninety-six subjects who had used marihuana prior to the use of other drugs were selected for closer inspection with special reference to their perception of marihuana as a drug used for kicks. Attention was directed to this group under the assumption that it offers a fertile point of departure, albeit crude, for exploring the transition process from marihuana to hard drug use. For this sample, information was available on one hundred and eighty-five persons regarding the first drug they used for kicks. (Eleven persons did not respond.) The following discussion looks intensively at this population. Data were obtained by an open-ended question, "What is the first drug that you can remember using for kicks?" This question offers an ideal means for identifying how marihuana is perceived by persons who by their own admission have moved from marihuana use to the use of hard drugs.

One hundred and thirty-five respondents (seventy-three percent) identified marihuana as the drug they first used for kicks. Two points are of interest here: (1) the fact that marihuana is perceived as a drug by an appreciable number, and (2) the fact that it is perceived as a drug used for kicks. It should be emphasized that neither in the open-end question concerning the drug first used for kicks or in any question prior to the marihuana experience question was any reference made to marihuana per se. Only the word "drug" was used. The question referring specifically to experience with marihuana appeared six questions after the question concerning the first drug used for kicks. It is not probable, however, that respondents were induced to list marihuana as a drug first used for kicks simply because a question appeared later with the word marihuana in it.

Fifty of the respondents (twenty-seven percent) who had in fact used marihuana prior to using other drugs did not list it as the drug they first used for kicks, but instead listed some other drug.

Judging from the responses of this sample it may be said that drug users, like non-drug users, vary in their perception of marihuana as a drug and as a vehicle for euphoria. This, of course, does not mean that marihuana may not have been used for kicks at the time it was initially used. It does mean, however, that in terms of recall and present perceptions, marihuana may or may not be perceived as a drug or as a drug which was first used for kicks.

The striking point is the high percentage of hard drug users who do perceive marihuana as a drug. This seems inconsistent with the increasing tendency and preference on the part of some, this observer among them, to place marihuana in a non-drug category. One would not be surprised to find hard drug users themselves in this group, but this is not in evidence here. Interesting too is the fact that hard-core heroin addicts also tend to perceive marihuana as a drug.[16] Of

---

[16] Hard-core heroin users are defined as those respondents who listed heroin, exclusive of marihuana, as the only drug they had used during preceding five year period.

fifty-seven hard-core heroin users—who had used marihuana prior to using other drugs and for whom data were available on the drug they perceived as the first drug used for kicks—forty-four (seventy-seven percent) listed marihuana as the first drug they remembered using for kicks.

There is some evidence to suggest that those who perceive marihuana as a drug used for its euphoric quality tend to be otherwise oriented toward marihuana. (See Table 1.) Those who perceive mari-

TABLE 1

Preference for and Experience with Marihuana During the Preceding Five Years by Those Experienced with Marihuana Who Perceive It as a Drug Used for Kicks and Those Who Do Not *

Preference-Experience with Marihuana	Marihuana as a Drug Used for Kicks	
	Perceivers	Non-perceivers
	a	b
Marihuana Listed as the Drug Preferred **	16 (13)	3 (6)
Marihuana Listed as a Drug Used During Previous Five Years **	c	d
	51 (50)	9 (20)

$X^2 = .08$, not significant.
Corrected by Yates correction for continuity.

* Percent of those responding to the question in parentheses. The number of respondents for cells a, b, c, and d are 124, 48, 101, and 45 respectively.
** This was an open-end question which asked that the respondent list the drug(s).

huana as a drug used for kicks, as opposed to those who do not, are more apt to list marihuana as a drug they used during the preceding five years, and by a slight margin are more apt to list marihuana as the drug preferred. The differences as measured by chi-square, however, were not statistically significant.

Using chi-square, the perceivers and non-perceivers were further compared on selected personal-social and drug-pattern variables to determine if there were any significant differences between the two groups.[17] Of the eleven variables investigated, two were statistically significant ($< .01$), education and drug preference. Non-perceivers as opposed to perceivers were less apt to be high school graduates with twenty and forty-three percent in this category respectively. Non-

---

[17] The personal-social variables were sex, marital status, race, prison and jail sentences served, parolee-probationer status, and age of first drug use; drug-pattern variables were drugs used during the preceding five years, drug preference, number of drugs used, and dangerous drugs used.

perceivers were slightly less apt to prefer marihuana as well as amphetamines, but were markedly less apt to respond "none" to the drug preference question. On the other hand, non-perceivers were more apt to list an opiate as the drug of preference. Seventy-three and forty-two percent of the non-perceivers and perceivers, respectively, listed an opiate as the preferred drug. The difference, however, was largely absorbed in the extent perceivers of marihuana as a drug used for kicks were inclined to say they did not prefer any drug. Forty percent and seventeen percent of the perceivers and non-perceivers respectively responded "none" to the drug preference question.

In sum, while firm conclusions are not possible, there is a tendency for perceivers as opposed to non-perceivers to be more oriented around a marihuana-use pattern (Table 1) and to respond "none" when asked what drug they preferred. While a "none" response may suggest a drug non-specific point of view, it seems a more probable explanation would be that it is a "non-drug" response, an orientation away from drugs. The two groups differed quite markedly with respect to formal education and drug preference and the differences were statistically significant.

DRUG-USE PATTERNS AND MARIHUANA EXPERIENCE

Experience with marihuana as it is related to selected drug-use patterns was selected for special attention. Basic data are presented in Table 2. Totals in the cells differ because of non-response on some items and the loss of cases in the cross-tabulation process.

Subjects with mixed-use patterns (opiates combined with amphetamines and/or barbiturates) as opposed to the opiate patterns are more apt to have experience with marihuana. The incidence of experience with marihuana, however, in no instance falls below seventy percent. The differences are even more marked with respect to the use of marihuana within the previous five years. Since the latter data were obtained by an open-end question (and in view of the marked differences in the two kinds of experiences) this could represent recall error and/or a commitment to the opiates.

Within the opiate category, hard-core heroin addicts are more apt to have experience with marihuana than the non-hard-core group. The difference is considerably diminished, however, when we turn to the use of marihuana during the preceding five years.

Preference for marihuana presents no marked differences pattern to pattern. It is of interest, however, that the opiate-amphetamine group, a mixed pattern, has the highest proportion of marihuana preferrers.

The higher incidence of marihuana use on the part of heroin addicts

TABLE 2

DRUG-USE PATTERNS AND EXPERIENCE WITH MARIHUANA

Drug-Use Patterns	Nature of Marihuana Experience [a]			
	Some Experience with Marihuana [b]	Marihuana First Drug Used for Kicks [c]	Used Marihuana in Previous Five Years [c]	Prefer Marihuana
Opiate	95 (82) N = 116	57 (52) N = 110	24 (20) N = 119	6 (5) N = 112
Opiate (excluding heroin only)	21 (70) N = 30	9 (32) N = 28	5 (16) N = 31	2 (7) N = 30
Heroin Only	74 (86) N = 86	48 (58) N = 82	19 (22) N = 88	4 (5) N = 82
Opiate-Amphetamine	69 (95) N = 73	39 (55) N = 71	42 (58) N = 73	11 (15) N = 72
Opiate-Barbiturate-Amphetamine	15 (100) N = 15	11 (79) N = 14	10 (67) N = 15	1 (7) N = 14

[a] Percentages in parentheses. The number of respondents on the particular item is expressed in the lower left corner of each cell. Marihuana experience was abstracted from four different questions; thus, there is a difference in the number of respondents for the several cells.

[b] Data obtained by a closed-end question.

[c] Data obtained by an open-end question.

as opposed to other users of opiates is consistent with the finding of Ball *et al.*[18] Unlike the latter study, the evidence here comes from a group which is largely a Northern addict population (Chicago and Oakland), and not from a comparison of Northern and Southern addicts where quite marked differences exist not only in the extent of experience with marihuana but in their characteristic drug-use pattern. Unfortunately, in the sample described here the hard-core heroin addicts represented the overwhelming proportion (seventy-four percent) of the opiate group thus vitiating the importance of the trend.

Time of experience with marihuana (not presented in table form) as related to drug-use patterns was recorded for those having this acquaintance prior to and about the same time as other drugs. For all patterns this acquaintance usually came before using other drugs. The opiate-amphetamine group was least likely (seventy-four percent) and the opiate-barbiturate-amphetamine the most likely (eighty-seven percent) to have marihuana experience as an antecedent event.

When the several kinds of experience with marihuana are combined,

---

[18] John C. Ball, Carl D. Chambers, and Marion J. Ball, *op. cit.*, note 9.

with two exceptions it is the opiate-mix patterns that are the most apt to have these collective experiences. Several patterns of collective marihuana experiences are presented in Table 3. Thirty-eight percent and forty percent of the opiate-amphetamine and the opiate-barbiturate-amphetamine groups respectively shared the first three marihuana experiences as presented in Table 3. The opiate-use pattern and the two opiate sub-patterns fall considerably short of these percentages. Note, however, that a rather high proportion, fifty-five percent, of the hard-core heroin users are experienced with marihuana and identify it as the first drug they used for kicks. Particularly noticeable in Table 3 is the marked drop-off in all patterns when preference for marihuana is added to the list of marihuana experiences.

TABLE 3

DRUG-USE PATTERNS AND EXTENT OF MARIHUANA EXPERIENCE

Drug-Use Patterns	Extent of Marihuana Experience [a]			
	Some Experience with Marihuana ———————→	Marihuana First Drug Used for Kicks ————————→	Used Marihuana in Previous Five Years ———→	Prefer Marihuana
Opiate N = 116	95 (82)	56 (48)	15 (11)	4 (3)
Opiate (Excluding heroin only) N = 30	21 (70)	9 (30)	2 (7)	2 (7)
Heroin only N = 86	74 (86)	47 (55)	13 (15)	2 (2)
Opiate-Amphetamine N = 73	69 (95)	39 (53)	28 (38)	6 (8)
Opiate-Barbiturate-Amphetamine N = 15	15 (100)	11 (73)	6 (40)	0 (0)

[a] Percent of the total population in a given drug category is expressed in parentheses. Thus, forty-seven (fifty-five percent) of the eighty-six "heroin only" users indicate that they had experience with marihuana *and* that it was the first drug they used for kicks.

CONCLUSION

The findings of this exploratory investigation provide additional support for the prevailing professional opinion in this area, namely, that marihuana use is not a necessary antecedent to the use of hard drugs. Perhaps more important are implications of the several rather clear patterns which emerge: (1) drug users who are experienced with marihuana differ in their perception of it as a drug they first used for kicks and (2) there is considerable variation in the kinds of experience with marihuana on the part of drug users characterized by different drug-use patterns.

It is recognized that the data do not permit generalizations, let alone conclusions, regarding the relationship of marihuana use to hard drug use. Neither are illuminating insights suggested about the transition process itself. Nevertheless, the varying experiences with marihuana as well as the marked differences in perception of it indicate that these are both interesting and important areas in the epidemiology of marihuana and narcotic drug use and should be subjected to further investigation.

Of particular interest is the tendency on the part of perceivers (those who see marihuana as a drug they used for kicks) to have more education; in terms of preference, perceivers tend to veer away from opiates and to be non-drug oriented as identified by "none" responses on the drug preference question. The fact, however, that no statistically significant differences were evident in the drug-use patterns of the perceivers and non-perceivers suggests a need for restraint in emphasizing the significance of the several differences between these two groups.

Viewed in terms of drug-use patterns per se there is a tendency for marihuana experience to increase as we move from opiate only to the opiate-mix patterns. A similar trend is evident when the various combinations of marihuana experiences for each of the several drug-use patterns are viewed collectively. These findings suggest but do not conclusively demonstrate that "spree" users or persons characterized by multihabituation are more apt to have experience with marihuana than are single pattern users.

It is believed that further investigation is needed along the lines projected in this paper. Research is necessary to build the body of epidemiological data apropos to marihuana use in the population, to develop an adequate typology of marihuana users, and especially to investigate those conditions involved in sustaining a marihuana-use pattern as opposed to those conditions involved in movement from marihuana experimentation use to a hard drug-use consumption pattern.

Assuming future investigations sustain the several differences or confirm other differences among drug users regarding marihuana use and perception, there is a need to establish their importance. Closer scrutiny of this kind of information should lead to a better understanding of the transition process that is involved in moving from marihuana use to the use of other drugs. There is, however, a need to develop with greater care and precision, than was possible in the present paper, the drug-use patterns themselves and to spell out the orientation and commitment to these patterns. A number of additional questions are also involved: To what extent are the several patterns transitory or permanent? What personal and social factors are associated with the patterns and what is their significance? When subjected to closer inspection will the differences in marihuana experiences be sustained? If so, a deeper probing is indicated concerning the nature of these orientations and to identify factors which are significantly related to them. With respect to marihuana, given the preliminary findings of this paper, there is a particular need to explore the extent there are differences in the experiential background of those persons representing drug-use patterns which seem to cluster around a complex of marihuana experiences in contrast to those who do not.

THE EFFECT OF A SYNTHETIC MARIHUANA-LIKE COMPOUND ON MUSICAL TALENT AS MEASURED BY THE SEASHORE TEST

C. Knight Aldrich

Musicians, particularly members of dance orchestras, are reputed to use marihuana for the purpose of enhancing their musical ability. Piel (*1*), in *Life* Magazine, reports that in the state of marihuana intoxication "the swing musician ascends to new peaks of virtuosity." Medical writers, however, are inclined to question this belief, and Walton (*2*) states that "there is very little probability that an individual's performance is in any degree improved over that of his best capabilities. As judged by objectively critical means, the standards of performance are no doubt lowered." In an endeavor to discover the cause of the common misapprehension, he says: "There is an increased sensitivity to sound and a keener appreciation of rhythm and timing," but he feels that "these phenomena, as judged by objective criteria, probably do not exist except during the early phases of the drug's effects." He suggests that the release of inhibitions by marihuana may result in bringing latent talents to the surface or in evoking a

Reprinted from *Public Health Reports,* March 31, 1944, pp. 431–33, with the permission of the publisher.

more intense emotional performance. He also recognizes, with Bromberg (*3*) and others, that a subject's evaluation of his own performance is enhanced.

PROCEDURE

The synthesis of the pyra-hexyl compound (1-hydroxy-3-n-hexyl-6,-6,9-trimethyl-7,8,9,10-tetrahydro-6-dibenzopyran) by Professor Adams (*4*) has facilitated the study of marihuana by furnishing a stable drug of uniform potency and consistent effect. Experienced marihuana users report that the psychological effects of this compound are qualitatively identical with those of marihuana. The present experiment was set up to study the effect of this compound on performance as measured by the Seashore tests of musical talents (*5*), in order to determine objectively whether or not marihuana affects musical ability.

The Seashore tests were used because they seemed to offer the most carefully standardized tests available of musical capability. Although they have been criticized for their low reliability and their value in individual diagnosis has been questioned, for group work they are, as Mursell (*6*) says, "outstandingly the most important battery of tests in the field of music."

The six tests are played on phonograph records. The first consists of 50 pairs of notes of progressively diminishing degree of difference in pitch; the subject indicates whether he considers the second note of the pair to be higher or lower than the first. Three other tests are similarly constructed, with differences in loudness, time, and timbre. Two consist of 30 double series of notes, in one of which the subject decides whether two rhythm patterns are the same or different, and in the last he identifies by number one note which is changed in the second of two otherwise similar tone patterns.

Twelve healthy white male patients volunteered for the experiment. All were serving prison sentences for violation of the Marihuana Tax Act. One was 47 years of age; the ages of the others varied between 23 and 36 years. They had used marihuana from 3 to 18 years with an average of 9½ years. Of the 12 subjects, 2 were professional musicians and 2 had musical ambitions. Each patient was given the test three times, at intervals of 1 week; twice without any drug, and the third trial 4½ hours after ingestion of 60 mg. of pyra-hexyl compound. This quantity and time were found to produce a "kick" comparable to a satisfying amount of marihuana in most cases, although individual variations were noted.

The average of the results, summarized in table 1, shows improve-

ment in all tests on the second trial and a return to approximately
the original level under the influence of pyra-hexyl compound. One
exception is seen in the case of rhythm in which the change between
the second and third trials is negligible. In general the pyra-hexyl
compound seems simply to have obliterated the gain due to practice.

TABLE 1

	Pitch (50)	Loudness (50)	Rhythm (30)	Time (50)	Timbre (50)	Tonal memory (30)
First trial	35.9	39.2	23.4	34.7	41.8	21.2
Second trial	37.2	40.5	24.1	36.7	43.1	23.3
After pyra-hexyl	35.3	39.8	24.2	33.9	41.9	21.8

Average number correct: 12 patients.

The Seashore test measures only sensory musical capacity and leaves
out of account factors such as motor speed and coordination, release
of inhibitions and fatigability, which could conceivably influence the
playing of present-day music. The subjective reports, however, emphasize the extent of the self-deception brought out by marihuana. Eight
of the patients, when asked if they noticed any differences in their own
performances, felt sure that they had improved with marihuana; 3 felt
that they remained the same, and 1 "couldn't say." Actually, 9 out of
12 subjects achieved lower scores on the third than on the second
trials.

Subject D, a professional saxophone player, said after the third
trial, "I am convinced I was better ... I'm sure the medicine helped;
I know it does on my horn as I hear the notes more distinctly." He
stated that the medicine made him " 'high' but not quite to the peak—
about three-fourths I'd say." His scores, indicating in general a poorer
performance with the drug, are shown in table 2.

TABLE 2

	Pitch (50)	Loudness (50)	Rhythm (30)	Time (50)	Timbre (50)	Tonal memory (30)
First trial	33	43	26	39	44	27
Second trial	40	47	24	39	47	29
After pyra-hexyl	33	46	26	35	44	27

Patient "D" number correct.

SUMMARY OF RESULTS

No improvement was observed in the musical capability, as tested by the Seashore measures of musical talents, of 12 former users of marihuana after ingestion of satisfying amounts of pyra-hexyl compound, a synthetic, marihuana-like substance.

Although 9 out of 12 subjects achieved poorer scores after using the drug than on the previous trial, 8 out of 12 expressed the opinion that their scores had improved, and none recognized a loss in efficiency.

CONCLUSION

Pyra-hexyl compound, a marihuana-like synthetic, appears to improve an individual's subjective impression of his own musical ability rather than the ability per se as measured by the Seashore test.

REFERENCES

(1)   Piel, Gerard: *Narcotics. Life* Magazine, 15 (3):15–82 (July 19, 1943).

(2)   Walton, Robert P.: *Marihuana, America's New Drug Problem.* Lippincott, Philadelphia, 1938.

(3)   Bromberg, Walter: "Marihuana, a psychiatric study." J. Am. Med. Assoc., 113:4 (1939).

(4)   Adams, R.: *Marihuana* (Harvey Lecture). Bull. N.Y. Acad. Med., 18: 1705 (1942).

(5)   Seashore, Carl E.: *Psychology of Music.* McGraw-Hill, New York, 1938.

(6)   Mursell, James L.: *Psychology of Music.* Norton, New York, 1937.

THE ASSOCIATION OF MARIHUANA
SMOKING WITH OPIATE ADDICTION
IN THE UNITED STATES

John C. Ball, Carl D. Chambers
and Marion J. Ball

The question has been repeatedly raised as to whether the smoking
of marihuana cigarettes leads to opiate addiction in the United States.[1]
Extreme viewpoints have been advanced. Marihuana use has been
viewed as an insidious and invariant precursor of opiate addiction and
enslavement.[2] Conversely, it has been regarded as an innocuous narcotic
with beneficial social qualities.[3] These extreme positions may now be
dismissed as polemical statements without substantiation.[4] Still, the

---

[1] For a recent discussion of this issue see the Report by the President's Commission on Law Enforcement and Administration of Justice, *The Challenge of Crime
in a Free Society* (Washington: U.S. Government Printing Office, 1967) 224–225.
A definitive bibliography on marihuana has recently been compiled, United Nations, Economic and Social Council, Commission on Narcotic Drugs, *The Question
of Cannabis: Cannabis Bibliography* (E/CN.7/479, September 15, 1965).

[2] Anslinger & Tompkins, *The Traffic in Narcotics* 20–22 (1953).

[3] Solomon (Ed.), *The Marihuana Papers* xiii–xxi (1966).

[4] The smoking of marihuana cigarettes does not necessarily lead to opiate addiction (this report, Tables 1–3); conversely, use of marihuana is not without unpleasant or adverse effects for some persons. On this latter point see, Mayor's
Committee on Marihuana, *The Marihuana Problem in the City of New York*
(Lancaster, Pennsylvania: The Jaques Cattell Press, 1944), p. 38; also see Howard

Reprinted from *The Journal of Criminal Law, Criminology and Police Science*
59 (June 1968): 171–82, with the permission of the publisher and John C. Ball.

question remains: To what extent and under what conditions is marihuana smoking associated with a subsequent addiction to opiates?

The logical possibilities with respect to the association of marihuana and opiate drugs may be depicted as shown in Figure 1.

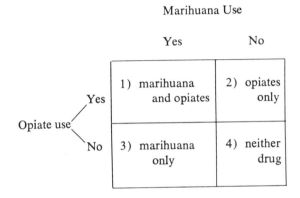

FIGURE 1

Box 1 includes users of both marihuana and opiates; Box 2 those who use opiates but not marihuana; Box 3 those who only use marihuana; and Box 4 consists of those who use neither marihuana nor opiates. The nondrug using population—the normal or control comparison—is found in Box 4 which, presumably, includes the major portion of the United States population. The question of association involves Boxes 1, 2 and 3. The opiate only category, Box 2, is relevant as it indicates no association between marihuana and opiates, as does Box 3, the marihuana only category. Thus, a positive association is found only in Box 1.

There are two principal ways of considering the association of marihuana and opiate use. The first is an epidemiological or community approach: to determine the prevalence of marihuana use in a given population, such as a city or state, and then to record the prevalence of opiate use within the marihuana group as well as in the population selected. This community based approach has been effectively employed in St. Louis by Robins and Murphy.[5] It is pertinent to note that such epidemiological studies take a broad view of the question from the

---

Becker's case report of adverse effects, *Becoming a Marihuana User, 59 Amer. J. Soc.* 241 (1953).

[5] Robins & Murphy, *Drug Use in a Normal Population of Young Negro Men, 57 Amer. J. Public Health* 1580–1596 (1967).

community level to the target subjects—the telescope is focused upon the community.

The second general approach in considering the association of marihuana and opiate use is to focus upon the target subjects themselves, to start with the positive association. This has been a traditional method in both medicine and sociology: to study the clinical disease state or the deviant individual. In the present study, this second approach is employed. Analysis of a national sample of opiate addicts was undertaken in order to ascertain whether or not marihuana smoking was associated with their addiction—the telescope was focused upon the target subjects.

Because of the current interest in the topic of marihuana use in the United States and the concomitant confusion as to popular versus scientific sources of data, it may be pertinent to state explicitly the scope and purpose of this paper. The precise research question under investigation is: Given existing social conditions and laws, is the smoking of marihuana in the United States associated with the subsequent use of opiate drugs? If so, under what conditions? If not, under what conditions?

SUBJECTS AND SOURCE OF DATA

The subjects were 2,213 addict patients admitted to the Lexington and Fort Worth hospitals during 1965.[6] The demographic characteristics of this national patient sample have been previously described.[7] The probable representativeness of the 50,070 addicts who have been admitted to the two hospitals since 1935 with respect to the universe of opiate addicts in the United States has also been considered.[8] It is relevant to note in the present context that the addict patients at the two federal hospitals do not consist of a lower-class homogeneous prisoner population. Thus, the 2,213 addicts included both voluntary admissions and federal prisoners, males and females, Negroes and whites, laborers and housewives, prostitutes and physicians, lawyers and forgers, and drug sellers as well as users. Forty-six of the fifty states were represented and the range in age was from 16 to 75 years.

---

[6] The 2,213 subjects included all addict patients admitted to the Lexington hospital from February 1, 1965 through December 31, 1965 and those admitted to the Fort Worth hospital from April 20, 1965 through December 31, 1965.

[7] Ball, O'Donnell & Cottrell, *Selected Social Characteristics of Consecutive Admissions to Lexington in 1965*, 4 *Criminologica* 13–16 (1966).

[8] Ball, *Two Patterns of Narcotic Drug Addiction in the United States*, 56 J. *Crim. L., C. & P. S.* 210 (1965); Ball & Bates, *Migration and Residential Mobility of Narcotic Drug Addicts*, 14 *Social Problems* 67–68 (1966).

n sum, this hospitalized population reflects the diverse sub-groups which comprise the universe of known opiate addicts in the United States.[9]

The principal source of data was the admission summary sheet completed by a clerk at the time each patient enters the hospital. Further nformation was available from patients' medical records; this included a medical history, current drug diagnosis, psychiatric diagnosis, employment experiences, criminal history, family relationships, educational records and other varied clinical and administrative documents. An extended interview was conducted with 337 of the subjects at the Lexington hospital in 1965 to secure additional information related to drug use.[10] From these interviews a reliability check of the admission data was undertaken.[11]

Early in 1965, additional information with respect to marihuana use, age at first arrest, and age at first opiate use became available on all new admissions to the two federal hospitals.[12] Specifically, each patient was asked (1) whether he had ever used marihuana, (2) at what age he was first arrested, (3) at what age he first used opiates, (4) present drug used, (5) method of administration, and (6) from whom drugs were obtained. The present study is focused upon an analysis of these six items from the revised admission summary sheet, although reference is made to other sources of data as seems appropriate.

THE DISTRIBUTION OF MARIHUANA USE IN THE UNITED STATES

In Table 1, the percentage of subjects with and without a history of marihuana use is tabulated for each state. Three types of conditions

---

[9] O'Donnell & Ball (Eds.), *Narcotic Addiction* 9–10 (1966).

[10] During 1965, 337 Lexington patients were interviewed by the staff of the Addiction Research Center. A detailed occupation and addiction history was obtained for each patient.

[11] At the time of hospital admission a clerk asked each subject whether he had ever used marihuana. Subsequently, during the detailed interview by staff he was also asked whether he had ever used marihuana. Of the 337 subjects, 30 changes in use were reported: 19 reported use to the interviewer after having answered "no use" to the admission clerk, while 11 denied use after having answered "yes" to a history of marihuana use. Thus, 5.6 percent of the 337 subjects reported more use of marihuana to the interviewer and 3.3 percent reported less use. In sum, there was a 2.4 percent net increase. Reliability of the item response was 91.7 percent. For an analysis of the reliability of 20 items contained in the patients' records, see Emily S. Cottrell, *Reliability of Admission Data*, Working Paper, Addiction Research Center, SS 67–1.

[12] For comparative data from 1936–1937, see Michael J. Pescor, *A Statistical Analysis of the Clinical Records of Hospitalized Drug Addicts, Public Health Reports*, Supplement No. 143, 1–30 (1938).

were found to exist with respect to marihuana and opiate use in th
United States (Figure 2). First was the positive association betwee
marihuana and opiate use found in 16 states, the District of Columbi
and Puerto Rico. In each of these high addiction states,[13] more tha

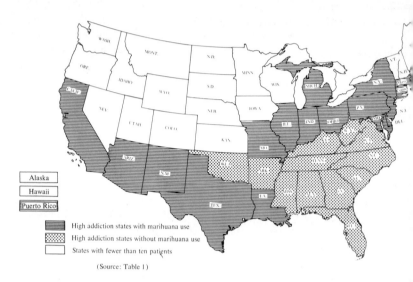

High addiction states with marihuana use

High addiction states without marihuana use

States with fewer than ten patients

(Source: Table 1)

FIGURE 2

High opiate addiction states, with and without marihuana use,
for 2,208 patients from Lexington and Fort Worth hospitals, 1965

50 percent of the subjects have used marihuana as well as opiates. Th
16 "marihuana states" consist of two contiguous sets. Five of the mari
huana states border on Mexico or the Gulf of Mexico: California
Arizona, New Mexico, Texas, and Louisiana. The other 11 marihuan
states are located in the Eastern-Midwestern metropolitan belt, on th
Atlantic from Boston to New York to Washington, D.C. and westwar
from Pittsburgh to Chicago to St. Louis. Included within this groupin
of states are the District of Columbia and Puerto Rico.[14] (The mari
huana states are those with ruled lines on map in Figure 2.)

A second type of association is found in 12 states wherein most o
the opiate addicts have never used marihuana. These "opiate only
states" (shown by dots in Figure 2) are found in the South and con
stitute a regionally based area from Miami to Oklahoma to Virginia. I

---

[13] O'Donnell & Ball, *op. cit. supra* note 9, at pp. 8–9.
[14] Puerto Rico, although not contiguous to these states, is closely tied to the
East Coast by virtue of migration and rapid air transportation.

previous research,[15] the pattern of drug abuse in these states has been referred to as the "southern pattern" of opiate addiction in the United States. It involves the use of opiates other than heroin and it is not associated with marihuana use.

The third condition, or type of association, shown in Figure 2 is that of low addiction states with or without marihuana use. The 22 states shown in white are low addiction areas on the basis of admissions to the Lexington and Fort Worth hospitals in 1965.[16] Most of these states also have low rates of opiate addiction as computed from the active file of the Federal Bureau of Narcotics.[17] Previous analyses of rates of opiate addiction by state generally confirm the present contiguous groupings, although some changes in rates and rank order for particular states occur.[18]

There are, then, two quite distinct patterns of opiate use in the United States. The first pattern of addiction is associated with marihuana use and is concentrated in the metropolitan states—New York, Illinois, California and Texas. The second pattern of opiate use is that found in the Southern states and it is not associated with marihuana smoking. The question arises as to why marihuana use is associated with the one pattern of opiate addiction, but not the other?

HIGH ADDICTION STATES WITH AN ILLICIT-DRUG SUBCULTURE

In the metropolitan centers in which marihuana and heroin use are prevalent, an illicit-drug subculture exists. Marihuana smoking and heroin use can only be steadily pursued in an environment in which there is continuous contact with underworld sources of supply, since neither drug can be legally prescribed nor dispensed in the United States. Although the structure and dynamics of the addict subculture as an enduring group and cultural process, as distinct from an individual and psychological experience, has still to be adequately investigated, some of the basic facets are well known. The importance of learning to smoke marihuana [19] or to use a needle when injecting heroin,[20] the

---

[15] Ball, *op. cit. supra* note 8 at pp. 203–211.

[16] Table 1.

[17] O'Donnell & Ball, *op. cit. supra* note 9.

[18] Ball, *op. cit. supra* note 8, at p. 207.

[19] Becker, *op. cit. supra* note 4, at pp. 235–242.

[20] Ball, *The Onset of Heroin Addiction in a Juvenile Population: Implications for Theories of Deviancy,* paper read at the annual meeting of the American Sociological Association, August 31, 1966, p. 4.

TABLE 1

STATE * OR PLACE OF RESIDENCE OF 2,213 ADDICT PATIENTS BY SELECTED DEMOGRAPHIC AND DRUG HISTORY FACTORS

Residence	Demographic Factors								Addiction Factors				First Arrest	Mean Age	
	Male Number	Female Number	Total Number	1st Adm. %	Vol. Adms. %	From SMSA %	Non-White %	With Arrest History %	Mari-huana History %	Heroin Diag. %	Intra-venous Route %	Drugs from Pusher %		1st Opiate Use	At Hosp. Adm. in 1965
1. Alabama	47	13	60	56.7	95.0	58.3	6.7	63.3	20.0	1.7	55.0	28.3	20.8	29.5	39.2
2. Arizona	18	1	19	73.7	78.9	100.0	5.3	94.7	68.4	84.2	84.2	73.7	17.2	21.5	29.9
3. Arkansas	7	3	10	70.0	100.0	30.0	10.0	30.0	10.0	0.0	50.0	0.0	31.3	35.2	47.3
4. California	135	5	140	82.1	43.6	98.6	9.3	96.4	92.1	93.6	95.0	93.6	17.0	20.7	30.8
5. Colorado	6	3	9	100.0	88.9	100.0	11.1	88.9	88.9	66.7	88.9	77.8	15.1	22.3	27.8
6. Connecticut	32	0	32	78.1	96.9	100.0	25.0	100.0	75.0	78.1	90.6	90.6	18.9	19.1	25.7
7. Delaware	1	1	2	100.0	100.0	100.0	100.0	100.0	100.0	100.0	100.0	100.0	19.5	19.0	30.5
8. Dist. of Columbia	50	12	62	71.0	12.9	100.0	95.2	100.0	77.4	95.2	98.4	96.8	20.1	21.3	31.1
9. Florida	23	11	34	76.5	100.0	85.3	5.9	61.8	44.1	11.8	47.1	35.3	24.6	29.0	39.7
10. Georgia	49	26	75	54.7	100.0	80.0	9.3	78.7	24.0	4.0	49.3	24.0	23.8	28.8	38.8
11. Idaho	1	0	1	100.0	100.0	0.0	0.0	100.0	0.0	0.0	0.0	0.0	20.0	29.0	40.0
12. Illinois	177	58	235	52.8	77.4	99.6	58.3	90.2	82.6	76.6	90.2	83.8	19.2	21.5	31.8
13. Indiana	44	5	49	57.1	69.4	89.8	42.9	85.7	69.4	42.9	69.4	61.2	19.0	23.7	37.5
14. Iowa	1	0	1	100.0	100.0	33.3	0.0	100.0	0.0	0.0	0.0	0.0	40.0	20.0	42.0
15. Kansas	3	0	3	66.7	100.0	45.9	0.0	100.0	66.7	33.3	100.0	33.3	25.3	26.3	48.3
16. Kentucky	31	6	37	62.2	97.3	87.8	5.4	75.7	32.4	0.0	43.2	27.0	21.8	33.0	42.5
17. Louisiana	36	5	41	73.2	73.2	87.8	43.9	85.4	70.7	70.7	80.5	73.2	20.1	22.5	31.5
18. Maine	1	0	1	100.0	100.0	100.0	0.0	100.0	0.0	0.0	0.0	0.0	23.0	27.0	47.0
19. Maryland	38	5	43	72.1	86.0	100.0	34.9	100.0	83.7	86.0	95.3	95.3	17.6	20.0	27.7
20. Massachusetts	16	2	18	88.9	77.8	100.0	33.3	94.4	66.7	55.6	55.6	55.6	18.2	21.8	32.4
21. Michigan	28	10	38	68.4	89.5	86.8	36.8	73.7	60.5	36.8	57.9	36.8	21.5	25.1	35.7
22. Minnesota	5	0	5	100.0	100.0	100.0	0.0	100.0	60.0	0.0	100.0	40.0	16.4	18.6	22.8
23. Mississippi	12	3	15	66.7	100.0	20.0	0.0	66.7	33.3	0.0	60.0	40.0	22.5	28.5	42.3

State															
24. Missouri	70	12	82	81.7	84.1	96.3	84.1	95.1	87.8	84.1	89.0	85.4	16.5	20.2	31.5
25. Montana	1	2	3	100.0	100.0	33.3	0.0	33.3	33.3	33.3	66.7	33.3	18.0	37.3	44.0
26. Nebraska	1	0	1	100.0	100.0	100.0	0.0	100.0	0.0	0.0	0.0	0.0	25.0	21.0	31.0
27. Nevada	4	1	5	80.0	80.0	100.0	20.0	100.0	100.0	80.0	100.0	100.0	17.8	22.4	26.6
28. New Jersey	64	6	70	77.1	87.1	94.3	37.1	88.6	82.9	87.1	85.7	90.0	18.3	20.5	27.8
29. New Mexico	30	3	33	72.7	69.7	81.8	0.0	93.9	81.8	87.9	87.9	87.9	15.1	20.1	26.9
30. New York	371	53	424	55.2	75.5	99.8	42.7	91.3	85.6	92.5	91.3	94.6	19.4	19.3	29.0
31. North Carolina	34	10	44	34.1	97.7	36.4	2.3	79.5	22.7	0.0	54.5	22.7	24.4	30.0	45.8
32. North Dakota	1	1	2	100.0	100.0	0.0	0.0	100.0	0.0	0.0	100.0	0.0	15.5	20.5	29.0
33. Ohio	47	16	63	55.6	87.3	81.0	44.4	81.0	55.6	25.4	55.6	34.9	21.1	25.5	38.3
34. Oklahoma	17	4	21	47.6	90.5	61.9	4.8	76.2	42.9	14.3	52.4	38.1	19.9	24.4	39.1
35. Oregon	4	2	6	100.0	83.3	83.3	16.7	100.0	66.7	66.7	83.3	83.3	19.6	21.3	26.2
36. Pennsylvania	48	7	55	63.6	87.3	96.4	60.0	83.6	72.7	67.3	81.8	69.1	17.8	22.7	35.0
37. Rhode Island	1	1	2	100.0	50.0	100.0	50.0	100.0	100.0	100.0	100.0	100.0	19.5	18.5	30.5
38. South Carolina	12	5	17	58.8	100.0	41.2	0.0	52.9	11.8	5.9	35.3	23.5	27.1	35.2	46.2
39. Tennessee	31	10	41	63.4	92.7	56.1	2.4	65.9	9.8	0.0	31.7	12.2	24.5	30.1	40.9
40. Texas	204	20	224	73.7	74.1	96.4	6.3	96.0	69.2	82.1	87.5	83.5	17.9	21.6	30.2
41. Utah	3	1	4	100.0	100.0	75.0	0.0	75.0	25.0	25.0	25.0	50.0	11.0	20.5	27.5
42. Virginia	18	3	21	61.9	95.2	52.4	4.8	81.0	42.9	9.5	61.9	23.8	19.7	25.9	37.6
43. Washington	5	4	9	77.8	100.0	100.0	44.4	88.9	77.8	22.2	88.9	55.6	18.1	23.0	33.3
44. West Virginia	11	4	15	33.3	100.0	33.3	6.7	60.0	13.3	0.0	66.7	33.3	22.2	32.5	48.7
45. Wisconsin	2	0	2	100.0	100.0	50.0	50.0	100.0	100.0	50.0	50.0	50.0	17.0	21.0	37.0
46. Wyoming	2	0	2	100.0	50.0	0.0	0.0	50.0	50.0	50.0	50.0	50.0	32.0	44.5	49.5
47. Hawaii	1	0	1	0.0	100.0	100.0	100.0	100.0	100.0	100.0	100.0	100.0	25.0	25.0	40.0
48. Puerto Rico	123	8	131	75.6	95.4	90.1	20.6	74.0	93.9	100.0	96.2	100.0	20.6	19.0	25.8
49. Foreign	4	1	5	100.0	20.0	—	0.0	100.0	60.0	100.0	100.0	100.0	14.8	18.2	30.8
Total: Percent or Mean	84.5	15.5	100.0	65.3	78.9	88.8	31.8	86.8	70.4	67.1	80.5	74.0	19.3	22.5	32.4
Total Number	1,870	343	2,213	1,445	1,746	1,961	703	1,921	1,558	1,486	1,781	1,637	1,916	2,211	2,213

* There were no admissions from four states: New Hampshire, South Dakota, Vermont, and Alaska.

dominant influence of the adolescent peer-group in the commencement of drug use,[21] the association of opiate addiction with crime,[22] the difficulty of rehabilitation,[23] and the high death rate among addicts have all been described.[24] In the present analysis, the intent is to delineate some of the relevant characteristics of addicts who inhabit the illicit-drug world, contrast them with what may be termed licit-opiate addicts, and consider the probable significance of marihuana use among these two types of addicts.

In 16 states, the District of Columbia and Puerto Rico, most of the addicts had a history of marihuana use and were also diagnosed as dependent upon heroin at hospital admission in 1965. There was, then, a close association between the use of the two illicit drugs, marihuana and heroin, among residents of the marihuana states. Of the 2,213 addicts, 1,759 were residents of these 16 states, the District of Columbia and Puerto Rico, and of these addicts 80 percent had used marihuana and 82 percent were heroin users.

The concentration of the addicts from the marihuana states in metropolitan areas was marked. Over 59 percent of the 1,759 addicts were from the 12 largest Standard Metropolitan Statistical Areas in the United States; only 3.8 percent lived outside of SMSA's.

With respect to sex, race and age, the addict residents of the marihuana states were 87 percent male, 38 percent non-white and had a mean age of 30.4 years in 1965 (Table 2). The significance of minority group status is under-represented by the non-white percentage as this does not include Puerto Rican and Mexican-American addicts.

The extent of involvement by these metropolitan addicts in the illicit-drug subculture is seen from the data on criminality and addiction history. Over 90 percent of the 1,759 addicts from the marihuana states had been arrested; the mean age at time of first arrest was 18.7 years. In 1965, 25 percent of these addicts were federal prisoners at Lexington or Fort Worth, while many of the voluntary admissions were

---

[21] Chein, Gerard, Lee & Rosenfeld, *The Road to H* Ch. 5 (1964).

[22] Finestone, *Narcotics and Criminality,* 22 *Law & Contemp. Prob.* 69–85 (1957); O'Donnell, *Narcotic Addiction and Crime,* 13 *Social Problems,* 374–385 (1966).

[23] U.S. Department of Health, Education and Welfare, *Rehabilitation in Drug Addiction* (Washington: U.S. Government Printing Office, Revised 1964).

[24] O'Donnell, *A Follow-Up of Narcotic Addicts: Mortality, Relapse and Abstinence,* 34 *Amer. J. Orthopsychiatry* 948–954 (1964); Helpern & Yong-Myun Rho, *Deaths From Narcotism in New York City,* 66 *New York State J. Medicine* 2391–2408 (1966).

TABLE 2

Addicts from 16 Marihuana and Opiate States * Compared ** with
Addicts from 12 Opiate Only States on Selected Demographic
and Drug History Characteristics (N = 2,149)

Characteristic	Addicts from 16 Marihuana and Opiate States (N = 1,759)		Addicts from 12 Opiate Only States (N = 390)	
	Number	Percent	Number	Percent
A. Demographic				
1. Male	1,531	87.0	292	74.9
2. Non-White	670	38.1	21	5.4
3. Residence in SMSA in 1965	1,692	96.2	222	56.9
B. Addiction and Criminality				
4. History of Marihuana Use	1,415	80.4	99	25.4
5. History of Arrest	1,590	90.4	272	69.7
6. Heroin Diagnosis, 1965	1,441	81.9	14	3.6
7. Use of Intravenous Route, 1965	1,543	87.7	189	48.5
8. Drugs Obtained from Pushers, 1965 .	1,497	85.1	100	25.6
9. Federal Prisoners, 1965	446	25.4	11	2.8
	Number	Mean Age	Number	Mean Age
C. Mean Age at,				
10. First Arrest	1,588	18.7	271	23.0
11. Onset of Opiate Use	1,759	20.9	390	29.8
12. Hospital Admission in 1965	1,759	30.4	390	41.3
13. Of First Admissions, in 1965	1,166	28.6	220	37.0

* Includes the District of Columbia and Puerto Rico, see text.
** For all 13 characteristics, highly significant differences were found between the residents of the two sets of states (P < .001). Characteristics 1–9 were compared by chi square test, the mean ages by t-test.

under legal pressure from local authorities.[25]

The mean age at onset of opiate use for these 1,759 metropolitan addicts was 20.9 years. The dominant opiate used in 1965 was heroin, by 82 percent of the addicts, and it was commonly (by 85 percent) procured from underworld peddlers. The intravenous route of administration was utilized by 83 percent of these addicts. In sum, these young adults had had an early involvement in both delinquency and marihuana use before they became further enmeshed in the illicit-drug subculture to the extent of using opiates.

[25] Levine & Monroe, *Discharge of Narcotic Drug Addicts Against Medical Advice,* 79 *Public Health Reports* 13–18 (1964).

The question of the sequence of events—marihuana, delinquency opiate use—requires elaboration. From interviews with 337 patients a stratified sample of the 2,213 subjects, it was found that the dominan sequence of events as determined from mean ages was marihuana smoking, arrest and then opiate use. The respective mean ages for these three events were: first marihuana use at 17, arrest at 19, and onset o heroin use at 20.[26]

For the entire 16 marihuana states, the District of Columbia and Puerto Rico, the mean age at first arrest was less than the mean age of first opiate use in 13 of the states and the District of Columbia; in the case of New York it was 19 years for both and in Puerto Rico it was reversed (Table 1). A separate analysis of sequence by the 1,755 individuals supported the finding based on means.[27]

HIGH ADDICTION STATES WITH
A LICIT-DRUG SUBCULTURE

The 12 states shown in the "dotted" areas of Figure 2 are high addiction states in which less than 50 percent of the patients had a history of marihuana use. These southern, or opiate only states have a licit-drug subculture in the sense that legally manufactured drugs, such as morphine, dilaudid and paregoric, are used and these are not secured from underworld sources of supply. In these states, then, a quite different pattern of drug abuse obtains—and neither marihuana nor heroin use is prevalent.

The southern "opiate only" pattern of addiction is less markedly a metropolitan phenomenon than within the marihuana states. Although 57 percent of the 390 addicts were residents of SMSA's, in 6 of the 12 states more than half of the addicts were from outside SMSA's. This pattern of addiction is, then, less concentrated and less metropolitan than the illicit-drug type (Tables 1 and 2).

Of the 390 addicts from the 12 opiate only states, 75 percent were

---

[26] Of the 337 addicts in the stratified sample, complete sequential data was available on 210; the principal reason for omissions were no arrest or no marihuana use, particularly among the 167 females included in this sample. Of the 210 addicts, 182 (87 percent) had used marihuana before opiates and 28 (13 percent) had first used it after the onset of opiate use. With respect to the sequence of marihuana use and arrest, 142 (68 percent) used marihuana first, while 68 (32 percent) were arrested first.

[27] Of the 1,755 addicts from the 16 state "lined" area, 168 or 9.6 percent had no arrest reported (no data was available for 4 subjects). Of the 1,587 with an arrest history, 52.7 percent were arrested before the onset of opiate use, 32.8 percent used opiates before their first arrest, and 14.6 percent were arrested and started to use opiates during the same year.

male and only 5 percent were non-white. At the time of hospitalization in 1965, their mean age was 41.3 years. This older age was not simply a result of recidivism as the age at onset of opiate use (29.8 years) and the mean age of first admission patients in 1965 (37.0 years) were both significantly older than that found among the addicts from the marihuana states (Table 2).

A markedly different type of involvement in a drug subculture is evident among the 390 addicts from the 12 opiate only states. Although from states with high addiction rates, only 3.6 percent of these Southern residents were heroin users at time of hospital admission in 1965. Further, most received their drugs from doctors or drugstores—only 26 percent secured their drugs from underworld pushers (Table 2). Also, the intravenous route of administration was employed by less than half of these addicts.[28]

With respect to criminality, the 390 southern addicts were less likely to have an arrest history, and if arrested this occurred at a later age (23 years). Among the 70 percent who had been arrested, this event commonly preceded the onset of opiate use, although the fact that 30 percent were without an arrest should be noted. As might be expected, few of these addicts were federal prisoners—only 2.8 percent.

In these 12 opiate only states, only 25 percent of the 390 addicts had a history of marihuana use. Although by the operational definition employed marihuana use could not be prevalent in any of these states, the fact remains that there were 12 high addiction states in which marihuana use was uncommon. In addition, these same 12 states were characterized by a different pattern of subcultural involvement.

WITHIN-AREA COMPARISON BY MARIHUANA HISTORY

The gross differences obtained between residents of the marihuana and opiate only states, although important in themselves, tend to obscure the issue of the positive association of marihuana smoking with opiate addiction. In order to transcend the marked effect of region, a within-area comparison of marihuana users and non-users, controlled for sex and race, was undertaken.

Of the 970 white male addicts from the 16 illicit-drug states, 77.8 percent had a history of marihuana use and 21.2 percent had never used marihuana (Table 3). Those who had used marihuana were more likely to be metropolitan residents, arrested at an earlier age and

---

[28] For a discussion of the historical development of this means of administration in the United States, see: O'Donnell & Jones, *Diffusion of the Intravenous Technique Among Narcotic Addicts in the United States, J. Health & Soc. Behavior* (forthcoming).

arrested before the onset of opiate use. The 764 marihuana users were twice as likely (85 vs. 45) to be heroin addicts, to use the intravenous method of administration and to secure their drugs from underworld pushers or sellers than the 206 addicts without a history of marihuana use. In addition, the earlier age at arrest (17 years), at onset of opiate use (19 years), and of Lexington or Fort Worth hospitalization (27 years) of the marihuana group indicates that marihuana use is associated with an early age of entrance into a deviant subculture. Statistically significant differences on all nine variables between the addicts with a marihuana history from those without such a history are presented in Table 3.

There were 277 white male addicts from the 12 opiate only states. Of these, 26.0 percent had a history of marihuana use and 74.0 percent had never used marihuana. The 72 marihuana users were more likely to be metropolitan residents, more often arrested before the onset of opiate use, and arrested at an earlier age (19 vs. 23 years). The marihuana users were more than three times as likely to be securing their drugs from pushers, and twice as likely to be taking drugs intravenously.

TABLE 3

Within Area Comparison of White Male Addicts with and without a History of Marihuana Use, for "Lined" and "Dotted" State Residents Separately by Selected Variables

Comparison Groups	N	(A) Vol. Patients in 1965, Percent	(B) In SMSA, Percent	(C) Arrest Before Opiate Use, Percent	(D) Heroin Diag., Percent	(E) Intravenous Route, Percent	(F) Pushers as Source of Drugs, Percent	(G) Age at 1st Arrest, Mean	(H) Age at Onset of Opiates, Mean	(I) Age at Hospital Admission, 1965 Mean
"Lined" States, with Marihuana History	764	78.3	96.3	49.7	84.9	93.7	88.9	17.7	19.1	27.8
"Lined" States, No Marihuana Use	206	88.3	87.9	42.6	44.7	59.2	49.5	21.1	27.2	40.2
"Dotted" States, with Marihuana History	72	94.4	65.3	61.1	8.3	83.3	50.0	19.7	21.8	35.5
"Dotted" States, Never Used Marihuana	205	98.5	51.7	48.0	0.0	41.5	15.6	23.5	32.4	43.6
Statistical Test				χ^2 test					*t*-test	
"Lined" States Comparison: P =		< .01	< .001	< .001	< .001	< .001	< .001	< .001	< .001	< .001
"Dotted" States Comparison: P =		< .10	< .05	< .001	< .001	< .001	< .001	< .003	< .001	< .001

Heroin addiction was uncommon in these 12 states, only 6 heroin users were included among the 277 addicts. As in the previous comparison within the "lined" states, the addicts with a marihuana history were notably younger at first arrest, at onset of opiate use, and at time of 1965 hospitalization (Table 3). Within the "dotted" states, then, those addicts who had a marihuana history were significantly different from those without such a history, on 8 of the 9 variables compared. These differences were often marked—age at onset of opiate use was ten years earlier for the marihuana subjects—and *in all eight instances* they were in the same direction as in the previous comparison within the lined states.

A similar statistical comparison between marihuana users and non-users was undertaken for the non-white and female addicts. The 703 non-white addicts were almost exclusively Negroes [29] from the "lined" states residing in metropolitan areas. Thus, the only meaningful comparison of the non-white addicts was between the marihuana users and non-users in the 16 "lined" states. There were 561 male Negro addicts from these states; 502 of this number (89.5 percent) had a history of marihuana use and 59 did not have a marihuana history. Meager but statistically significant differences between the 502 users and the 59 non-users were found with respect to: use of heroin (94 vs. 85 percent), use of the intravenous route (95 vs. 88 percent), and securing opiates from pushers (96 vs. 86 percent). More meaningful age differences between the two male Negro groups were found. Among the 502 addicts with a history of marihuana use, the mean age at first arrest was 18.5 years, mean age at onset of opiate use was 20.1 years, and the mean age at the time of hospitalization for addiction in 1965 was 30.2 years. The comparable mean ages of the 59 Negro addicts without a history of marihuana use for these three events were: first arrest 20.6 years, onset of opiates 24.0 years and current hospitalization 32.8 years; each of these age differences was statistically significant.[30]

Of the 109 Negro females from the 16 "lined" states, 83 had used marihuana and 26 had not. All 109 subjects were residents of SMSA's in 1965. For the comparisons other than age, the only statistically significant difference was with respect to intravenous use—those with a marihuana history were more likely to be using opiates intravenously (94 vs. 73 percent). The other differences were in the same direction as reported in Table 3, although not statistically significant. With

---

[29] Of the 703 non-white addicts, 699 were Negro, 2 Chinese, 1 Hawaiian and 1 Philippino.

[30] The *t*-test probabilities were: arrest $P < .05$, onset $P < .001$, and hospitalization $P < .005$.

respect to the three age variables, the marihuana group was younger at first arrest (19.8 vs. 22.9 years), younger at onset of opiate use (20.2 vs. 24.1 years), and younger at time of hospitalization at Lexington (29.2 vs. 32.2).[31]

In sum, the Negro addicts who had used marihuana were notably different from those who had not by a younger age involvement in deviancy—arrest, onset of opiate use, and hospitalization for addiction. The other intergroup differences (on variables A, C, D, E and F, Table 3), even if statistically significant, were attenuated by comparison with the differences noted between the white marihuana users and non-users who were residents of these same 16 states, the District of Columbia and Puerto Rico.

MARIHUANA USE AMONG WHITE FEMALE ADDICTS

Of the 119 white female addicts from the "lined" states, 66 had used marihuana and 53 had not. Those female addicts with a history of marihuana use were more likely than those without such a history to be metropolitan residents (97 vs. 87 percent), twice as likely to be heroin users (82 vs. 45 percent), using intravenously (85 vs. 47 percent) and securing their drugs from pushers (89 vs. 49 percent). Again, there was marked evidence of earlier involvement in deviancy among the marihuana users: mean age at first arrest (19.4 vs. 23.9), mean age at the onset of opiates (19.3 vs. 27.4), and mean age at 1965 hospitalization (26.8 vs. 35.6).[32]

The female addicts from the 12 "dotted" states were less likely to have used marihuana than those from the "lined" states. Of the 92 white female addicts from the "dotted" states, only 12 had a history of marihuana use. These 12 were three times more likely to be using drugs intravenously (83 vs. 25 percent), and three times as often securing drugs from underworld pushers (50 vs. 15 percent). The two groups did not differ (in terms of statistical significance) with respect to voluntary status at the hospital, residence in SMSA, (although 75 percent of users vs. 51 percent of non-users were SMSA residents), or heroin addiction.[33] As in all previous within area comparisons, the addicts with a history of marihuana use became involved in deviancy at an earlier age than those who did not use marihuana. The mean age at first arrest for the 12 white female marihuana subjects was 23.9 years,

---

[31] The probabilities were (*t*-test): <.05, <.01, and <.08.
[32] Probabilities (*t*-test): <.003, <.001, and <.001.
[33] Only 3 of the 92 females were heroin users in 1965.

mean age at onset of opiate use was 23.0 years, and mean age at Lexington hospitalization was 31.8 years. The comparable figures for the 80 white female addicts without a history of marihuana use from the 12 "dotted" states were: first arrest 28.9 years, onset of opiates 32.7 years, and 1965 hospitalization 43.5 years.[34]

INTERPRETATION OF THE RESEARCH FINDINGS

Before considering the particular question of the association of marihuana use with opiate addiction in the United States, several more general points require comment. The absence of Negro addicts from the Southern states in the present national sample as well as similar findings from previous studies[35] supports the contention that ethnicity is an important variable with respect to addiction liability. The high addiction rates among Negroes and Puerto Ricans in northern metropolitan areas also support this contention.[36] It appears, however, that drug addiction as a form of deviance: (1) affects some ethnic populations more than others (the lack of opiate use among Japanese-Americans, Polish or Italian immigrants may be contrasted with the prevalence of addiction among the Chinese-Americans and northern Negroes), and (2) depends upon a suitable host environment. This latter factor accounts for the differential prevalence of addiction among Negroes in the United States. In addition to differential liability by ethnicity and host environment, opiate addiction is affected by cultural changes in a given society with the result that the prevalence of addiction with respect to specific populations and geographical designations also changes. Thus, opiate addiction among infants, females, and Chinese-Americans has markedly decreased during the twentieth century in the United States.[37] Conversely, addiction among young male metropolitan members of certain racial or ethnic groups has increased.[38]

The present research findings provide inferential evidence that marihuana smoking has become more common among opiate addicts in recent years. The older age of the 655 addicts without a history of marihuana use (40.3) when contrasted with the 1,558 who had smoked marihuana (29.1) provides substance for such an interpretation. Furthermore, the absence of references to marihuana use among opiate

---

[34] Probabilities (*t*-test): <.02, <.001, and <.001.
[35] Bates, *Narcotics, Negroes and the South*, 45 *Social Forces*, 61–67 (1966).
[36] Ball & Bates, *op. cit. supra* note 8.
[37] Ball & Lau, *The Chinese Narcotic Addict in the United States*, 45 *Social Forces* 68–72 (1966).
[38] Chein *et al., op. cit. supra* note 21, Chaps. 1–4.

addicts by Terry and Pellens [39] (1928) and Pescor's findings in 1937 that only a few Lexington patients had used marihuana before opiates seems significant when contrasted with the dominant pattern of marihuana use followed by opiate abuse reported by Fort,[40] Finestone,[41] Chein,[42] and Ball [43] in more recent years. The available evidence suggests, then, that marihuana smoking has increased among opiate addicts in the United States.

A further general comment concerning the significance of dependence upon specific opiate drugs is relevant. At the time of hospitalization in 1965, 1,486 of the 2,213 patients were diagnosed as heroin users. The other opiates being abused were: morphine (by 201 addicts), dilaudid (135), paregoric (131), meperidine (108), codeine (86), and the remaining 66 patients were using methadone, percodan, pantopon, opium, cocaine and numorphan. The association of heroin dependence with a history of marihuana use within each of the two regional high addiction areas has been delineated. What is not apparent, however, is the extent to which opiate use may be drug-specific for some persons. Thus, most of the 129 meperidine and methadone users have never used heroin and only 16 have ever used marihuana. The point being that within the general addict population one finds particular drug-specific behavioral patterns which appear to insulate the individual from other types of drug abuse.[44]

As to the issue of association, marihuana smoking is seen as a predisposing influence in the etiology of opiate addiction in the United States. Among metropolitan residents of the high addiction eastern and western states, opiate use is commonly preceded by the smoking of marihuana cigarettes and arrest. Thus, both marihuana use and delinquency are predisposing factors within the metropolitan host environment.

But what is the relative effect of marihuana use with respect to subsequent addiction? Is it of greater import than delinquency, or an unstable home? An adequate answer to this question is not possible. Still, enough is now known about the association of marihuana and opiate

---

[39] Terry & Pellens, *The Opium Problem* (1928).

[40] Fort, Jr., *Heroin Addiction among Young Men,* 17 *Psychiatry,* 251–259 (1954).

[41] Finestone, *Cats, Kicks and Color,* 5 *Social Problems* 3–13 (1957).

[42] Chein *et al., op. cit. supra* note 21, Ch. 6.

[43] Ball, *Marihuana Smoking and the Onset of Heroin Use,* paper read at the annual meeting of the Committee on Problems of Drug Dependence, National Research Council, February, 1967.

[44] Rasor & Crecraft, *Addiction to Meperidine (Demerol) Hydrochloride,* 157 *J. Amer. Med. Assoc.* 654–657 (1955).

use to delineate the dominant relationship of these two events.

The incipient addict is predisposed to opiate addiction by his use of marihuana for the following reasons: marihuana is taken for its euphoric effects—it produces a "high"; both marihuana and heroin are only available from underworld sources of supply; both are initially taken within a peer-group recreational setting; both are illegal; the neighborhood friends with whom marihuana use begins are often the same friends who initiate the incipient addict to the use of opiates. A principal effect, then, is one of differential association—becoming part of a drug-taking group.

In considering the association of marihuana and opiate use attention has been focused only upon the type 1 situation depicted in Figure 1. It has now been shown that a type 2 situation also prevails in the United States—opiate addiction without marihuana use. It is evident that there are several patterns of behavior which lead to drug addiction. Data of the present study support the conclusion that marihuana use is closely associated with opiate addiction in the high drug use metropolitan areas of the East and West, but not associated with opiate addiction in 12 southern states.

COMPARISON OF THE EFFECTS OF MARIHUANA AND ALCOHOL ON SIMULATED DRIVING PERFORMANCE

Alfred Crancer, Jr., James M. Dille, Jack C. Delay, Jean E. Wallace, and Martin D. Haykin

We have determined the effect of a "normal social marihuana high" on simulated driving performance among experienced marihuana smokers. We compared the degree of driving impairment due to smoking marihuana to the effect on driving of a recognized standard—that is, legally defined intoxication at the presumptive limit of 0.10 percent alcohol concentration in the blood. This study focused attention on the effect of smoking marihuana rather than on the effect of ingesting $\triangle^9$-tetrahydrocannabinol ($\triangle^9$-THC), the principal active component.

Weil et al. (1) have studied the clinical and psychological effects of smoking marihuana on both experienced and inexperienced subjects. They suggest, as do others (2), that experienced smokers when "high" show no significant impairment as judged by performance on selected tests; they also establish the existence of physiological changes that are useful in determining whether a subject smoking marihuana is "high." A review of the relation of alcohol to fatal accidents (3) showed that

Reprinted from *Science* 164 (May 1969): 851–54, copyright 1969 by the American Association for the Advancement of Science, with permission of the publisher and Alfred Crancer, Jr.

nearly half of the drivers fatally injured in an accident had an alcohol concentration in the blood of 0.05 percent or more.

Crancer (4) found a driving simulator test to be a valid indicator for distinguishing driving performance; this result was based on a 5-year driving record. Further studies (5) indicated that a behind-the-wheel road test is not significantly correlated to driving performance. We therefore chose the simulator test, which presents a programmed series of emergency situations that are impractical and dangerous in actual road tests.

Subjects were required to be (i) experienced marihuana smokers who had been smoking marihuana at least twice a month for the past 6 months, (ii) licensed as a motor vehicle operator, (iii) engaged in a generally accepted educational or vocational pursuit, and (iv) familiar with the effects of alcohol. The subjects were given (i) a physical examination to exclude persons currently in poor health or under medication, and (ii) a written personality inventory (Minnesota Multi-phasic Personality Inventory) to exclude persons showing a combination of psychological stress and inflexible defense patterns. Seven of the subjects were females and 29 were males (mean age, 22.9).

We compared the effects of a marihuana "high," alcohol intoxication, and no treatment on simulated driving performance over a 4½-hour period. We used a Latin-square analysis of variance design (6) to account for the effects of treatments, subjects, days, and the order in

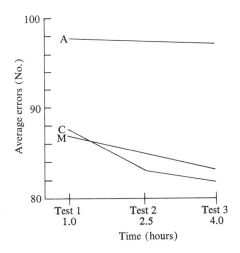

FIGURE 1

DISPLAY OF THE EFFECT OF EACH TREATMENT ON SIMULATOR ERROR SCORES OVER A 4-HOUR PERIOD. ALCOHOL (A), MARIHUANA (M), AND CONTROL (C).

which the treatments were given. To measure the time response effects of each treatment, simulator scores were obtained at three constant points in the course of each experimental period. A sample of 36 subjects was determined to be sufficient in size to meet the demands of this experimental design.

Three treatments were given to each subject. In treatment M (normal social marihuana "high"), the experimental subject stated that he experienced the physical and psychological effects of smoking marihuana in a social environment comparable to his previous experiences. This subjective evaluation of "high" was confirmed by requiring a minimum consumption of marihuana established with a separate test group, and by identifying an increase in pulse rate (1).

In treatment M, the subjects smoked two marihuana (7) cigarettes of approximately equal weight and totaling 1.7 g. They completed smoking in about 30 minutes and were given their first simulator test 30 minutes later.

Some confirmation that the amount of marihuana smoked was sufficient to produce a "high" is found in Weil's (1) study. His subjects smoked about 0.5 g of marihuana of 0.9 percent $\triangle^9$-THC.

In treatment A, subjects consumed two drinks containing equal amounts of 95 percent alcohol mixed in orange or tomato juice. Dosage was regulated according to subject's weight with the intended result of a 0.10 blood alcohol concentration as determined by a Breathalyzer reading (8). Thus, a subject weighing 120 pounds received 84 ml of 95 percent laboratory alcohol equally divided between two drinks. This was equivalent to about 6 ounces of 86 proof liquor. The dosage was increased 14 ml or ½ ounce for each additional 15 pounds of body weight. A Breathalyzer reading was obtained for each subject about 1 hour after drinking began; most subjects completed drinking in 30 minutes.

Treatment C consisted of waiting in the lounge with no treatment for the same period of time required for treatments M and A. The experimental subject stated that his physiological and psychological condition was normal. Subjects were requested to refrain from all drug or alcohol use during the time they were participating in the experiment.

A driver-training simulator was specially modified to obtain data on the effect of the treatments. The car unit was a console mockup of a recent model containing all the control and instrument equipment relevant to the driving task. The car unit faced a 6 by 18 foot screen upon which the test film was projected. The test film gave the subject a driver's eye view of the road as it led him through normal and emergency driving situations on freeways and urban and suburban streets.

From the logic unit, located to the rear of the driver, the examiner started the automated test, observed the subject driving, and recorded the final scores.

A series of checks was placed on the 23-minute driving film which monitored driver reactions to a programmed series of driving stimuli. The test variables monitored were: accelerator (164 checks), brake (106 checks), turn signals (59 checks), steering (53 checks), and speedometer (23 checks). There was a total of 405 checks, allowing driver scores to range from zero to 405 errors per test. Errors were accumulated as follows.

1) Speedometer errors: Speedometer readings outside the range of 15 to 35 mile/hour for city portion of film and 45 to 65 mile/hour for freeways. The speed of the filmed presentation is not under the control of the driver. Therefore, speedometer errors are not an indication of speeding errors, but of the amount of time spent monitoring the speedometer.

2) Steering errors: Steering wheel in other than the appropriate position.

3) Brake errors: Not braking when the appropriate response is to brake, or braking at an inappropriate time.

4) Accelerator errors: Acceleration when the appropriate response is to decelerate, or deceleration when it is appropriate to accelerate.

5) Signal errors: Use of turn signal at an inappropriate time or position.

6) Total errors: An accumulation of the total number of errors on the five test variables.

Two rooms were used for the experiment. The lounge, designed to provide a familiar and comfortable environment for the subjects, was approximately 12 feet square and contained six casual chairs, a refrigerator, a desk, and several small movable tables. The room was lighted by a red lava lamp and one indirect red light, and contemporary rock music was played. Snacks, soft drinks, ashtrays, wastebaskets, and a supply of cigarettes were readily available. Subjects remained in this room except during simulator tests.

The driving simulator was located in a larger room about 50 feet from the lounge. The simulator room was approximately 20 by 30 feet and was kept in almost total darkness.

Each subject took three preliminary tests on the driving simulator to familiarize himself with the equipment and to minimize the effect of learning through practice during the experiment. Subjects whose error scores varied by more than 10 percent between the second and third tests were given subsequent tests until the stability criterion was met.

The experiment was conducted over a 6-week period. Six subjects were tested each week. On day 1, six subjects took a final test on the driving simulator to assure recent familiarity with the equipment. A "normal" pulse rate was recorded, and each was given two marihuana cigarettes of approximately 0.9 g each. Subjects smoked the marihuana in the lounge to become acquainted with the surroundings and other test subjects, and with the potency of the marihuana. A second pulse reading was recorded for each subject when he reported that he was "high" in order to obtain an indication of the expected rate increase during the experiment proper. They remained in the lounge for approximately 4 hours after they had started smoking.

Three of the subjects were scheduled for testing in the early evening on days 2, 4, and 6; the remaining three subjects for days 3, 5, and 7. A single treatment was given each evening. Within a given week, all subjects received treatments in the same order. Treatment order was changed from week to week to meet the requirements of a Latin-square design. Procedure for each evening was identical except for the specific treatment.

Subject 1 arrived at the laboratory and took the simulator warm-up test. Treatment A, M, or C was begun at zero hour and finished about ½ hour later. One hour after treatment began, subject 1 took simulator test 1, returning to the lounge when he was finished. He took simulator test 2 2½ hours after treatment began, and test 3 4 hours after treatment began. Pulse or Breathalyzer readings, depending on the treatment, were taken immediately before each simulator test.

Subject 2 followed the same schedule, beginning ½ hour after subject 1. Time used in testing one subject each evening was 4½ hours, with a total elapsed time of 5½ hours to test three subjects.

The three simulator tests taken after each treatment establish a time response effect for the treatment. For each treatment the total error scores for each time period were subjected to an analysis of variance. Table 1 presents the analysis of variance for period 1 scores; results comparable to these were obtained for scores in periods 2 and 3.

The simulated driving scores for subjects experiencing a normal social marihuana "high" and the same subjects under control conditions are not significantly different (Table 1). However, there are significantly more errors ($P < .01$) for intoxicated than for control subjects (difference of 15.4 percent). This finding is consistent with the mean error scores of the three treatments: control, 84.46 errors; marihuana, 84.49 errors; and alcohol, 97.44 errors.

The time response curves for "high" and control treatments are comparable (Fig. 1). In contrast, the curve for alcohol shows more total

TABLE 1

ANALYSIS OF VARIANCE OF TOTAL DRIVING SIMULATOR ERROR SCORES
FOR THREE TREATMENTS; MARIHUANA (M), CONTROL (C), AND ALCOHOL (A).

Source of variation	Sum of squares	Degrees of freedom	Mean square	Mean square ratios
Treatments	2,595.1	2	1,297.5	6.7 *
M versus C	(11.7)	(1)	11.7	0.1
A versus M and C	(2,583.4)	(1)	2,583.4	13.3 †
Days	738.5	2	369.3	1.9
Subjects	40,872.5	24	1,703.0	9.7 †
Squares	13,708.5	11	1,247.2	6.4 †
Pooled error	13,253.8	68	194.9	
Total	71,168.4	107		

* $P < .05$.
† $P < .01$.

errors ($P < .01$). These higher error scores for alcohol persist across all three time periods with little evidence of the improvement shown under the other two treatments.

A separate Latin-square analysis of variance was completed for each test variable to supplement the analysis of total errors (Table 2). In

TABLE 2

Significant treatment differences from Latin-square analysis of variance ($P < .05$). Accelerator, signal, and total errors are significantly correlated with driving performance for normal drivers. No correlation was found for brake, speedometer, and steering errors; $A > C$, $M > C$ indicate that error scores for alcohol (A) or marihuana (M) treatment are greater than control (C).

Simulator Test	Test variable errors					
	Accelerator	Signal	Total	Brake	Speedometer	Steering
Period 1	$A > C$	$A > C$	$A > C$	None	$A > C$ $M > C$	None
Period 2	$A > C$	$A > C$	$A > C$	$A > C$	None	None
Period 3	None	$A > C$	$A > C$	$A > C$	None	None

comparison of intoxicated and control subjects, significant differences ($P < .05$) were found for accelerator errors in periods 1 and 2, for signal errors in periods 1, 2, and 3, for braking errors in periods 2 and 3, and for speedometer errors in period 1. In the comparison of marihuana smokers and controls, a significant difference ($P < .05$) was found for speedometer errors in period 1. In all of these cases, the number of errors for the drug treatments exceeded the errors for the control treatment.

Other sources of variation are Latin squares, subjects, and days. In all of the analyses, the effect of subjects and Latin squares (representing groups of subjects) were significant ($P < .05$). In contrast, the effect of days was not significant, thus indicating that no significant amount of learning was associated with repeated exposure to the test material.

For normal drivers, Crancer (4) found a significant correlation ($P < .05$) between the three simulator test variables (signals, accelerator, and total errors) and driving performance. An increase in error scores was associated with an increase in number of accidents and violations on a driving record. In the same study, error scores for brake, speedometer, and steering were not correlated with driving performance.

It may not be valid to assume the same relationship for persons under the influence of alcohol or marihuana. However, we feel that, because the simulator task is a less complex but related task, deterioration in simulator performance implies deterioration in actual driving performance. We are less willing to assume that nondeterioration in simulator performance implies nondeterioration in actual driving. We therefore conclude that finding significantly more accelerator, signal, and total errors by intoxicated subjects implies a deterioration in actual driving performance.

Relating speedometer errors to actual driving performance is highly speculative because Crancer (4) found no correlation for normal drivers. This may be due in part to the fact that the speed of the filmed presentation is not under the control of the driver. However, speedometer errors are related to the amount of time spent monitoring the speedometer. The increase of speedometer errors by intoxicated or "high" subjects probably indicates that the subjects spent less time monitoring the speedometer than under control conditions.

This study could not determine if the drugs would alter the speed at which subjects normally drive. However, comments by marihuana users may be pertinent. They often report alteration of time and space perceptions, leading to a different sense of speed which generally results in driving more slowly.

Weil *et al.* (1) emphasize the importance and influence of both subject bias (set) and the experimental environment (setting). For this study, the environmental setting was conducive to good performance under all treatments.

Traditional methods for controlling potential subject bias by using placebos to disguise the form or effect of the marihuana treatment were not applicable. This is confirmed by Weil *et al.* (*1*); they showed that inexperienced subjects correctly appraised the presence or absence of a placebo in 21 of 27 trials.

The nature of selection probably resulted in subjects who preferred marihuana to alcohol and, therefore, had a set to perform better with marihuana. The main safeguard against bias was that subjects were not told how well they did on any of their driving tests, nor were they acquainted with the specific methods used to determine errors. Thus, it would have been very difficult intentionally and effectively to manipulate error scores on a given test or sequence of tests.

A further check on subject bias was made by comparing error scores on the warm-up tests given before each treatment. We found no significant difference in the mean error scores preceding the treatments of marihuana, alcohol, and control. This suggests that subjects were not "set" to perform better or worse on the day of a particular treatment.

In addition, an inspection of chance variation of individual error scores for treatment M shows about half the subjects doing worse and half better than under control conditions. This variability in direction is consistent with findings reviewed earlier, and we feel reasonably certain that a bias in favor of marihuana did not influence the results of this experiment.

A cursory investigation of dose response was made by retesting four subjects after they had smoked approximately three times the amount of marihuana used in the main experiment. None of the subjects showed a significant change in performance.

Four additional subjects who had never smoked marihuana before were pretested to obtain control scores, then given marihuana to smoke until they were subjectively "high" with an associated increase in pulse rate. All subjects smoked at least the minimum quantity established for the experiment. All subjects showed either no change or negligible improvement in their scores. These results suggest that impairment in simulated driving performance is not a function of increased marihuana dosage or inexperience with the drug.

A significant difference ($P < .01$) was found between pulse rates before and after the marihuana treatment. Similar results were reported (*1*) for both experienced and inexperienced marihuana subjects. We found no significant difference in pulse rates before and after drinking.

Thus, when subjects experienced a social marihuana "high," they accumulated significantly more speedometer errors on the simulator than under control conditions, but there were no significant differences in accelerator, brake, signal, steering, and total errors. The same subjects intoxicated from alcohol accumulated significantly more accelerator, brake, signal, speedometer, and total errors than under control conditions, but there was no significant difference in steering errors. Furthermore, impairment in simulated driving performance apparently is not a function of increased marihuana dosage or inexperience with the drug.

REFERENCES AND NOTES

1. A. T. Weil, N. E. Zinberg, J. M. Nelsen, *Science* 162, 1234 (1968).

2. Mayor's Committee on Marihuana, *The Marihuana Problem in the City of New York* (1944).

3. W. J. Haddon and V. A. Braddess, *J. Amer. Med. Ass.* 169, No. 14, 127 (1959); J. R. McCarroll and W. J. Haddon, *J. Chronic Dis.* 15, 811 (1962); J. H. W. Birrell, *Med. J. Aust.* 2, 949 (1965); R. A. Neilson, *Alcohol Involvement in Fatal Motor Vehicle Accidents in Twenty-Seven California Counties in 1964* (California Traffic Safety Foundation, San Francisco, 1965).

4. A. Crancer, *Predicting Driving Performance with a Driver Simulator Test* (Washington Department of Motor Vehicles, Olympia, 1968).

5. J. E. Wallace and A. Crancer, *Licensing Examinations and Their Relation to Subsequent Driving Record* (Washington Department of Motor Vehicles, Olympia, 1968).

6. A. E. Edwards, *Experimental Design in Psychological Research* (Holt, Rinehart & Winston, New York, 1968), pp. 173–174.

7. The marihuana was an assayed batch (1.312 percent $\triangle^9$-THC) from NIH through the cooperation of Dr. J. A. Scigliano.

8. L. A. Greenberg, *Quart. J. Studies Alcohol* 29, 252 (1968).

THE MARIHUANA PROBLEM
IN THE CITY OF NEW YORK

George B. Wallace

The widespread publicity describing the dangerous effects of marihuana usage in New Orleans and other southern cities, especially among school children, had its repercussion in the city of New York, and some anxiety was experienced as to the possibility that similar conditions were present or might develop here. Because of this, Mayor La Guardia asked The New York Academy of Medicine for an opinion as to the advisability of studying the whole marihuana problem. The Academy recommended that such a study be made and outlined its scope in general terms. Following this, the Mayor appointed a committee empowered to make the study. This committee consisted of two internists, three psychiatrists, two pharmacologists, and one public health expert, and the Commissioners of Correction, of Health, and of Hospitals, and the Director of the Division of Psychiatry of the Department of Hospitals, ex officio.

Reprinted with permission from *The Marihuana Problem in the City of New York,* by The Mayor's Committe on Marihuana, copyright 1944, The Ronald Press Company, New York, pp. 213–20.

The Committee formulated a plan for the study, and the expenses were arranged for through grants by the New York Foundation, the Friedsam Foundation and the Commonwealth Fund. The study was begun in April 1940.

The first phase of the study concerned the extent of marihuana smoking in New York City, its incidence among school children, its relation to crime, and its effects on individuals using it. For obtaining this information, the Commissioner of Police assigned to the Committee six police officers, four men and two women, who served as "plain clothes" investigators. These investigators circulated in the districts in which marihuana appeared to be most widely used, particularly Harlem, associated with marihuana users, and found out as much as possible about sources of supply, means of distribution, and effects of marihuana on users. Included in this survey were a careful watch on school children in both grade and high schools and interviews with school principals.

As a result of this investigation the Committee came to the conclusion that marihuana distribution and usage is found mainly in Harlem, the population of which is predominately Negro and Latin-American, and to a less extent in the Broadway area extending from 42nd to 59th Streets. The local supply comes from individual peddlers and from "tea-pads," which are establishments for marihuana smoking. There are no figures available as to the number of marihuana users in New York City, but a conservative estimate is that there are some 500 peddlers and 500 "tea-pads" in Harlem.

The marihuana users with whom contact was made in this study were persons without steady employment. The majority fall in the age group of 20 to 30 years. Idle and lacking initiative, they suffer boredom and seek distraction. Smoking is indulged in for the sake of conviviality and sociability and because it affords a temporary feeling of adequacy in meeting disturbing situations.

The confirmed user smokes from 6 to 10 cigarettes a day. The effects are easily recognized by the smoker, the desirable stage being what is known as "high." When this is reached, the smoking is stopped. If a "too high" state is reached, the taking of beverages such as beer or sweet soda pop, or a cold bath are considered effective countermeasures.

In most instances, the behavior of the smoker is of a friendly, sociable character. Aggressiveness and belligerency are not commonly seen, and those showing such traits are not allowed to remain in "tea-pads."

The marihuana user does not come from the hardened criminal class and there was found no direct relationship between the commission of crimes of violence and marihuana. "Tea-pads" have no direct association with houses of prostitution, and marihuana itself has no specific stimulant effect in regard to sexual desires.

There is no organized traffic in marihuana among New York City school children, and any smoking that occurs in this group is limited to isolated instances.

Smoking marihuana can be stopped abruptly with no resulting mental or physical distress comparable to that of morphine withdrawal in morphine addicts.

The second division of the study was the clinical one, the purpose of which was to ascertain the effects of marihuana on the individual user. There were two phases of this work, the general medical study and the psychological study. Wards in the municipal hospital on Welfare Island (now known as Goldwater Memorial Hospital) were made available by the Commissioner of Hospitals. The subjects for the study were drawn from the prison population at the Penitentiary on Riker's Island, as arranged by the Commissioner of Correction. They were under sentence for terms varying from three months to three years, most of them for what would be called minor criminal offenses. They volunteered for the study, the purpose and procedure of which had been fully explained to them. They were kept in the hospital in groups of 6 to 10, for a period of study of approximately a month. The subjects afforded the sample especially desired, for over half of them were marihuana smokers and the others of the class from which marihuana smokers come. The personnel conducting the study consisted of a physician in charge, with an assistant physician, three psychologists, and a secretary. The subjects were under the constant supervision of the medical staff, nurses and attendants.

In studying the effects of marihuana on the 77 subjects selected for the study, the drug was given either in the form of an extract taken by mouth, or was smoked in cigarettes. The dose given to produce definite systemic reactions ranged from a minimal one of 1 cc. to a maximum of 22 cc. of the extract, and from 1 to 10 cigarettes. The effects of smoking appeared immediately and usually passed off in from one to three or four hours. Those from the extract came on more gradually and persisted for a longer time, in some instances for twenty-four hours or more. As the dose for any individual was increased, the effects usually were more marked and of longer duration, but the effect of any given dose varied with the individual subjects.

Although some of the subjects became restless and talkative under marihuana influence, a mental state characterized by a sense of well-being, relaxation and unawareness of surroundings, followed by drowsiness, was present in most instances when the subject was left undisturbed. Generally, there was observed a difficulty in focusing and sustaining mental attention. In company, the subjects were lively and given to talkativeness, fits of laughter and good-natured joking. The pleasurable effects, classed as euphoric, were frequently interrupted or replaced by a state of apprehension of varying degree.

In a limited number of the subjects there were alterations in behavior giving rise to antisocial expression. This was shown by unconventional acts not permitted in public, anxiety reactions, opposition and antagonism, and eroticism. Effects such as these would be considered conducive to acts of violence. However, any tendency toward violence was expressed verbally and not by physical actions, and in no case was restraint by force needed.

In addition to its effect on mental states, physical symptoms resulting from the administration of marihuana were recorded. Of these, tremor, ataxia, dizziness, a sensation of floating in space, dilation of the pupils, dryness of the throat, nausea and vomiting, an urge to urinate, hunger, and a desire for sweets were the most striking. Tremor and ataxia and dizziness were of the greatest frequency. These symptoms may be disturbing to the subject, and if marked enough, cause anxiety and interrupt the euphoric state.

On some occasions, instead of the marihuana concentrate, preparations supplied by Dr. Roger Adams were given. These were tetrahydrocannabinol, made from cannabidiol, corresponding to a principle found in the plant, a synthetic tetrahydrocannabinol, an isomer of the natural one, and a synthetic hexyl-hydrocannabinol. They all produced effects similar in character to those from the concentrate. Their relative potency could be determined only approximately. The rough estimate was that 1 cc. of the concentrate had as its equivalent 15 mg. of the natural tetrahydrocannabinol, 60 mg. of the hexyl-hydrocannabinol, and 120 mg. of the synthetic tetrahydrocannabinol.

In the total group studied, what are known as psychotic episodes occurred in 9 of the subjects. In 6 instances, they were of short duration, persisting for from three to ten hours, and were characterized by mental confusion and excitement of a delirious nature with periods of laughter and of anxiety. These effects correspond to those often reported in marihuana literature and are examples of acute marihuana intoxication which in many ways is similar to acute alcoholic intoxication. In the other 3 cases, one subject had a mild psychotic reaction after smoking one cigarette. Later, a typical psychotic state came on four hours after the subject had taken tetrahydrocannabinol and persisted for six days. This subject subsequently was found to have a history of epileptic attacks so that the psychotic episode was probably related to epilepsy. The second subject had previously been a drug addict. She was given marihuana on several occasions, at times showing only euphoric effects and other times confusion and worriment. She left the hospital depressed and moody, and a week later was committed to a State hospital with the diagnosis of psychosis. After six months, she was discharged as cured. The third subject showed no unusual effects of marihuana which was given on several occasions during his stay at the hospital. Some days after his return to the penitentiary he developed a psychotic state diagnosed "Psychosis with psychopathic personality." This was considered an example of what is known as "prison psychosis," a condition which has been noted in persons emotionally unstable subjected to the depressing atmosphere of prison incarceration. The precise role of marihuana in the psychotic states in the three unstable subjects is not clear. In the case of the second and third subjects, the fact that they were sent back to prison to complete their sentences must be considered an important if not the main factor in bringing on the psychosis.

In the clinical study of the effect of marihuana on functions of various organs of the body, there were found an increase in pulse rate and blood pressure and an increase in blood sugar and metabolic rate. No changes were found in the circulation rate and vital capacity. Tests on renal and liver function were negative. No changes were found in blood counts and hemoglobin, or blood nitrogen, calcium and phosphorus concentrations. The electrocardiogram showed no abnormalities which could be attributed to direct action on the heart, and from a few observations made, marihuana appeared to be without effect on gastric motility and secretion. The positive results found, as well as the occurrence of nausea and vomiting, an increase in the frequency of urination, and the sensation of hunger and an increase in appetite, may be considered results of central nervous excitation, producing peripheral effects through the autonomic nervous system.

The psychological study, planned and carried out by experienced psychologists, was concomitant with the general medical one and was devoted to determining the effects of marihuana on psychomotor responses and certain special abilities, on intellectual functioning, and on emotional reactions and personality structure.

For psychomotor effects, procedures were followed which gave records affording quantitative measurement. Static equilibrium and hand steadiness were the functions most strongly affected by marihuana. The body swaying was general in direction and not greater in one axis than in others. These effects came on during the first hour after the extract was given, reached a peak in about four hours, and persisted for some eight hours. After smoking, the effects came on much sooner —within a few minutes—and were of shorter duration, about three hours. Complex hand and foot reactions showed impairment, but simple reaction time, the strength of grip, speed of tapping, auditory acuity and musical ability, and estimation of short time intervals and small linear distances were unchanged. The findings in the women corresponded to those in the male subjects. In both groups there was marked individual variability, irrespective of dosage.

It was found that marihuana in an effective dose impairs intellectual functioning in general. Included under this heading are adverse effects on speed and accuracy in performance, on the application of acquired knowledge, on carrying out routine tasks, on memory, and on capacity for learning.

Marihuana does not change the basic personality structure of the individual. It lessens inhibition and this brings out what is latent in his thoughts and emotions but it does not evoke responses which would otherwise be totally alien to him. It induces a feeling of self-confidence, but this is expressed in thought rather than in performance. There is, in fact, evidence of a diminution in physical activity. While suggestibility may be increased by small doses, larger ones tend to induce a negativistic attitude.

From the study as a whole, it is concluded that marihuana is not a drug of addiction, comparable to morphine, and that if tolerance is acquired, this is of a very limited degree. Furthermore those who have been smoking marihuana for a period of years showed no mental or physical deterioration which may be attributed to the drug.

The lessening of inhibitions and repression, the euphoric state, the feeling of adequacy, the freer expression of thoughts and ideas, and the increase in appetite for food brought about by marihuana suggest therapeutic possibilities. From limited observations on addicts undergoing morphine withdrawal and on certain types of psychopathic disturbances, the impression was gained that marihuana had beneficial effects, but much more extensive and controlled study is required for definite conclusions to be drawn concerning therapeutic usage. It should be borne in mind that the effects of marihuana, more than in the case of other drugs, are quite variable in different individuals and in the same one at different times.

The chapter on the pharmacology of marihuana, prepared by Dr. Loewe, reviews the results of collaborative work of three laboratories (The Pharmacological Laboratory at the Cornell Medical College, the William Albert Noyes Laboratory at the University of Illinois, and the Laboratory of the Bureau of Narcotics at Washington, D.C.) which led to the discovery of the active principles, the elucidation of their origin, and the assembling of data on the relationship between chemical structure and biological activity. The chapter is introduced by a survey of the geographical distribution and botanical relationships of plants with marihuana activity.

The principles involved in bioassay are discussed and a method for marihuana assay described. The synthetic tetrahydrocannabinol of Adams was taken as the standard of reference and the characteristic reaction of ataxia in dogs measured quantitatively for the degree of activity. By this method the potency of samples and preparations of marihuana and of natural and synthetic principles has been determined and relationships between chemical structure and pharmacological activity elucidated.

The main components which have been isolated from marihuana oil containing the active principles are cannabidiol, cannabinol and isomeric tetrahydrocannabinols. The first two, but not the last, have been obtained as crystalline substances. The chemical structure and synthesis of these compounds have been described by Adams.

The typical effects of marihuana on man are ascribed to actions on the central nervous system. In dogs, the characteristic effect is ataxia. A delayed increase in pulse rate, a decrease in respiratory rate and blood pressure, and retching and vomiting were also observed. These effects are produced by tetrahydrocannabinol but not by cannabinol or cannabidiol. A derivative of the latter, tetrahydrocannabidiol, after a latent period of from thirty to seventy minutes following intravenous injection, had a specific convulsant action on the dog.

In rabbits a characteristic effect of marihuana extracts is corneal areflexia. This is also not produced by cannabidiol or cannabinol but does occur after tetrahydrocannabinol. However, impure oil mixtures have this action to a greater extent, from which it is suggested that a third unknown principle is present in the plant.

Cannabidiol has a synergistic hypnotic action with pernoston in mice. Neither cannabinol nor the synthetic tetrahydrocannabidiols had this effect.

The ataxia action of marihuana was considerably increased by a central stimulant, benzedrine.

No evidence was found of an acquired tolerance for the drug.

In examination of the data presented in the detailed clinical study it is seen that the effects reported were in the main those produced by the extract of marihuana taken by mouth. With the extract, the absorption is gradual and the action persists as long as the active principles are circulating throughout the body. The doses given were fixed ones and once taken the effects were beyond the subjects' control. Giving the extract thus afforded a longer period for study and insured greater accuracy in dosage. In New York, as far as is known, marihuana is rarely if ever taken in this form but is smoked in cigarettes. However, it is shown in the study that the effects from smoking correspond in kind to those from the extract. The difference is that, in smoking, the effects come on promptly and are of much shorter duration. How marked the reaction becomes depends on the number of cigarettes smoked and this is entirely under the subjects' control. The sensations desired are pleasurable ones—a feeling of contentment, inner satisfaction, free play of imagination. Once this stage is reached, the experienced user realizes that with further smoking the pleasurable sensations will be changed to unpleasant ones and so takes care to avoid this.

PART **4**

THE QUESTION
OF CONTROL

POT BUST AT CORNELL

David Sanford

Mark Barlow, the vice president of Cornell University, went to a very intimate cocktail party three Sundays ago in Ithaca. Some pretty responsible people on the faculty were there. At one point conversation got around to the subject of pot. "We all agreed," Barlow recalls, "that if someone at that moment had a package of marijuana we'd probably smoke it for the hell of it, to see what it's like."

This attitude of experimentation seems a bit odd for someone on the other side of the generational gap, especially when he is the student affairs vice president of a university which routinely reports students caught smoking, selling, buying or possessing marijuana to the police. It is all the more remarkable, considering that in New York the result of a conviction for possessing more than an ounce of marijuana is a mandatory five years in jail.

But these are strange times. The Federal Narcotics Bureau, a branch of the Treasury Department, has recently discovered that marijuana

Reprinted by permission of *The New Republic,* © 1967, Harrison-Blaine of New Jersey, 156 (April 15, 1967): 17–20.

is no longer a kick enjoyed more or less exclusively by Negro jazz musicians, hippies and other low-life but that it is fairly common among decent, middle-class, educated, otherwise conventional people who no longer believe that pot is a dangerous drug.

The burgeoning marijuana traffic, plus the radical change in attitudes toward pot, has been a source of grief to the Narcotics Bureau, which has the job of keeping it under control. Arrests involving pot have doubled in the past two years, narcotics agents have had to be diverted from the more important work of suppressing heroin, and this year the bureau had to come hat in hand to Congress for more money for more agents. The new permissiveness toward pot is seen by Narcotics Bureau Commissioner Henry L. Giordano as "just another effort to break down our whole American system."

Some universities, not Cornell, look the other way when students are arrested in pot "busts"; some parents worry not because their children are smoking pot but because they might be arrested; courts are increasingly reluctant to impose fixed minimum sentences and therefore refuse to bring convictions; even the Narcotics Bureau has stopped saying that smoking pot results directly in rape, murder and insanity.

In its 448 pages a new book, *The Marijuana Papers,* tells more than anyone would ever want to know about pot. David Solomon, its editor, is all for pot and believes that "millions of other Americans" are beginning to learn that "marijuana is both pleasurable and harmless."

Marijuana comes from the flowering tops and leaves of the *Cannabis sativa* or hemp plant, and grows without cultivation in most climates. A few puffs on a reefer give one the sensation of relaxation and a heightened awareness of light and sound. Pot was made illegal by the federal Marijuana Act of 1937, largely as a result of the lobbying of the Narcotics Bureau and its Commissioner Harry Anslinger. Most states subsequently enacted anti-pot legislation of their own. Since the late thirties the Narcotics Bureau has changed its line from an insistence that smoking marijuana is itself hazardous, to the belief that its use leads to other things, notably heroin addiction.

"THE POT HAZARD"

If marijuana did not lead to heroin addiction prior to 1937 but does now, David Solomon argues, perhaps it is because, as an illegal drug, it now must be obtained through the same channels through which other illegal drugs flow. "The marijuana user thus found himself able to purchase heroin from merchants who had previously sold only marijuana." In any event, the "attempt to suppress the use of marijuana in

he United States through police power and by means of heavy penalties
;hows no signs of succeeding."

The Narcotics Bureau is clearly on the defensive about marijuana.
[n his testimony before a House appropriations subcommittee February
3, Commissioner Giordano attributed the rise in illicit marijuana traffic
(7,000 arrests in 1964; 15,000 in 1966) to "free expression" groups
'hat have told young people to do whatever they like, without regard
:o the mores of society. "We seem to have a lot of people today trying
.o convince our youth that there is nothing really wrong with marijuana,"
ie said.

But strangely, nowhere in the commissioner's remarks to the sub-
:ommittee did he detail the hazards of marijuana, except to reiterate
:hat it is a stepping stone to stronger stuff. He draws this conclusion
'rom studies of known heroin addicts who say that they earlier smoked
marijuana. However, there are no studies available to suggest, as Giordano would like to believe, that the converse is true, that even a small
percentage of pot smokers graduate to heroin addiction. The assumptions of the Narcotics Bureau, which has something of a vested interest
in keeping marijuana a "problem," were questioned by the recent President's Crime Commission Report which said that "there are too many
marijuana users who do not graduate to heroin" and that "there is no
scientific basis for [the stepping-stone] theory."

Two weeks ago the American College Health Association, an organization of university and college health service professionals, met in
Washington to discuss their common interests (ranging from birth control
to football injuries). The panel discussions on the campus drug scene attracted the most interest. Marijuana, according to the panelists, is by
far the most prevalent and least alarming of the so-called hallucinogenic
drugs to be found on campuses today. (One rough guess has 25 percent
of the students at the University of California smoking pot, and UC is
not unique.) Woodrow W. Burgess, a psychiatrist at the University of
California at Davis, calls marijuana a "negligible source of emotional
disturbance in college students." He said that "in an active practice of
psychiatry of twenty years I have never had anyone come to me and
say they were in trouble from taking marijuana." Duke D. Fisher, a
physician with the Neuropsychiatric Institute at the University of California at Los Angeles and an authority on LSD, said "We don't see
adverse reactions to marijuana." His concern with pot is not its danger
(LSD *is* dangerous, he insists) but its illegality. Robert S. Liebert, a
Columbia University physician, thinks occasional use of the drug a
normal developmental phase among college kids. "The case could be
made," he said, "that if a male goes through four years of college on

many campuses now, without the experience, this abstinence bespeaks a rigidity in his character structure and fear of his impulses that is hardly desirable." Dr. Liebert stopped short only of suggesting that colleges "screen out all seniors who have never tried marijuana and insist that they go to the counseling service."

The problem of pot has in a real sense become a problem of law, not of medicine. Recently I visited the campuses of two universities which have lately experienced marijuana busts—Cornell and Wayne State. Both have noted an increase in the use of drugs by students; both consider it a problem. But that is where the similarities stop. Cornell reports student offenders to the cops. Where there is a conviction for selling, Cornell is inclined to kick the student out of school.

The dean of students at Wayne State in Detroit says the university has not and would not cooperate with narcotics agents and would most likely not suspend a student even after he had been convicted of a narcotics violation.

GETTING HIGH ABOVE CAYUGA'S WATERS

Cornell has developed something of a reputation for its drug problem. Last month a Cornell grad student was arrested along with 10 other persons in Ithaca, 11 in New York and one in Montreal in what the Thompkins County district attorney called the largest LSD buy in the state's history ($3,000 worth of LSD; $600–$700 of marijuana). The state narcotics bureau's undercover agent who was instrumental in the arrest was posing as a Cornell student and was allegedly getting the drugs for his friends at Cornell. In fact, the number of cases involving Cornell students has been small and university officials, while recognizing that marijuana is more widely used than ever before, do not think Cornell's difficulties are unusual.

Last year Cornell's health service answered a questionnaire from Senator Robert Kennedy about the use of LSD. Of 27 colleges and universities replying to the senator's query, Cornell was reported as having the most known LSD cases—eight (it later turned out that some of the cases reported by Cornell were not LSD at all but morning glory seeds, peyote and other drugs).

In 1965 Cornell's President James A. Perkins decided to face up to the drug problem and instituted a policy of issuing press releases whenever Cornell students were caught with drugs, reporting violations to Thompkins County DA, Richard Thaler, and declaring Cornell's unequivocal abhorrence of narcotics law violations. The policy has had uneven results. In one instance a university announcement forced

Thaler's hand and he had to make arrests before he felt that he had the goods on all the drug users involved.

Thaler prosecutes with zeal the cases Cornell turns over to him, and when he plans a bust he tells Cornell officials so they can be in on it. His investigative work has involved paid informants (in one case a university employee), paid amateur sleuths, and student rats. Two years ago he hired a New York City detective to come to Ithaca and hang around Cornell and the nearby Ithaca College, posing as a pothead. The agent, Edward Manet, befriended Mona Silverman, an Ithaca College girl (in court her lawyer said they had become very good friends indeed). He gave her $20 to buy some pot for him in New York, and when she did he had her arrested. The case became quite involved. In court Thaler was asked by the judge whether he had imported an undercover man to "make love" to the girl. Thaler replied that a kiss is not making love.

The Silverman girl was convicted by the Thompkins County court of selling and possessing marijuana, which under New York law may carry up to 20 years in prison. The conviction for selling, however, was ultimately overthrown by the New York Supreme Court, which concluded that Miss Silverman had not profited from the exchange (most student "pushers" sell marijuana as a not-for-profit favor) and had merely done what Thaler's man had asked her to do. "One who acts solely as the agent of the buyer," the court concluded, "cannot be convicted of the crime of selling narcotics."

Thaler says the community has not been much moved by his narcotics campaign, since many people think he is just interested in publicity and in serving his own political ambitions. They think, and he denies, he has an interest in the state legislature. Thaler's methods, though, especially the question of entrapment, were issues in his 1965 reelection campaign and have alarmed some university officials because Cornell is so willing to entrust its students to Thaler's care. One Ithaca resident wrote the local newspaper demanding Thaler resign. He wondered, "Can we possibly ask parents to send their children into a town whose public officials, through carelessness or ambition, allow their agents to use guile in enticing youngsters into wrongdoing?"

The tactics used by those who would suppress marijuana often seem to result in more serious problems than pot itself. Thaler points out that the courts have ruled that getting someone to purchase marijuana and then setting him up for the kill when he turns over the stuff is not illegal entrapment. Pot is a serious offense, he emphasizes, and extraordinary methods are necessary to ferret out offenders. Cornell feels constrained to cooperate with such activities, and once again the reason is law. It is a crime in New York to know of the commission of a crime and not report it.

One high university official said privately that "one has to separate a principle of cooperation from how one is going to cooperate specifically with the constabulary you happen to be working with. There's a lot of stuff I'd do in principle, but Thaler would have to subpoena me before he'd get the information out of me, and then I'd even consider civil disobedience."

Of course, not everyone at Cornell feels this way. Proctor Lowell George says Thaler merely uses the same procedures that "they use in the city of New York" to apprehend dope peddlers. You don't just walk up to people and ask them if they are pushing marijuana. "You've got to obtain evidence and to do this you need an undercover man." I asked Proctor George whether he approves of entrapment, paid student informers, and agents posing as students. His reply was, "Do they do it any differently in New York?"

NO ONE TO TRUST

A plethora of agencies is involved in controlling drug traffic: the Federal Narcotics Bureau (marijuana, heroin), the Food and Drug Administration's new Bureau of Drug Abuse Control (LSD, amphetamines, barbiturates), customs agents, state narcotics bureaus, state police, local police.

There is some cooperation among these agencies although there is just as much overlap of activity. Just before the March arrests in Ithaca the Thompkins DA heard from his spies that the state narcotics bureau was taking motion pictures of persons having contact with known pushers and also that FDA people were on the scene, but he never heard directly from either agency and the state narcotics bureau has yet to reply to his request to see their movies.

Educational institutions also become involved in the police function through their own campus cops, and sometimes in more indirect ways. Dr. Henry B. Bruyn, director of student health at the Cornell Memorial Hospital at UC in Berkeley, said at the recent American College Health Association meetings that in 1962 the city of Berkeley passed an ordinance which had the effect of requiring a campus physician to report the name of any patient who had suffered an adverse drug reaction—a law which effectively destroys the confidential doctor-patient relationship in drug cases and makes one's physician an agent of the state.

Cornell held discussions with officials at the University of Rochester, which also has had trouble with illicit drugs, during which it was suggested that room maids might keep their eyes open for drug users. Cornell denies that such reports are encouraged or received.

Students have been recruited as paid informers; and, in the recent case at Fairleigh Dickinson University, police officers have registered for and attended classes as students. The result of all this activity is a fear on the part of some students that they are being spied upon from all directions and that they cannot trust anyone, even one another.

Richard Thaler feels that it is important to play on this fear reaction, that the more frightened students become of an arrest the less likely they are to experiment with drugs. "You can treat people through fear, fear that they're going to get caught, fear that the consequences are going to be personally disastrous, fear that the stigma that's going to be attached to their activities is going to be irrevocable," he says, "or you can treat them with force, that is, by making arrests, by making whoever is involved go through the expense, and the time, and the publicity of standing trial."

Thaler says, "From what I've been told—of course not having any personal knowledge—marijuana in and of itself is apparently not that dangerous." Students, he says, wonder why then he is so eager to prosecute cases. "I have no choice. It's defined in the law as a crime, and therefore I'm charged with the duty of prosecuting."

David Radin, the editor of the student *Cornell Daily Sun,* said that before the most recent pot bust at Cornell, marijuana was "really rampant on campus. There were many students who had large holdings." Since the bust he believes the town is clean, but that after spring vacation pot will be back on campus. Sam Roberts, managing editor of the *Sun,* said most students rather take pot for granted. "But not Thaler. He'll go looking around and he'll feel so proud when he's discovered one exchange, when 100 a week are taking place."

In the final analysis, most doctors and university administrators beg the question of the harmfulness of marijuana and view it pragmatically as a violation of law. At Wesleyan University (Connecticut) the college physician, C. B. Crampton, sent a frank "personal message" to the students. It said in part: "When you spend five dollars for a nickel-bag of marijuana you are contributing directly to the most vicious criminal elements in your country—the individuals and groups who deal in narcotics. No decent human being will subsidize the narcotics rings knowingly, but many do so unwittingly. Parenthetically, I should point out that stiff penalties are imposed not only for selling narcotics and hallucinogenic drugs, but for having them in your possession. A man can be (and some individuals have been) sentenced to five years in prison for possessing a single packet of marijuana or a few milligrams of LSD."

THE MARIHUANA PROBLEM—
MYTH OR REALITY?

Alfred R. Lindesmith

The primary fact about marihuana which ought to be taken into account by legislators but is not, is that it is not a habit-forming drug. By this is meant that the regular use of marihuana does not produce tolerance, and its abrupt cessation does not lead to withdrawal distress. As a consequence the problem of controlling or regulating its use is sharply different from that presented by the genuine drugs of addiction, i.e., the opiates such as heroin and morphine and their synthetic equivalents. Nevertheless, by federal legislation in 1951 and 1956, the increased penalties imposed on opiate users and peddlers were also applied to the users and distributors of marihuana. This extension was made casually with little discussion or investigation and with no apparent appreciation that the use of marihuana is something almost totally different from the use of heroin.

Reprinted from Alfred Lindesmith, *The Addict and the Law,* copyright © 1965 by Indiana University Press, with permission of the publisher.

EFFECTS OF SMOKING MARIHUANA

Marihuana is ordinarily used in this country by smoking. The effects it produces are experienced as exhilaration, loss of inhibitions, a changed sense of time, and other psychological effects which have sometimes been described and extravagantly praised by those who have experienced them. These effects are in a general way comparable to the stimulating effects produced by alcohol in the sense that they are intoxicating, although they differ qualitatively from those of alcohol.

Intrinsically, however, marihuana is less dangerous and less harmful to the human body than is alcohol. It is, for example, not habit-forming, whereas alcohol is. While the alcoholic commonly substitutes alcohol for food, marihuana sharply stimulates the appetite. Chronic alcoholism is associated with various psychotic conditions and diseases such as Korsakoff's psychosis and cirrhosis of the liver. In comparison, the smoking of marihuana produces relatively trivial physical effects, although it does appear that immoderate use of the more concentrated products of the hemp plant also produce deleterious bodily effects. Such effects, however, are not conspicuous among American reefer smokers, probably because of the relatively small quantities of the essential drug that are ingested from the poor quality marihuana ordinarily consumed in this country. The American marihuana smoker who inadvertently uses too much when he switches, let us say, to the more potent ganja plant raised in Mexico and the West Indies is likely to experience nothing more alarming than going to sleep and waking up hungry.

USE OF MARIHUANA IN OTHER COUNTRIES

Marihuana consists of the dried and crumbled stems, leaves, and seed pods of a plant known as Indian hemp or *Cannabis sativa*. These materials are often mixed with tobacco and in the United States are ordinarily smoked. In many other parts of the world a special type of hemp plant of unusual potency, known commonly as *ganja*, is used in a similar manner or it may be brewed and drunk as ganja tea—a common practice in the West Indies, where this drink is prized for its alleged therapeutic efficacy. In India the uncultivated hemp plant is smoked as marihuana is here and is also drunk. It is known there as *bhang*. The essential drug of the hemp plant is *cannabis indica* or *cannabinol* and it, of course, can be taken in this form. This essential drug is derived primarily from the resin of the female hemp plant. This concentrated hemp resin is commonly known as *hashish* and is immensely more powerful than either ganja or marihuana. The comparison of hashish and marihuana is like that between pure alcohol and beer. Lurid accounts of the psychological effects and dangers of hemp are often based upon observations made by and upon hashish users. The mixture smoked as marihuana ordinarily contains very small quantities of the drug and its effects are correspondingly less spectacular, less dangerous, and less harmful than those of hashish.[1]

The medical use of *cannabis indica* has declined in Western medicine but it is still extensively used in the Ayurvedic and Unani systems of indigenous medicine in India. In various parts of the world folk beliefs attribute great therapeutic and even divine virtues to the drug. In Jamaica it is known to many persons of the lower classes as "the wisdom weed" and it is alleged that it stimulates good qualities in the person who uses it and brings him closer to God. The use of ganja there is supported by references to various Biblical passages which recommend the "herbs of the field." The same passages, incidentally, are taken by the devotees of peyote (a cactus containing mescaline) to refer to that plant. A back-to-Africa protest cult in Jamaica, known as the Ras Tafari, has adopted ganja as a symbol of the movement and its members sometimes refer to themselves as the "herb men." In defiance of the Government, members of this cult, and others who are simply impressed by the fact that ganja is a more profitable crop than any other, grow and harvest the plant and use some of it themselves. Ganja tea is regarded as a prime ameliorative agent in the folk treatment of many diseases including asthma, tuberculosis, venereal disease, and many others, especially all types of respiratory ailments. Ganja cigarettes are extensively used by the workers in the sugar cane fields and some foremen of the sugar producing companies state that, were it not for ganja, they would have difficulty finding workingmen to harvest their crops.[2]

On the book jacket of Professor Robert P. Walton's 1938 book entitled, *Marihuana: America's New Drug Problem,* Frederick T. Merrill and Mr. Anslinger are quoted. The latter observed: "It is a new peril—in some ways the worst we have met, and it concerns us all." Merrill was even more emphatic and alarmed: "If the abuse of this narcotic drug is not stamped out at once, the cost in crime waves, wasted human lives, and insanity will be enormous." Quoting Walton, Merrill notes that marihuana often produces "uncontrollable irritability and violent rages, which in most advanced forms cause assault and murder." He continues: "Am-

---

[1] For general discussions of marihuana see: Robert P. Walton, *Marihuana: America's New Drug Problem* (Philadelphia: Lippincott, 1938), and Norman Taylor, *Flight from Reality* (New York: Duell, Sloan and Pearce, 1949).

[2] From observations and interviews with Jamaicans by the writer during a visit to that island.

nesia often occurs, and the mania is frequently so acute that the heavy smoker becomes temporarily insane. Most authorities agree that permanent insanity can result from continual over-indulgence." Marihuana has had no noticeable effect in increasing the population of our mental institutions and whatever crimes of violence it may instigate are as nothing when compared to those that are linked with the use of alcohol.

Norman Taylor notes that the hemp plant, called *Cannabis sativa* by Linnaeus in the eighteenth century, probably originated in Central Asia or in China, where it was described in a book on pharmacy written by one Shen Nung nearly three thousand years before the birth of Christ.[3] The euphoric potential of the resinous female plant was known then and troubled Chinese moralists, who called it the "Liberator of Sin." Nung, however, recommended the medicine from this plant for "female weakness, gout, rheumatism, malaria, beri-beri, constipation and absent-mindedness." From China the use of hemp spread westward to India, to the Middle East, and along both sides of the Mediterranean, and ultimately reached Europe and the Western hemisphere. Nowhere has its use been eradicated, even after thousands of years of effort in some instances. Recent publications of the United Nations comment on the apparent continued spread of the practice.

The evil reputation of hemp was enhanced when, during the eleventh century, it became linked with a cult headed by one Hasan which initiated a new political tactic of secret assassination to cleanse the Moslem world of false prophets. Hasan's full name was Hashishin and he was called the Old Man of the Mountain. The terms *hashish* and *assassin* are linked with the name of *Hasan* and his cult.

USE BY LOWER CLASSES

It is possible that the bad reputation of marihuana and other forms of this drug reflects in part the bias of upper classes against an indulgence of the lower strata. Since hemp grows luxuriantly without cultivation in many parts of the world, it is available to many of its devotees at extremely low cost—in India, for example, at about one-twentieth the price of good quality whiskey in 1894, when the English carried out an extensive inquiry into the subject.[4] Denunciations of the weed come characteristically from persons of those classes which prefer whiskey, rum, gin, and other alcoholic beverages and who do not themselves use marihuana. Such persons, overlooking the well-known effects of alcohol,

---

[3] N. Taylor, *Flight from Reality*, p. 27.
[4] *Report of the Indian Hemp Drug Commission* (7 vols.; Simla, India, 1894), cited by N. Taylor, *Flight from Reality*, p. 34.

commonly deplore the effects of hemp upon the lower classes and often believe that it produces murder, rape, violence, and insanity.

Despite the prevalence of these beliefs among the drinkers of rum and whiskey and the upper classes generally, impartial investigations invariably have shown no such results. The moderate use of hemp, according to the Indian Hemp Drug Commission in 1894, does not produce significant mental or moral injuries, does not lead to disease, nor does it necessarily or even usually lead to excess any more than alcohol does. Excess, the Commission said, is confined to the idle and dissipated.[5] Many years later in New York City similar conclusions were stated on the basis of experimental study and from an examination of violent crimes committed in that city over a period of years.[6]

In Jamaica, where the lower classes regard the drug with favor, persons of high social status commonly assert that ganja is a potent cause of much of the personal violence which is relatively frequent there among the working classes. This is staunchly denied by the ganja users, who contend that the effects are usually in the opposite direction but admit that ganja may bring out the evil in some persons who are already evil. Police examination of violent crimes in Jamaica suggest that ganja has little connection with them and that they arise rather from sexual jealousy and the highly informal manner in which sexual matters are arranged on that island among the simpler people of the lower classes.

MARIHUANA AND ALCOHOL

In general, virtually all of the charges that are made against marihuana tend to shrink or dissolve entirely when they are closely examined by impartial investigators. The present tendency of the rank-and-file policeman, despite the enormous penalties attached to handling marihuana, is to regard it as a minor problem hardly deserving serious attention except for those who handle the weed in large amounts for mercenary purposes or who promote its use among the uninitiated.

Ironically, the accusations that are leveled at marihuana are all applicable to alcohol, as has been demonstrated by innumerable investigations. These studies indicate that much murder, rape, and homicide is committed by persons under the influence. The special psychoses and ailments of alcoholics are numerous and well delineated in countless scientific and literary productions. The menace of the drinking driver of

---

[5] N. Taylor, *Flight from Reality*, pp. 34–35.

[6] *The Marihuana Problem in the City of New York: Sociological, Medical, Psychological and Pharmacological Studies* by the Mayor's Committee on Marihuana, George B. Wallace, Chairman (Lancaster, Pa.: Jaques Cattell Press, 1944).

automobiles is well understood by all and is more or less accepted as one of the inevitable hazards of life in the modern world. It is well known, too, that the manufacturers of alcoholic beverages advertise their products and seek to enlarge their markets and that the use of alcohol spreads from those who already have the practice to those who do not. Why, then, so much excitement about marihuana? It is said that marihuana sometimes causes girls and women to lose their virtue and innocence, but the role of alcohol in this respect is infinitely more important. It seems inconsistent, therefore, that while the decision to drink or not to drink is viewed as a personal moral decision, the use of marihuana should be viewed as a heinous crime subject to long prison sentences.

Among those who have never used hemp or seen it used by others the belief is often found that marihuana acts as a sexual stimulant or aphrodisiac. Actually its effects, like those of opiates, are in exactly the opposite direction, tending to cause the user to lose interest in the opposite sex. Users more frequently than not report the absence of ideas of sex or say that Venus herself could not tempt them when they are under the influence of this drug.

THE EFFECTS OF ANTI-MARIHUANA LEGISLATION

In 1937 the Congress passed a Marihuana Tax Act, modeled after the Harrison Act. It was designed to curb the use of marihuana by the use of the federal police power, and like the Harrison Act imposed penalties upon both buyers and sellers. This Act was the result of a publicity campaign staged by the Federal Bureau of Narcotics under Mr. Anslinger's direction and leadership. The bill was passed with little discussion after brief hearings on the ground that marihuana was a highly dangerous drug inciting its users to commit crimes of violence and often leading to insanity.[7]

The beliefs concerning marihuana which led to this legislation may be represented in a pure and extreme form by turning to the writing of a hyperactive reformer and alarmist of the period, Earle Albert Rowell.[8] He claimed in 1939 that he had spent fourteen years campaigning

---

[7] See *Taxation of Marihuana:* Hearings before the Committee on Ways and Means, U.S. House of Representatives, 75th Cong., 1st sess., April and May, 1937 (hereafter called *House Marihuana Hearings, 1937*); and *Taxation of Marihuana:* Hearings before a Subcommittee of the Committee on Finance, U.S. Senate, 75th Cong., 1st sess., on H.R. 6906 (hereafter called *Senate Marihuana Hearings, 1937*).

[8] Earle Albert Rowell and Robert Rowell, *On the Trail of Marihuana, the Weed of Madness* (Mountain View, Cal.: Pacific Press Publishing Association, 1939). See also Earle Albert Rowell, *Dope: Adventures of David Dare* (Nashville, Tenn.: Southern Publishing Association, 1937).

against this weed, delivering more than four thousand lectures in forty states and personally pulling up and destroying many flourishing hemp fields. Mr. Rowell's zealous opposition to marihuana was only slightly less intense than his disapproval of alcohol and tobacco. The use of tobacco, he correctly observed, invariably precedes the smoking of the deadly reefer. Mr. Rowell came into disfavor with the Bureau of Narcotics around 1938 and this agency spent considerable energy and manpower in an attempt to silence and discredit him. This may have been because of Mr. Rowell's view that opiate addiction is a disease or perhaps because of his repeated allegations that the police were not sufficiently diligent in destroying marihuana.

Mr. Rowell summarized the effects of marihuana as follows:

> We know that marihuana—
> 1. Destroys will power, making a jellyfish of the user. He cannot say no.
> 2. Eliminates the line between right and wrong, and substitutes one's own warped desires or the base suggestions of others as the standard of right.
> 3. Above all, causes crime; fills the victim with an irrepressible urge to violence.
> 4. Incites to revolting immoralities, including rape and murder.
> 5. Causes many accidents both industrial and automobile.
> 6. Ruins careers forever.
> 7. Causes insanity as its specialty.
> 8. *Either in self-defense or a means of revenue, users make smokers of others, thus perpetuating evil.* [Italics in original.] [9]

In 1939 when Rowell published his book, marihuana was regarded as a relatively new drug menace in the United States. Mr. Rowell thought that he had already detected an increase of the population of mental hospitals because of it:

> Asylums and mental hospitals in this country are beginning to see and feel the influence of marihuana, and are awaking to its deleterious effects on the brain. As we traveled through the various states, superintendents of these institutions told us of cases of insanity resulting from marihuana. [10]

"The baleful mental effects of marihuana," he said, "begin soon after the first reefer is smoked. . . ." [11]

When Mr. Anslinger appeared before the Senate subcommittee which

---

[9] E. A. Rowell and R. Rowell, *On the Trail of Marihuana*, p. 33.
[10] *Ibid.*, p. 51.
[11] *Ibid.*

was investigating the illicit drug traffic in 1955 under the guidance of Senator Price Daniel, there were only a few offhand discussions of marihuana. Mr. Anslinger observed that the Bureau in its national survey was "trying to keep away from the marihuana addict, because he is not a true addict." The real problem, he said, was the heroin addict. Senator Daniel thereupon remarked:

"Now, do I understand it from you that, while we are discussing marihuana, the real danger there is that the use of marihuana leads many people eventually to the use of heroin, and the drugs that do cause complete addiction; is that true?" [12]

Mr. Anslinger agreed:

"That is the great problem and our great concern about the use of marihuana, that eventually if used over a long period, it does lead to heroin addiction." [13]

Senators Welker and Daniel pursued the subject, and Mr. Anslinger, when prompted, agreed that marihuana was dangerous. Senator Welker finally asked this question:

"Is it or is it not a fact that the marihuana user has been responsible for many of our most sadistic, terrible crimes in this nation, such as sex slayings, sadistic slayings, and matters of that kind?"

Mr. Anslinger hedged:

"There have been instances of that, Senator. We have had some rather tragic occurrences by users of marihuana. It does not follow that all crime can be traced to marihuana. There have been many brutal crimes traced to marihuana, but I would not say that it is a controlling factor in the commission of crimes." [14]

Eighteen years earlier, in 1937, the year in which the federal anti-marihuana law was passed, Mr. Anslinger had presented a very different picture of marihuana. Prior to 1937 Mr. Anslinger and the Bureau of Narcotics had spearheaded a propaganda campaign against marihuana on the ground that it produced an immense amount of violent crime such as rape, mayhem, and murder, and that many traffic accidents could be attributed to it. During the 1937 hearings before a House subcommittee, Representative John Dingell of Michigan asked Mr. Anslinger: "I am just wondering whether the marihuana addict graduates into a heroin, an opium, or a cocaine user."

---

[12] *Daniel Subcommittee Hearings,* Part 5, 1955, p. 16.
[13] *Ibid.*
[14] *Ibid.,* p. 18.

Mr. Anslinger replied: "No, sir; I have not heard of a case of that kind. I think it is an entirely different class. The marihuana addict does not go in that direction." [15]

A few months later in the same year, before a Senate subcommittee which was considering the antimarihuana law which the Bureau of Narcotics had asked for, Mr. Anslinger commented: "There is an entirely new class of people using marihuana. The opium user is around 35 to 40 years old. These users are 20 years old and know nothing of heroin or morphine." [16]

The theme stated by the Commissioner of Narcotics in 1955, that the main threat in marihuana is that it leads to the use of heroin, is now ordinarily cited as the principal justification for applying to it the same severe penalties that are applied in the case of heroin. Reformer Rowell in 1939 was more logical and consistent than either the Senators or the Commissioner when he emphasized that cigarette smoking invariably preceded reefer smoking. Mr. Rowell told of a shrewd gangster whom he engaged in what now appears as a prophetic discussion of the prospects of the dope industry.[17]

> The gangster remarked: "Marihuana is the coming thing."
> "But," I protested in surprise, "marihuana is not a habit-forming drug like morphine or heroin; and, besides, it's too cheap to bother with."
> He laughed. "You don't understand. Laws are being passed now by various states against it, and soon Uncle Sam will put a ban on it. The price will then go up, and that will make it profitable for us to handle."

The gangster, according to Mr. Rowell, then commented on the shrewd manner in which the tobacco companies had popularized cigarettes among the soldiers of the First World War and on the enormous increase in cigarette consumption by young persons. He grew eloquent: "Every cigarette smoker is a prospect for the dope ring via the marihuana road. Millions of boys and girls now smoke. Think of the unlimited new market!"

Mr. Rowell got the idea and commented as follows to his readers: "Slowly, insidiously, for over three hundred years, Lady Nicotine was setting the stage for a grand climax. The long years of tobacco using were but an introduction and training for marihuana use. Tobacco, which was first smoked in a pipe, then as a cigar, and at last as a cigarette, demanded more and more of itself until its supposed pleasures palled, and some of the tobacco victims looked about for something stronger. Tobacco was no longer potent enough."

---

[15] *House Marihuana Hearings, 1937*, p. 24.
[16] *Senate Marihuana Hearings, 1937*, pp. 14–15.
[17] E. A. Rowell and R. Rowell, *On the Trail of Marihuana*, pp. 69–74.

Mr. Rowell was not optimistic about the future: "Marihuana will continue to be a problem for both police and educators, because it is so easy to grow, to manufacture, and to peddle, and is such a quick source of easy money. The plant can be grown anywhere; it can be harvested secretly, prepared in twenty-four hours without a penny of investment for equipment; and every cigarette user is a prospect. As our laws are enforced and the weed becomes scarcer, the price will rise, and greater profit accrue to venturesome and successful peddlers. Whereas now it is usually peddled by lone wolves, as soon as the weed becomes scarcer and the price rises, organized crime will step in and establish a monopoly." [18]

While Mr. Rowell, in the manner of reforming alarmists, exaggerated the evil with which he was preoccupied, the above appraisal of the effects of the Marihuana Tax Act has been reasonably well borne out by subsequent events. Certainly it was a more realistic assessment of the law's effects than any that were made by the legislators who passed the bill or by the officials who promoted it. Mr. Rowell was also completely right in pointing out that virtually every marihuana smoker graduated to this practice from cigarette smoking. His gangster informant was correct in his calculation that state and federal laws prohibiting marihuana would make the weed more expensive and more profitable for peddlers to handle, and also correctly foresaw that with the same merchants handling both marihuana and heroin it would become a simple matter for marihuana users to switch from the less to the more dangerous drug, as they have done.

In the United States during the nineteenth century, and the early decades of the twentieth, addiction to opiates frequently developed from the abuse of alcohol. This still occurs to some extent and is frequently reported from other parts of the world, for morphine provides a potent means of relieving the alcoholic hangover. An American doctor once advocated as a cure of alcoholism that alcohol addicts be deliberately addicted to morphine, arguing with considerable plausibility that of the two habits the latter was obviously the lesser evil.[19] Moreover, he practiced what he preached and recommended his technique with considerable enthusiasm for use by others.

The truth of the matter, of course, is that very few cigarette smokers go on to marihuana, very few marihuana users go on to heroin, and very few alcohol users graduate to the use of heroin. Since some barbiturate and amphetamine users progress to heroin it should be added that it is also only a very small proportion who do. If all of these substances were

---

[18] *Ibid.*, pp. 88–89.
[19] J. R. Black, "Advantages of Substituting the Morphia Habit for the Incurably Alcoholic," *Cincinnati Lancet-Clinic,* XXII, n.s. (1889), Part I, 537–41.

to be prohibited because they are sometimes involved in the progression toward heroin addiction there is little doubt that the illicit traffic in marihuana and heroin would be expanded to include the other offending substances and that the movement from less to more serious habits would be greatly facilitated.

No one, of course, recommends the use of marihuana nor does anyone deny that there are evil effects and consequences associated with using it. The fact that the use of marihuana is outlawed, for example, means that it is often obtained through association with unsavory types, often used in an underworld environment, and the user takes the risk of criminal prosecution. It is also undeniable that marihuana intoxication may sometimes lead to automobile accidents and to irresponsible or criminal acts. The controversy with respect to marihuana is solely concerning the relative prevalence or frequency of such results in comparison to similar consequences following from the use of alcoholic beverages. All empirical investigations indicate that alcohol constitutes a far greater social danger than does marihuana.

MAYOR LAGUARDIA'S COMMITTEE ON MARIHUANA

Mayor LaGuardia's Committee on Marihuana, on the basis of a close examination of the matter in New York City, stressed the relative triviality of the effects of marihuana use in a report published in 1945.[20] In the July 1943 issue of the *Military Surgeon,* the editor, Colonel J. M. Phalen, commented as follows in an editorial on "The Marihuana Bugaboo":

> The smoking of the leaves, flowers and seeds of *Cannabis sativa* is no more harmful than the smoking of tobacco or mullein or sumac leaves. ... The legislation in relation to marihuana was ill-advised ... it branded as a menace and a crime a matter of trivial importance. ... It is hoped that no witch hunt will be instituted in the military service over a problem that does not exist.[21]

Similar statements have been made by many other competent investigators and observers.

On the other hand, as has been pointed out, a sharply divergent view has been presented by law enforcement officials, particularly by the Federal Bureau of Narcotics, and also by many individual writers. The sharp divergence of views among the scientifically oriented evidently depends upon the manner in which the research is done. Investigators who rely on the opinions of high echelon officials, who have no direct acquaint-

---

[20] *The Marihuana Problem in the City of New York.*
[21] Cited by N. Taylor, *Flight from Reality,* p. 36.

ance with the use of marihuana and who base their opinions on anecdotes rather than actual statistical data, usually reach the conclusion that marihuana is a highly dangerous drug which produces much violent crime and insanity. These conclusions, as we have suggested, may be a reflection of upper-class hostility toward an unfamiliar lower-class indulgence. More critical and skeptical investigators, who look for basic statistical evidence, invariably fail to find it and end up writing debunking articles for which they are roundly abused by the moralists.

It is often felt that, even if the dangers of marihuana are exaggerated, these exaggerations and misstatements should be allowed to stand so that they may frighten adolescents away from the drug. The implication that adolescents are influenced to any appreciable degree by articles appearing in scientific journals is probably absurd. Those who use marihuana probably come to do so on the basis of personal associations and direct observations of their own.

The deliberate circulation of false information is self-defeating in that the adventurous, experimentally inclined youth can quickly discover for himself, by trying the weed or talking to those who have smoked it, that much of the officially circulated view is false. He is then prepared to believe that everything he has been told about narcotics is equally wrong.

When Mayor LaGuardia's Committee on Marihuana made its report, it was strongly attacked by those committed to a belief in the marihuana menace. The *Journal of the American Medical Association* in 1943 published a letter from Mr. Anslinger in which he criticized an article by Drs. Allentuck and Bowman on findings derived from the New York study in which they had participated.[22] There were rumors that the New York marihuana study was to be suppressed, but after considerable delay, it was ultimately released in 1945. On April 28, 1945, the *Journal of the American Medical Association* editorially assailed the report, using language and arguments of a type not ordinarily found in learned journals:

> For many years medical scientists have considered cannabis a dangerous drug. Nevertheless, a book called "Marihuana Problems" by the New York City Mayor's Committee on Marihuana submits an analysis by seventeen doctors of tests on 77 prisoners and, on this narrow and thoroughly unscientific foundation, draws sweeping and inadequate conclusions which minimize the harmfulness of marihuana. Already the book has done harm. One investigator has described some tearful parents who brought their 16 year old son to a physician after he had been detected in the act of smoking marihuana. A noticeable mental deterio-

---

22 *J.A.M.A.*, 121, No. 3 (Jan. 16, 1943), 212–13.

ration had been evident for some time even to their lay minds. The boy said he had read an account of the LaGuardia Committee report and that this was his justification for using marihuana. He read in *Down Beat*, a musical journal, an analysis of this report under the caption "Light Up, Gates, Report Finds Tea a Good Kick."

A criminal lawyer for marihuana drug peddlers has already used the LaGuardia report as a basis to have defendants set free by the court. . . .

The book states unqualifiedly to the public that the use of this narcotic does not lead to physical, mental or moral degeneration and that permanent deleterious effects from its continued use were not observed on 77 prisoners. This statement has already done great damage to the cause of law enforcement. Public officials will do well to disregard this unscientific, uncritical study, and continue to regard marihuana as a menace wherever it is purveyed.[23]

Despite the fact that this editorial continues to be cited and reproduced to discredit the New York study, the conclusions of the report enjoy considerable status and are undoubtedly far closer to the realities of the situation than is the view represented by the A.M.A. editorial. Indeed, if one judges the law enforcement agencies by their actions rather than their words, it appears that even the police, to a considerable extent, have swung over to the viewpoint of the Mayor's committee.

MARIHUANA ARRESTS

After 1951 the budget and field force of the Federal Bureau of Narcotics were substantially enlarged. Nevertheless, the number of marihuana arrests has steadily declined and by 1960 it was close to the vanishing point, with only 169 such cases. In previous years the numbers of federal marihuana violations were reported as follows: [24]

1952	1,288
1954	508
1956	403
1958	179

Of the 169 federal marihuana violations reported in 1960, 88 occurred in California, 16 in Maryland, and 13 in Kentucky. No other state had as many as ten and no violations were reported from 28 states. We have already noted that the Bureau does not bother to count marihuana users in its national survey of addiction and does not regard marihuana as an

---

[23] *J.A.M.A.*, 127, No. 17 (April 28, 1945), 1129.

[24] From the annual reports of the Bureau of Narcotics for the years indicated. In 1962 the number of marihuana cases was 242. (*Traffic in Opium and Other Dangerous Drugs, 1962*, p. 62.)

addicting drug. The above figures on enforcement suggest that, at the federal level at least, the marihuana laws are being largely ignored since it is not claimed that the use of marihuana is diminishing.

Statistics on marihuana prosecutions as such are extremely difficult to obtain and data that are available are very unreliable and incomplete. The Federal Narcotics Bureau presented to the Daniel Subcommittee a summary of marihuana prosecutions for the year 1954, giving both federal and nonfederal cases. It is not claimed that the latter are complete; they are merely figures from some of the main cities in the indicated states.

TABLE 1

MARIHUANA ARRESTS—FEDERAL AND LOCAL BY STATES—1954 [25]

State	Federal	Local	State	Federal	Local
Alabama	2	6	New Hampshire	0	0
Arizona	25	4	New Jersey	5	26
Arkansas	2	0	New Mexico	23	10
California	51	1,101	New York	5	407
Colorado	28	1	North Carolina	0	0
Connecticut	2	6	North Dakota	0	0
Delaware	0	1	Ohio	25	23
District of			Oklahoma	2	13
Columbia	3	17	Oregon	1	8
Florida	4	30	Pennsylvania	3	50
Georgia	4	1	Rhode Island	0	0
Idaho	0	2	South Carolina	4	0
Illinois	13	327	South Dakota	0	0
Indiana	0	14	Tennessee	11	1
Iowa	0	8	Texas	325	612
Kansas	2	0	Utah	4	0
Kentucky	39	8	Vermont	0	0
Louisiana	17	105	Virginia	0	1
Maine	0	0	Washington	22	10
Maryland	2	30	West Virginia	0	0
Massachusetts	5	1	Wisconsin	0	47
Michigan	30	270	Wyoming	4	0
Minnesota	0	5	Alaska	5	0
Mississippi	0	1	Hawaii	14	23
Missouri	9	15			
Montana	0	6	Totals	713	3,205
Nebraska	1	13			
Nevada	16	2	Grand Total		3,918

From this table it will be seen that 3,263 of the total of 3,918 arrests were made in the six states of California, Texas, Illinois, Michigan, New York, and Louisiana. These states are, in one way or another, centers

---

[25] *Daniel Subcommittee Hearings,* 1955, pp. 267–71, exhibit 7. Note the unexplained discrepancy between the federal total given here and that of the preceding citation.

of the marihuana traffic. High arrest rates in California, Texas, and Louisiana no doubt arise from the fact that considerable quantities of marihuana are smuggled into the country there from Mexico and the Caribbean area. The rates in Illinois, Michigan, and New York reflect mainly police activity in the three large cities of Detroit, Chicago, and New York, all of them narcotics distribution centers. Heroin arrests are also highest in the states of California, New York, Illinois, and Michigan, while Texas and Louisiana are farther down on the list.

The penalty provisions applicable to marihuana users under state and federal law are about the same as those applied to heroin users. These penalties are entirely disproportionate to the seriousness of the offending behavior and lead to gross injustice and undesirable social consequences. For example, it is well known that many jazz musicians and other generally inoffensive persons use or have used marihuana. To send these persons to jail is absurd and harmful and serves no conceivable useful purpose. The moderate or occasional marihuana user is not a significant social menace. Jails and prisons, chronically overcrowded, should be used for those who present a genuine threat to life and property. The absurdity is compounded when an occasional judge, ignorant of the nature of marihuana, sends a marihuana user to prison to cure him of his nonexistent addiction. The writer was once in court when a middle-aged Negro defendant appeared before the judge charged with having used and had in his possession one marihuana cigarette during the noon hour at the place where he had worked for a number of years. This man had no previous criminal record and this fact was stated before the court. Nevertheless, a two-year sentence was imposed to "dry up his habit."

The President's Advisory Commission which reported on narcotic and drug abuse in 1963 took cognizance of the relatively trivial nature of the marihuana evil by suggesting that all mandatory sentences be eliminated for crimes involving it and that judges be granted full discretionary power in dealing with offenders.[26] These suggestions are excessively timid and not entirely logical, for there is no good reason why a mere user of marihuana should be subjected to a jail sentence at all. The marihuana user probably ought to be dealt with by the law along the same lines that are used with persons who drink alcohol.

If it is deemed in the public interest to punish smokers of marihuana, such punishments should ordinarily consist of fines only, up to some maximum of perhaps $500.00, depending upon the offense and the defendant's ability to pay. These fines might be scaled down or eliminated

---

[26] *Final Report:* The President's Advisory Commission on Narcotic and Drug Abuse, p. 42.

entirely for persons who provided information concerning their source of supply. Police efforts should be focused primarily on the traffic rather than on the user. Persons driving automobiles under the influence of the drug might be fined and deprived of their driving license for a period of time. Crimes which could be shown to the satisfaction of a court of law to be linked with the use of marihuana ought to be dealt with about the way that crimes arising from the use of alcohol are handled.

Laws such as this, with penalties of a reasonable nature, would probably be more effective than those now in effect because they would be more enforceable and more in accord with the nature of the problem being dealt with. They would have the effect of reducing the discrepancy that now exists between the laws as written and the laws as they are actually enforced. A more matter-of-fact and realistic handling of the marihuana problem would also probably reduce the aura of sensationalism which now surrounds the subject and diminish the illicit glamor which is now attached to the hemp plant.

It is argued by some that the marihuana industry should be brought under control by legalization, taxation, licensing, and other devices like those used to control alcohol—and to exploit it as a source of revenue. Advocates of this view might well argue that there should be no unfair discrimination among vices; that if the greater evil of alcohol use is legal, the lesser one of marihuana smoking should be so as well. Since the smoking of marihuana will undoubtedly continue regardless of legislation against it, it can also be argued that it would be better to accept the inevitable than to wage war for a lost cause.

In opposition to this extremely permissive position, the more conservative reformer can call attention to the fact that, outside of a few Asian and African countries, the use of this substance is everywhere disapproved of and subject to legal restrictions. It is possible that legal sanctions exercise some deterrent effect and that without them the use of this drug might spread even more rapidly and assume more virulent forms. Should the use of marihuana become anywhere nearly as widespread as that of alcohol it might be too late to talk of effective restrictions since the users would command too many votes. A legal marihuana or ganja industry which advertised its product and sought to improve it through research and experimentation would be a distinct embarrassment to the nation as a whole as well as being a direct economic threat to the alcoholic beverage industries and possibly to the tobacco industry. A final and decisive argument seems to be that public opinion is not likely in the foreseeable future to accept indulgence in marihuana as an equivalent of, or substitute for, indulgence in alcohol.

The long history of the use of marihuana, the spread of the practice throughout the world in the face of determined and sometimes fanatical opposition, and the persistence of the practice once it is established—all suggest that the smoking of marihuana will continue in the United States for some time to come. The practical question seems to be one of minimizing and controlling the practice while avoiding the extreme tactics of prohibitionists. A comprehensive, impartial public inquiry into the matter, based on the assumption that marihuana is *not* the same as heroin, might help to bring about a more sober and rational approach to an indulgence which merits some concern but which is far less serious than is presently suggested by the harsh inflexibility of current laws.

MARIJUANA AT ISSUE

Lee Berton

"Let the punishment fit the crime."

That is the fundamental plea being sounded in courtrooms in many states on a subject often as emotional as abortion or birth control—marijuana. Civil liberties-minded lawyers are undertaking broad challenges of the laws governing its use, sale and possession.

The U.S. Constitution, particularly the Eighth Amendment forbidding "cruel and unusual punishments," is at the heart of these defenses, and the attorneys involved hope that the Supreme Court eventually will overturn the state laws they oppose.

But the courtroom activity is just one symptom of a legal and regulatory debate engaging law enforcement officers, educators and other public officials across the nation, not to mention the members of respectable families whose sons or daughters face fines or prison sentences on marijuana charges.

Reprinted from *The Wall Street Journal* 48 (November 20, 1967): 1, 18, with the permission of the publisher.

DISSENSION WITHIN THE GOVERNMENT

The controversy over "pot" is reaching into high circles of the Government, and two Federal agencies are on collision course. The Treasury Department's Federal Narcotics Bureau, which regulates the drug, continues to support present or even stronger controls on it.

But the thinking is different at the Food and Drug Administration, an arm of the Department of Health, Education and Welfare. A confidential memorandum recently circulated among top HEW officials over the signature of Dr. James L. Goddard, FDA commissioner, advocates such radical changes as removal of legal penalties for possession of marijuana when it is intended for personal use only.

"Legalize Pot" is a popular button and banner slogan among hippie demonstrators, but that is far from Dr. Goddard's intent, and no one expects complete legalization. But pressure is mounting for reexamination of marijuana laws and of the purported perils of the drug on which the laws are based.

Obviously, marijuana use has spread. Thirty years ago marijuana circulated mainly among criminals and their associates; now it can be bought on Main Street. Also, medical evidence reaching the public casts doubt on the dangers of marijuana—particularly the long-held notion that it leads to addiction to such drugs as heroin. But many observers see another major reason for the marijuana debate: Pot has climbed the social ladder.

THE DOCTOR AND THE LAWYER

"Nobody worried very much when police sent thousands of ghetto dwellers to languish in prison for years for puffing on one joint (marijuana cigaret)," asserts Alfred R. Lindesmith, an Indiana University sociologist and author of *The Addict and the Law*. "But now that the doctor, the lawyer, the teacher and the business executive and their children are facing the same fate, marijuana has become a cause celebre."

Some of the most vocal protests against marijuana laws are coming from professionals. In San Francisco, 1,952 persons, including physicians, college professors and other highly educated citizens, have signed affidavits calling marijuana a harmless drug. An elementary school principal in California, a 58-year-old woman, volunteered publicly that she had used marijuana for 18 years—whereupon she was suspended indefinitely from her job.

The Federal Narcotics Bureau, which says annual marijuana arrests have almost doubled since 1964, to about 15,000 a year, acknowledges that many of the new users are in the "upper and middle strata of society."

No one disputes that the penalties written into the marijuana laws are severe. A Federal statute enacted in 1937 provides for prison penalties ranging from 2 to 40 years, and it served as the pattern for state laws around the nation. In Georgia, a second conviction for selling to a minor can result in a death sentence.

THE PERILOUS DRUG

These are sentences ordinarily meted out for the most heinous felonies. How did this happen? Civil liberties lawyers and others point to the Federal Narcotics Bureau. When Congress was considering legislation in 1937, Harry J. Anslinger, the zealous former commissioner of the bureau, testified that marijuana was a "menace" leading to rape, homicide and other crimes and possibly to insanity as well.

That posture hasn't changed. In a Narcotics Bureau booklet entitled *Living Death: The Truth About Drug Addiction,* the current commissioner, Henry L. Giordano, writes, "Never let anyone persuade you to smoke even one marijuana cigaret. It is pure poison." Elsewhere in the booklet, he writes, ". . . it cannot be too strongly emphasized that the smoking of the marijuana cigaret is a dangerous first step on the road which usually leads to enslavement by heroin."

Such assertions to the contrary, many thousands of Americans can testify that a marijuana smoke hasn't led to their ruin.

"I'm not a hippie or a fringie, and I get along well with my parents," says a 22-year-old student at Harvard University's law school who occasionally smokes marijuana at parties with friends. "And I'm not taking pot for rebellion. It just happens to be a pleasant experience that heightens my perceptions. After one smoke, for instance, I heard for the first time the bass part in a piece of classical music, though I had listened to the selection many times before without pot."

But there has been no discernible agitation among state legislators or executives to change the laws. The reason seems clear: The subject of marijuana holds political peril. The FDA's Dr. Goddard discovered this some weeks ago when he suggested that marijuana was no more dangerous than alcohol.

The FDA chief soon qualified his statement, saying that both were dangerous, alcohol for its damage to mind and body, and marijuana for its legal consequences and possible long-term physical dangers yet unknown. But the reaction in Congress was stormy; Rep. Dan Kuykendall (D., Tenn.), among others, called for Dr. Goddard's resignation.

THE CONFIDENTIAL MEMO

The FDA commissioner has since been circumspect in public, although he did suggest that penalties for possession might be relaxed. However, the confidential FDA memo obtained by the Wall Street Journal shows that Dr. Goddard's position indeed is sharply divergent from the stand long taken on marijuana within the Government.

The most radical suggestion in the memo is the proposal to end penalties for possession when the marijuana clearly is intended for personal use. It would simply be seized, as is the far more dangerous hallucinogen LSD under Federal law (many state laws now classify LSD possession as a crime).

Dr. Goddard also would transfer jurisdiction over marijuana from the Narcotics Bureau to the FDA, where it could be classified as a mild hallucinogen and regulated under the Drug Control Abuse Act.

The present Federal law would be repealed under Dr. Goddard's recommendations. Illegal sale, manufacture and distribution of marijuana would remain felony violations—but without mandatory sentencing provisions such as those in the present Federal law.

HEW hasn't indicated what its public stance in the developing marijuana dispute will be. The Narcotics Bureau declines comment on the recommendations of the FDA memo. But Mr. Giordano made clear his position on some aspects of the controversy in testimony last Wednesday before the House Government Operations subcommittee.

"If there is no criminal sanction against possessing marijuana," he said, "many people will regard this as tacit approval of its use." Without stern penalties, he declared, marijuana use will "go through the roof."

Dr. Goddard has noted that LSD users don't face prosecution. But Mr. Giordano said Congress should be thinking of imposing penalties for possession of LSD, rather than relaxing penalties for possession of marijuana.

About 30 legal actions challenging state marijuana laws are under way or pending. The most publicized is a Boston case involving the Massachusetts statute that provides prison sentences ranging up to 25 years for marijuana violations.

"The marijuana menace is 85% myth, and I aim to dispel it," says Joseph S. Oteri, the defense attorney. He is representing two Philadelphia men charged with possession of the drug.

A county Superior Court judge in Boston is weighing a decision on Mr. Oteri's motion to rule the Massachusetts law unconstitutional. But an Albuquerque, N.M., defense based on the Oteri brief already has produced a sentence considered lenient by the attorney, Gerald D. Fowlie.

A CRACK IN THE WALL

Mr. Fowlie represented a 25-year-old college dropout "from a good family" caught selling marijuana. The judge imposed a sentence of four months imprisonment but suspended an additional three-year sentence.

A "new court climate concerning marijuana" is developing, Mr. Fowlie says. And he declares, "There are going to be a lot more defendants in marijuana cases trying to upset the laws now that it appears there's a crack in the legal wall."

One chief ingredient in the dispute over regulating marijuana is the acknowledged "information gap" on the drug's true effects. Dr. Roger Meyer, acting chief of the Center for Studies of Narcotic and Drug Abuse in Chevy Chase, Md., a National Institute of Mental Health facility, comments:

"On one hand, Federal enforcement officials insist marijuana stirs up hazardous mental aberrations, while many more liberal sociologists maintain many of its new users are intellectually bright youngsters who become more contemplative, relaxed and tranquilized after smoking it."

In addition to the medical questions, there is the Narcotics Bureau's contention that marijuana is associated with serious crime. Both issues got something of a full-scale airing in the 11-day hearing in Boston on Mr. Oteri's constitutionality motion. He produced 10 expert witnesses for the defense.

Dr. Joel Fort, a respected psychiatrist and drug consultant who has worked at the Federal Narcotics Hospital in Lexington, Ky., testified that he knew of no one who had been admitted to mental hospitals in this country "solely because of problems associated with marijuana use."

And Dr. Fort suggested that marijuana might even be useful for some agitated persons, "in that the tension they live under, the depression that they might suffer from, would be relieved or alleviated by a certain pattern of marijuana use." A pharmaceutical chemist said marijuana might have therapeutic value in medicine.

But Dr. Donald B. Louria, president of the New York State Council on Drug Addiction, testifying for the prosecution, said, "There is evidence from Morocco, where kif (a form of marijuana) is commonly smoked in excess of 10 cigarets a day, that heavy consumption is associated with a marked increase in mental derangement."

The crime question came into dispute too. A Greek police official and a physician from India said marijuana use in their nations was associated with violent crimes, dishonesty and vagrancy. But a New York sociologist, citing a three-year study of marijuana users in this country, said there was no evidence that the drug is associated with violent behavior, criminal acts or sexual promiscuity.

While the dispute over marijuana rages, enforcement of present laws is getting stiffer. The Federal Narcotics Bureau will sponsor 22 two-week seminars on narcotics and marijuana for local and state officials in 1968, double the number this year. And the trainees are going to work at home.

A $1,000 FINE

In the suburban community of Bridgewater, N.J., Det. Sgt. James Hoffman says he has arrested eight youths aged 17 to 24 in the past year on marijuana charges. One of them, an 18-year-old boy charged with possession, was fined $1,000 and put on five years probation. A second conviction could put him in jail for up to five years.

Sgt. Hoffman says he is investigating 50 students in a local high school. Much of his information, he says, comes from other students "who owe the police a favor." The sergeant adds: "A lot more are going to be picked up in the future unless parents begin cracking down on drug abuse."

Critics accuse the Narcotics Bureau of bearing down heavily on occasional users such as students who may be experimenting with the drug. But Donald Miller, counsel for the Narcotics Bureau, says only 8 of 667 persons arrested under the Federal law in 1966 were students.

"We're after the pusher, the trafficker, not the young school boy," he insists.

ENFORCEMENT TECHNIQUES

*Allan S. Morton, John Mueller, Joel Ohlgren,
Roger W. Pearson and Sheldon Weisel*

I. INTRODUCTION

Enforcement of the marijuana laws suffers from the same difficulties encountered in the enforcement of laws concerning other consensual crimes.[1] There is no victim to complain and there is little social pressure to conform to the law within the various subcultures involved.[2] The

---

[1] For a general discussion of the problems involved in enforcing consensual crimes *see* E. Schur, Crimes Without Victims (1965); L. Tiffany, D. McIntyre, & D. Rottenberg, *Detection of Crime* 208–13 (1967) [hereinafter cited as Tiffany]; Project, *The Consenting Adult Homosexual and the Law: An Empirical Study of Enforcement and Administration in Los Angeles County,* 13 U.C.L.A. L. Rev. 644, 686 (1965) [hereinafter cited as *Homosexual Project*].

[2] A subculture may be loosely defined as a "culture-within-a-culture, with its [own] distinctive values and behavior norms. . . ." E. Schur, *supra* note 1, at 85. Schur indicates that legal repression of some activities, such as homosexuality or the use of addictive narcotics, may in fact directly stimulate the creation of subcultures centered on those activities. *Id.* at 141–45. Marijuana, however, has been incorporated into the life style of existing subcultures such as those of the ghetto Negro and the Sunset Strip "hippie," rather than being the cause behind the creation of those subcultures.

Reprinted from "Marijuana Laws: An Empirical Study of Enforcement and Administration in Los Angeles County," *UCLA Law Review* 15 (September 1968): 1515–42, with the permission of the publisher.

police compensate for these difficulties by developing aggressive tech niques designed to ferret out the illicit activity, including the use of in formants, undercover operators, and field surveillance.[3]

The effectiveness of enforcement can be measured only by determin ing the ratio of arrests to violations. But the effectiveness of enforcemen of the marijuana laws is particularly difficult to determine because mari juana use is increasing so rapidly.[4] The police readily admit that tota enforcement of the marijuana laws is impossible.[5] However, the heav' penalties placed on marijuana use by the legislature plus community concern place considerable pressure on the police to close the eve widening gap between violations of the law and actual arrests. At some point increased police efficiency in uncovering violations is going to clash with court-imposed barriers on investigation.[6] The police response is pressure for relaxation of these barriers [7] and the development of means to work around them.[8] These efforts, however, have been largely inef fective. At present, the police still depend largely on fortuity in appre hending marijuana violators.

Another factor which complicates the enforcement of marijuana laws is the increased geographical range of the problem. In the past, the police could isolate particular problem areas because the traditional

---

[3] Jerome Skolnick notes that the police enjoy narcotics work because it requires skillful and efficient detective work initiated by the policeman himself. J. Skolnick, *Justice Without Trial* 117 (1966).

[4] To the extent that arrests are an indication of increased illegal activity the record is striking. During the period 1960 through 1966 adult arrests for mari juana violations in Los Angeles County increased 217% from 2,704 in 1960 to 8,564 in 1966. Juvenile arrests in the county increased from 694 in 1960 to 2,636 in 1966, a gain of 280%. Cal. Dep't of Justice, Bureau of Criminal Statistics, *Drug Arrests and Dispositions in California* 6–7 (1966) [hereinafter cited as *Dis positions* 1966].

[5] Chief Thomas Reddin of the Los Angeles Police Department admits that all the police can do is try to keep marijuana under control. L.A. Times, Dec. 4, 1967, § 2, at 6, col. 1.

[6] This results from two alien views on what should be the primary emphasis of the criminal process. The police believe the process should be geared to ef ficiency in the discovery of those violating the law. The courts, interpreting the law, emphasize the rights of an individual to be free from certain police tactics even if this means a reduction in police efficiency. *See* Packer, *Two Models of the Criminal Process,* 113 *U. Pa. L. Rev.* 1 (1964).

[7] Police pressure resulted in the passage of a new evidence code section allowing the judge discretion in deciding whether to require the police to reveal their in formant where probable cause to arrest or search is the sole issue. *Cal. Evid. Code* § 1042 (West 1965). *See* State of California, *Final Report of the Special Study Commission on Narcotics* 43–47 (1961) [hereinafter cited as *Special Study*].

[8] This does not necessarily mean illegal actions by the police, but includes tech niques not prohibited by law designed to circumvent informant disclosure or probable cause requirements. *See* Section IV *infra.*

users were Mexican-Americans, Negroes, and "artists" who lived within particular areas.[9] Now, the rapid increase in use among 15 to 24-year olds[10] has spread the problem far beyond its traditional neighborhoods,[11] and there are no longer any local police agencies which deny having a marijuana problem.[12]

Arrest reports probably do not give an entirely accurate picture of the relative use of marijuana in particular areas. For example, although there are considerably more arrests in the Hollywood area than in West Los Angeles,[13] the difference may not be due entirely to greater incidence

---

[9] *See* testimony of Luke McKissick, in *Hearings on Marijuana Laws Before the Cal. Senate Pub. Health & Safety Comm.*, Oct. 18, 1967, at 87 [hereinafter cited as *Hearings*]. The percentage of adults arrested for marijuana offenses in Los Angeles County of Negro descent has remained fairly constant during the period from 1960 to 1966. In 1960, 33.6% of adult arrestees were Negro; in 1966, the figure was 31.0%. However, the corresponding figures for Whites and Mexican-Americans have changed significantly. In 1960, the percentage of arrestees who were White was 44.3%; in 1966, 53.6%. During the same period the equivalent percentages among Mexican-Americans declined from 21.0% to 14.6%. Compare *Dispositions* 1966, *supra* note 4, at 56, *with* Cal. Dep't of Justice, Bureau of Criminal Statistics, *Narcotic Arrests and Their Dispositions in California* 17 (1960).

[10] This age grouping represents a consensus drawn from responses of local enforcement agencies when asked what age group was primarily responsible for the increase in marijuana arrests.

[11] The traditional marijuana problem areas were the Watts area with its high Negro population, the East Los Angeles area with its high Mexican-American population, and the Hollywood and Venice areas with a high percentage of "artists" and fellow-travelers as residents. While these areas still provide the most arrests, there has been a spectacular increase in arrests, particularly among juveniles, in the traditionally respectable White middle-class areas. For example, the Covina Police Department reports a 700% increase in arrests within a one year period (1966–67). This is a fairly typical suburban community.

Juvenile arrests also increased dramatically in two Los Angeles Police Divisions located in the predominately White San Fernando Valley. Arrests by the West Valley Division went from 32 in 1965 to 430 in 1967 while arrests by the Van Nuys Division increased from 28 in 1965 to 278 in 1967.

Lieutenant William Pettit of the Manhattan Beach Police Department estimates that 30% of the students of Manhattan Beach High School have tried marijuana. Interview in Manhattan Beach, Jan. 16, 1968 [hereinafter cited as Pettit Interview]. Attorney Marvin Cahn makes a similar estimate of 90% of the students at Hollywood High School. Interview in Los Angeles, Jan. 3, 1967 [hereinafter cited as Cahn Interview]. In a recent poll of students at UCLA, 3377 of the 9589 responding claimed to have tried marijuana at least once. UCLA Daily Bruin, Jan. 4, 1968, at 3, col. 3.

[12] Of the enforcement agencies responding, the percentage of marijuana arrests to total arrests ranged from 1% in Culver City to 16% in Pasadena. Pasadena has a separate narcotics unit which may account, in part for the higher percentage.

[13] Of the 738 adult arrests studied, 90 were made by the Hollywood Division of the Los Angeles Police Department and 13 by the West Los Angeles Division. In 1967 (through November) 368 juveniles had been arrested by the Hollywood Division as compared with 228 by the West Los Angeles Division.

of marijuana use in Hollywood. Part of the difference may be due to heavier police patrols in the Hollywood area, and part to the overt use of marijuana by the "hippie-type" youth in Hollywood (as opposed to more covert use by the student and young adult population of West Los Angeles).

Given the current spread of marijuana use, both numerically and geographically, and the limitations placed upon investigatory techniques, the primary means of increasing the percentage of apprehensions is to devote more manpower to the task. However, the investigation required to uncover consensual activities such as marijuana possession and sale requires great amounts of time [14]—time which must be taken away from the investigation of other more violent crimes. This time commitment, along with the other social costs involved, should reflect a rational measure of the comparative importance of present marijuana laws.

II. THE DISTRIBUTIONAL SYSTEM

Los Angeles is a distribution center from which marijuana flows to the rest of the country.[15] Over 90 percent of the marijuana in Los Angeles County is grown in Mexico [16] and about 72 to 80 percent of this amount is shipped to Los Angeles by a group of separate, loosely knit syndicates that are organized particularly for this purpose.[17] It is purchased by Mexican-based members of the syndicate for five to eight dollars a kilogram, processed locally, and shipped over the border by plane, boat, or special vehicles known as "mules." [18] After arriving in Los Angeles, the transporter calls a designated telephone number for

---

[14] *See* J. Skolnick, *supra* note 3, at 139. Not only is this time spent on patrol and investigation, but it includes time spent by the police in court pursuant to a marijuana prosecution. Police responses indicated that the successful prosecution of the average marijuana case requires from four to eight hours of court attendance by the arresting officer.

[15] The Van Nuys News and Valley Greensheet, Sept. 12, 1967, at 16-a, col. 5 (central ed.).

[16] *Special Study, supra* note 7, at 19.

[17] The bulk of the information presented in this section was obtained from an interview with Mr. John Warner, Field Supervisor of the California Bureau of Narcotic Enforcement, in Los Angeles, Jan. 9, 1967. His assertion that continuing operations account for most of the imported marijuana is disputed by others, including attorney Marvin Cahn and sociologist Jerry Mandel. They claim that marijuana is too bulky and the eventual profit too low to make a continuing organization possible. Cahn Interview, *supra* note 11. Mandel, *Myths and Realities of Marihuana Pushing,* in *Marihuana Myths and Realities* 58, 76 (J. Simmons ed. 1967).

[18] The "mule" is an ordinary truck or automobile which has been specially outfitted to transport up to 1100 kilograms of marijuana.

instructions. He is told to deposit the cargo in a particular spot, such as a service station restroom, or he may be told to park the vehicle on a side street where the dealer will pick it up later. At no point is there any contact between the transporter and the stateside dealer.[19] Once the dealer receives his shipment he "stashes" it in a concealed place. The stash is later divided into smaller quantities for distribution to local pushers or for transportation out of Los Angeles.

Marijuana not shipped by these syndicates comes across the border in the possession of small-scale pushers, usually individuals who have purchased the marijuana primarily for their own use and who bring back some extra to make a small profit by selling to their friends.

The last link in the distributional chain is the pusher. In the past, most marijuana use was in heavily patrolled low income areas where the pusher had a firsthand knowledge of police procedures. With the currently expanding market, however, the dealers have recruited "amateurs" from middle or upper income areas [20] whose previous contact with the police has been minimal and who are thus less circumspect in their dealings.

There is some dispute whether marijuana pushers also sell heroin and other hard narcotics. Some enforcement agencies, notably the Federal Bureau of Narcotics, claim that the marijuana pusher often switches to selling heroin.[21] However, this claim is disputed by defense attorneys and other enforcement agencies who state that marijuana is usually sold exclusively.[22] The claim of exclusivity is supported by the negative connotation heroin has to the marijuana user and pusher. Heroin users form a separate subculture and rarely come into contact with casual marijuana users.[23] There appears, however, to be an increasing connection between the use of marijuana and the use of pills, such as the

---

[19] The precautions are so elaborate that the transporter may park an empty car, observe who gets in it and follow him to be sure he isn't a police plant. Warner Interview, *supra* note 17.

[20] This is necessary because a successful pusher must be integrated into the community in which he sells. Narcotics users will seldom buy from a total stranger and few experienced pushers desire to sell to total strangers. The new breed of pusher is typically a student, who started as an occasional user and began picking up extra money by selling to acquaintances.

[21] Interview with an agent of the Federal Bureau of Narcotics, in Los Angeles, Mar. 19, 1967 [hereinafter cited as FBN Interview].

[22] Cahn Interview, *supra* note 11; Interview with Luke McKissick, Attorney, in Hollywood, Mar. 13, 1968; Warner Interview, *supra* note 17.

[23] Interviews with enforcement agencies indicate that, even in areas where there is a high incidence of both marijuana and heroin use, undercover agents are advised to deal in one drug or the other, since an agent buying both heroin and marijuana would be suspect.

amphetamines, particularly among juveniles.[24] Since both pills and marijuana are used by the same groups for similar purposes, it is reasonable
to infer that the same pushers may be supplying them both.

III. ORGANIZATION AGAINST THE PROBLEM

Each law enforcement agency concerned with marijuana is organized
to combat a particular aspect of the overall narcotics flow from importation down to use: the Federal Bureau of Narcotics and the California
Bureau of Narcotics Enforcement combat the flow at the importation
and major traffic levels; the various special narcotics units of local
enforcement agencies are organized to uncover the local dealers and
pushers; and the individual patrolman has the responsibility of ap-
prehending the individual user.

The Federal Bureau of Narcotics (FBN) is vested with the broad
authority to enforce all the laws of the United States pertaining to marijuana and narcotic drugs.[25] In point of fact it is concerned only with
major traffic, its policy being to stop the flow of marijuana at its source.[26]
To accomplish this end the FBN has agents spread throughout the world
and has been the influential force behind the present international control agreements.[27] The FBN claims to work closely with local and state

---

[24] Statistics compiled on juvenile arrests in 1967 by the Los Angeles Police
Department, Juvenile Narcotics Division, indicate a rapid increase over 1966 in
both dangerous drug arrests and marijuana arrests. As of December, arrests
through the first 11 months of each year were:

	1966	1967
Dangerous Drugs	397	1062
Marijuana	1522	2910

Interviews with high school teachers indicate that the use of amphetamines and
other dangerous drugs is becoming as severe a problem as marijuana use among
high school students.

In our sample of 204 juvenile cases, 58 of those arrested had pills as well as
marijuana.

[25] 26 U.S.C. § 7607(2) (1964). As this project was being prepared, President
Johnson submitted a government reorganization plan which abolished the Federal
Bureau of Narcotics and the Bureau of Drug Abuse Control as separate agencies,
and combined them into a new organization, The Bureau of Narcotics and
Dangerous Drugs, under the Department of Justice. The reorganization became
effective April 8, 1968. Sterba, *The Politics of Pot, Esquire* 119 (Aug. 1968).

[26] FBN Interview, *supra* note 21.

[27] The present United Nations Treaty is known as the Single Convention on
Narcotic Drugs. It urges member nations to take measures to control marijuana,
but not necessarily to prohibit it. The former commissioner of the Federal Narcotics Bureau, Harry Anslinger, continually sought to keep the United Nations
committed to the position that marijuana is an addictive drug. *See* McGlothlin,
Toward a Rational View of Marihuana, in *Marihuana Myths and Realities* 191–
93 (J. Simmons ed. 1967).

agencies, but this claim is disputed by some of those agencies. They claim that the Bureau prefers to develop its own information and that it is generally uncooperative.

The California Bureau of Narcotics Enforcement is a part of the California Attorney General's Office.[28] Ostensibly given the duty of enforcing all of California's narcotics laws, its function has been narrowed by directives from the Attorney General's Office assigning it the "detection and apprehension of major traffic."[29] This Bureau depends primarily on arrestees of local agencies to supply it with information.[30]

Both the Federal and California Bureaus work with the United States Bureau of Customs and the Border Patrol in attempting to apprehend marijuana importers at the Mexican border. Border searches are a particularly useful enforcement device in view of the fact that they need not be accompanied by probable cause.[31] The border patrolmen receive instructions from state and federal agents to search particular vehicles coming over the border. This information is usually obtained from informants inside the United States.[32] The FBN also claims to get considerable cooperation from Mexican authorities.[33] The California Bureau, however, admits that it gets little assistance from Mexican officials and the FBN's claim is disputed by other commentators.[34]

The larger police departments and the Sheriff's Department in Los Angeles County have special narcotics units which concentrate on un-

---

[28] *Cal. Health & Safety Code* §§ 11100–07 (West 1964). The Code denominates the organization "Division of Narcotic Enforcement" but most people, including those within the organization, refer to it as the "Bureau of Narcotic Enforcement."

[29] The other assigned functions are to prevent the unauthorized use of licensed narcotics (which has nothing to do with marijuana since there is no authorized use for which it can be licensed) and to aid local agencies in narcotics enforcement (which the Bureau does not have the manpower to do anyway). Warner Interview, *supra* note 17.

[30] *See* text accompanying note 79 *infra*.

[31] The fourth amendment's prohibition against unreasonable searches has been held not to forbid border searches made without probable cause. The standard applied is one of mere suspicion that the vehicle might be carrying contraband goods. 19 U.S.C. § 482 (1964). *See* Carrol v. United States, 267 U.S. 132, 138 (1925); King v. United States, 348 F.2d 814 (9th Cir. 1965); Witt v. United States, 287 F.2d 389 (9th Cir. 1961), *cert. denied*, 366 U.S. 950 (1961). For a detailed discussion of border searches see Comment, *Intrusive Border Searches—Is Judicial Control Desirable*, 115 *U. Pa. L. Rev.* 276 (1966); 18 *W. Res. L. Rev.* 1007 (1967).

[32] Warner Interview, *supra* note 17.

[33] FBN Interview, *supra* note 21.

[34] Mandel, *supra* note 17, at 75. Mandel describes the various payoffs and concessions which must be made to the Mexican *Federales* to get them to show much interest in stopping the flow north.

covering local dealers and pushers.[35] In addition, these same agencies have separate juvenile narcotics divisions concerned with all juvenile offenders and with adults who supply them.[36] In the smaller agencies, responsibility for all narcotics enforcement usually lies with a couple of officers who devote only part of their time to the task.[37]

There appears to be a lack of any coordinated attack on marijuana traffic. Each of the law enforcement agencies involved operates at its designated level with only occasional contact with agencies at higher or lower levels. The California Bureau of Narcotics Enforcement does depend on local agencies for much of its information but can offer little help in return. The smaller police forces occasionally use undercover agents from the Sheriff's department and get the Sheriff's help in training their individual patrolmen. There is also some inter-agency cooperation in the chemical testing of seized marijuana for its presentation as evidence. Both the State Bureau and the smaller police forces depend on the Los Angeles Police Department or the Sheriff to do their testing.[38]

The training and selection procedures of the various narcotics units tend to perpetuate the existing bias against marijuana already present in the unit. The training is done by the present agents and the medical evidence presented is generally on the side of the anti-marijuana lobby.[39] Those individuals selected for the special units of the police must have considerable experience in law enforcement and a desire to become

---

[35] Of those agencies contacted three had special narcotics units. These were the Los Angeles Police Department, the Los Angeles County Sheriff, and the Pasadena Police Department.

[36] Interview with Sergeant Gene Zappey, Los Angeles Police Department Juvenile Narcotics Division, in Los Angeles, Jan. 11, 1967.

[37] The smaller agencies indicated that they often try to keep one man continually on narcotics matters but because of manpower shortage, this is difficult. If a large "bust" is planned practically the whole department may be used.

[38] The two tests used are the *Duquenois* and the *Bouquet* tests which indicate the presence of tetro-hydro cannabinol, the active ingredient present in marijuana, hashish, and other derivatives of the hemp plant (*cannabis sativa*). A positive result from the test is presumptive evidence that the material being tested is marijuana.

[39] Mr. John Warner of the State Bureau of Narcotics Enforcement said that he gave the lectures on the physical and psychological effects of marijuana to his trainees. The literature used in the talks is all anti-marijuana in nature. It all consists of reputable authorities, including the positions of the American Medical Association, the California Medical Association and the United Nations Committee on Drugs. In a recent speech at U.C.L.A. entitled "The Fuzz Looks at the Grass Problem" Warner concluded that marijuana is psychologically addicting, that it has many deleterious physical effects on the user, and that the use of marijuana leads to heroin addiction.

members.[40] Thus they have generally formed their attitudes prior to becoming narcotics officers.

The individual patrolman is the last link in the enforcement chain. He is responsible for the detection of the individual user. This job comes to him by default through the inability of any of the other organizations to afford the time and the manpower to actively seek out the individual user. He is given training on how to identify marijuana by sight and smell [41] and learns to recognize the characteristics of someone under the influence of the drug. As marijuana use has increased, this training has been given greater emphasis with the result that the individual patrolman has developed a heightened awareness of marijuana use. This awareness has been a partial factor in the increase in marijuana arrests.[42]

The attitudes of patrolmen toward marijuana users are harder to assess than those of narcotics agents. They are not interested primarily in narcotics and thus probably have a less definite view on marijuana. Of those patrolmen interviewed only one expressed any doubts as to the validity of the stiff marijuana laws and he stated this had no effect on his enforcement of them.

IV. METHODS OF ENFORCEMENT

A. Informants and Other Informational Sources

Before a narcotics unit can justify committing its limited manpower it must first have reliable information on which to proceed. Thus the initial and most important requirement of marijuana enforcement is the development of dependable sources of reliable information. These sources of information may be broken down into the following categories: (1) professional informants; (2) local contacts cultivated by the police who voluntarily provide frequent information concerning marijuana activity within a particular area; (3) individuals arrested for marijuana violations who cooperate in exchange for possible reduced charges or a

---

[40] For example, the Los Angeles Police Department's Juvenile Narcotics Division accepts applicants only if they have five years of service, an outstanding record, plus a strong desire to become a narcotics agent. Zappey Interview, *supra* note 36.

[41] The patrolman learns to identify marijuana by the wrapping used. "Bricks" (kilogram quantities) often come wrapped in tinfoil. "Lids" (ounce quantities) usually come in wax paper bags. "Joints" (marijuana cigarettes) look like hand-rolled cigarettes, twisted at both ends.

[42] This is a view expressed by both narcotics agents and defense attorneys. It is reasonable to assume that patrolmen more extensively trained to spot marijuana violators will be more perceptive to possible violations while on patrol.

recommendation of a lenient sentence; and (4) the occasional or one-time source of information.

1. Professional Informants.   The professional informant is the most valuable of these four sources to the local narcotics unit.[43] A good informant can make up to $50 a day in Los Angeles.[44] The pay scale is arbitrary depending on the individual agent's view of the quality and quantity of his informant's information. The only agency paying at a fixed rate is the United States Bureau of Customs which scales its compensation to the amount of marijuana uncovered by the information.[45] The narcotics officers interviewed, however, did not feel that money was the sole factor motivating the professional informant. The informant often works for the psychological feeling of importance he gets through cooperating with the police. The police try to find out the motivation of each informant, particularly with unproved sources, in order to avoid the possibility that the informant has planted the marijuana on the suspect for purposes of revenge.

The professional informant is the narcotic unit's eyes and ears within the community. A good professional will be able to provide continually reliable information used by the police for field investigation, and will often introduce police undercover agents to suspected dealers and pushers. Because of his continuing value, the police are careful to protect the professional informer's identity, a task which is hampered by the disclosure rules currently prevailing in California.

The California Supreme Court, in a series of decisions, has laid down rules requiring the police to disclose the identity of their informant whenever he is a material witness to an issue of the defendant's guilt.[46] This rule has been applied to require disclosure if the informant introduced an undercover agent to the defendant, even though the informant was not present when the illegal transaction occurred. The theory is that the

---

[43] Apparently the only agencies who pay informants are those with a separate narcotics unit. Of the nine agencies from whom information was collected, four did not pay their informants. These four were the smaller police departments without a separate narcotics unit.

[44] Interview with Sergeant George Barber, Los Angeles Police Department Narcotics Division, in Los Angeles, Jan. 10, 1967. The Los Angeles Police Department pays its informers out of a special fund budgeted for this purpose. Both the Federal Bureau of Narcotics and the State Bureau are allotted funds to pay their informers.

[45] FBN Interview, *supra* note 21.

[46] People v. McShann, 50 Cal. 2d 802, 330 P.2d 33 (1958); People v. Castiel, 153 Cal. App. 2d 653, 315 P.2d 79 (1957).

informant is aware of the defendant's identity which is a "material issue."[47]

Until 1967, the police in California were required to reveal their informant's identity whenever his information was the sole basis of probable cause to arrest or search.[48] Section 1042 of the California Evidence Code now gives the judge discretion to require disclosure under these circumstances.[49] The police officers interviewed claimed that judges usually require disclosure, while defense attorneys claimed the opposite. The police feel that the disclosure requirements have scared off many valuable professional informants, especially since police policy is to warn all prospective informants that their identity may be subject to disclosure at trial. If the police feel that the informant is particularly valuable or that his life might be in danger because of disclosure, they will refuse to identify him even though it might cost them the case.[50]

One method of protecting the informant's identity is the so-called "double duke-in" sale. The informant introduces undercover agent *A* to the suspect and then drops out of the picture. *A* makes several buys and then introduces agent *B* to the suspect. *B* makes several buys with *A* dropping out of the picture. The only sales charged to the suspect are those made to agent *B*. Although an alert defense attorney may trace back through the entire transaction, thus requiring the police to reveal their original informant, many defenders fail to probe beyond agent *A* thereby leaving the informant protected.[51]

The informant's identity may also be protected by arresting him (or the police undercover operator) along with the pusher. This decreases the possibility that the seller will be able to identify the informant as a police operative.[52]

The police claim that no immunity is granted to informants working for them. The claim is roundly disputed by defense attorneys who assert that the police allow their better informants to use marijuana without fear of arrest as long as they supply information.[53]

---

[47] People v. Durazo, 52 Cal. 2d 354, 340 P.2d 594 (1959).

[48] Priestly v. Superior Court, 50 Cal. 2d 812, 330 P.2d 39 (1958).

[49] Cal. Evid. Code § 1042 (West 1965).

[50] Barber Interview, *supra* note 44.

[51] Warner Interview, *supra* note 17.

[52] *See* Tiffany, *supra* note 1, at 258.

[53] There is little doubt that this is so with regard to heroin informants. *See* Goldstein, *Police Discretion Not to Invoke the Criminal Process: Low-Visibility Decisions in the Administration of Justice,* 69 Yale L.J. 543, 565–67 (1960). However, it seems less likely with marijuana informants since an individual does not become dependent on marijuana to the extent he does on heroin. What probably

2. *Local Contacts.*   A second source of information comes from local sources the police have cultivated who frequently come into contact with marijuana users and pushers. Through experience the police have learned that certain groups of individuals can provide reliable information about marijuana activity in a particular area and the police respond immediately to any proferred information from a member of these groups. They include prostitutes,[54] hotel and motel owners, bartenders, theatre operators, and generally any individual who deals with a transient clientele. Since these sources are not paid, their motives vary considerably: some want to curry favor with the police;[55] some are attempting to keep their establishments free of undesirables; some are genuinely concerned citizens; and others merely get a psychological kick out of participating in a police arrest.[56]

One of the most profitable of these regular sources is the school official. The juvenile narcotic units attempt to nurture a close working relationship with school principals, encouraging them to report any students under the influence of drugs and to report any suspicious individuals lurking near the school grounds.[57] The success of this police encouragement varies from school to school depending on the attitude of the individual principal. The principals of schools in smaller communities and in low income areas seem to report use of marijuana by students to the police more often than principals of higher income, urban schools, although use in some of the latter is the highest in the county.[58] It is claimed that the high school principal is also authorized to search

---

happens is that the narcotics unit will ignore use of marijuana by one of its informants as long as he is working for it. But if he is arrested separately by an individual patrolman, he is not given immunity.

[54] The information from prostitutes comes by way of the vice squad. Some attorneys claim that the police let prostitutes operate unmolested in return for narcotics information. The police, of course, deny this. Jerome Skolnick indicates that the police are willing to trade the arrest of a common prostitute for the arrest of a marijuana pusher, since the pusher has a higher moral culpability in the policeman's eye. J. Skolnick, *supra* note 3, at 118.

[55] Most owners of public establishments feel that it is smart to stay on the good side of the police by scrupulously avoiding any reputation of catering to a questionable clientele, which might result in the loss of their licenses.

[56] The police find that after turning in someone, the informant will often insist on being on the scene to witness the arrest. Participating in a live arrest gives an informant a feeling of importance which is psychologically gratifying. Barber Interview, *supra* note 44.

[57] The school officials usually call in directly to the juvenile narcotics office and the juvenile officers will give official advice on how to handle an unruly student, until the police arrive. Zappey Interview, *supra* note 36. Out of 110 juvenile arrest reports studied, eight of the arrests were initiated by school authorities.

[58] Estimates of marijuana use among high school students at Palos Verdes High (an upper-class Los Angeles suburb) range from 50% to 75% of the student body. *Time*, Aug. 30, 1968, at 44.

student lockers [59] and the police encourage this as a means of uncovering marijuana. However, while school authorities are likely to report the student who comes to class obviously under the influence of narcotics, they apparently do not fully exercise their authority to search lockers.[60]

3. Arrestee Informants.   A third type of informant is the arrestee who cooperates with the police in an attempt to obtain a recommendation for leniency from them. There is no lack of such potential cooperators since the first reaction of most marijuana arrestees is to ask what they can do to get off.[61] The police claim not to make any specific promises, but they do tell the arrestee that any assistance he gives will be reported to the district attorney or the probation officer and thus to the court. The police generally will not release an individual merely because he has promised to cooperate with them; he must first make bail.[62] Once out of jail the would be informant is on his own. He is told only to let the police know when he can give them some positive assistance. Such assistance requires that the arrestee inform against somebody who is actually selling marijuana and usually someone who is more than a minor pusher.[63] The arrestee is told that the more information he gives the better it will go for him. This practice has aroused much criticism since it places pressure on young arrestees to inform on their friends.[64] The

---

[59] This was the claim of the juvenile narcotics authorities. In actuality, there is no specific authorization for such a search under rules set down for the administration of the Los Angeles City Schools; but since there is no prohibition against it, the authority is assumed.

[60] A check with principals in the West Los Angeles area indicated that none of them ever search their students' lockers.

[61] The police claim that they do not bring up the subject of "finking"; they only respond when an arrestee asks if he can do anything to help his case. However, defense attorneys claim that arrestees who are believed to have valuable information are encouraged by the police to cooperate. This is more likely to happen in small towns where the police have no special narcotics unit and where any one arrestee may be able to tie the police in with most of the marijuana activity in town.

[62] This is the announced policy of the Los Angeles Police Narcotics Unit.

[63] This would follow from the claims of the narcotic units that they are interested only in the professional pusher or dealer. Defense attorneys, however, claim that the police will try to get the arrestee to "turn" anyone he knows. It is possible that this happens in some of the smaller cities where the local police may view any use of marijuana as a serious offense. One of the defense attorneys interviewed had an affidavit taken from a 19-year-old arrested by a small southern Los Angeles County community. The youth claimed he had been required to "turn" several of his friends, none of whom were regular pushers, in return for police recommendation of a reduced sentence. Cahn Interview, *supra* note 11.

[64] The pressures placed on arrestees to cooperate can be extremely severe in the hands of some police. For example, the police can threaten the arrestee with exorbitant bail if he does not cooperate. *See* testimony of Luke McKissick, in *Hearings, supra* note 9, at 78.

police tend to obtain as much information as possible from such an informant before giving any favorable recommendation. The Federal Bureau of Narcotics, for example, requires that the arrestee set up a transaction between the police and the individual on whom he is informing before it will give any recommendation. Such an initial "turn" by the arrestee may start a chain of successive arrests followed by more "turns" leading eventually to the ultimate desired end, the apprehension of a major dealer.

The arrestee informant is employed by the police in a variety of ways to initiate the transaction necessary for an arrest for the sale of marijuana. The informant will introduce an undercover agent to a pusher or will make the buy himself. The latter method, called a "witness sale," requires the informant to be stripped and searched, sent to make the purchase, and stripped and searched again when he returns. This procedure prevents any possible frameup by the informant or any successful challenge in court when the marijuana is sought to be admitted as evidence.[65] The police maintain as close a surveillance as possible at all times during the sale, often through the use of field glasses in an adjoining building, or through the use of an electronic eavesdropping device attached to the informant.[66]

The police will often use a witness sale to provide probable cause for a subsequent search of the seller's apartment, rather than charging him with that particular sale. There are two possible reasons for this. The first is that using the information solely for probable cause permits the judge to exercise his statutory discretion to protect the informant's indentity, which he could not do if the informant was a material witness to the sale.[67] The second reason is that the judge may be less sympathetic to a possible claim of entrapment against the informant where the only issue is probable cause.[68]

The police allow the arrestee informant to set up buys [69] without supervision.[70] The possibility of entrapment here is greater than where

---

[65] The use of women informants is inconvenient for this purpose since the vagina can be used as a hiding place. Thus the skin search must be done with female personnel. Tiffany, *supra* note 1, at 255.

[66] Barber Interview, *supra* note 44.

[67] There is still a possibility, however, that the informant may be held to be a material witness to the defendant's guilt. *See* text accompanying note 46 *supra*.

[68] It is doubtful whether the defendant can raise the issue of entrapment to defeat probable cause, since theoretically entrapment is an implied defense to the substantive crime and is therefore inapplicable when sought to be invoked to defeat probable cause. *See* text accompanying note 78 *infra*.

[69] Five of the nine agencies responding stated that they do not use cooperating informants to actually make purchases. However, these informants are used to set up transactions where an undercover agent makes the purchase.

[70] None of the agencies interviewed indicated that they gave a potential informant instruction on how to set up a transaction.

a purchase is set up by another type of informant or by a police under-cover agent. This is so for two reasons: (1) the arrestee is under great pressure to set up a transaction in order to obtain a reduced charge or a more lenient sentence; and (2) the arrestee is likely to make the pur-chase from a personal friend and use the friendship as a lever to extract a sale which the friend might not ordinarily make.

Entrapment is an affirmative defense to a criminal charge based on the rationale that the police have induced an individual into committing a crime which he would not have otherwise committed.[71] Although arrestees and any other type of informants working for the police are subject to entrapment rules,[72] the defense is an extremely hard one to prove. The defendant is required to show that the intent to commit the crime originated in the mind of the police, *i.e.,* the informant.[73] The prosecution can rebut this defense by showing a willingness on the part of the defendant to make the sale.[74] Because of the difficulties of proof involved, the doctrine of entrapment is rarely used by defense attor-neys.[75]

When the purchase of marijuana is made by an undercover agent from an on-the-street pusher, there is a sound argument for placing the burden of proof on the defendant to show lack of intent. A rigid en-trapment rule applied in this case would make the apprehension of pushers aware of the work of undercover agents extremely difficult.[76]

---

[71] Sorrels v. United States, 287 U.S. 435 (1932); People v. Benford, 53 Cal. 2d 1, 345 P.2d 928 (1959); People v. Adams, 213 Cal. App. 2d 536, 29 Cal. Rptr. 57 (1963).

[72] People v. Perez, 62 Cal. 2d 769, 775, 401 P.2d 934, 937 (1965) ("someone acting in cooperation with the authorities"). *See* Comment, *The Defense of En-trapment in California,* 19 *Hastings L.J.* 825 & n.2 (1968). The issue of just who is a police agent for purposes of applying entrapment rules has never been ade-quately discussed. Courts have treated, without discussion of their status, paid informers and those acting under promises of immunity, as government agents. *See* Donelly, *Judicial Control of Informants, Spies, Stool Pigeons, and Agent Provocateurs,* 60 *Yale L.J.* 1091, 1109 (1951).

[73] People v. Jackson, 42 Cal. 2d 540, 547, 268 P.2d 6, 11 (1954); People v. Cordero, 240 Cal. App. 2d 826, 829, 49 Cal. Rptr. 924, 926 (1966). *See* Com-ment, *The Defense of Entrapment in California, supra* note 72, at 842.

[74] People v. Sweeney, 55 Cal. 2d 27, 49, 357 P.2d 1049, 1062, 9 Cal. Rptr. 793, 806 (1960); People v. Harris, 210 Cal. App. 2d 613, 26 Cal. Rptr. 850 (1962).

[75] None of the enforcement agencies responding felt the entrapment laws were a barrier to enforcement. Out of 738 arrest reports studied, only three defendants were acquitted because of entrapment.

[76] There is probably more justification for a liberal entrapment rule in narcotics transactions than in homosexual solicitations. The narcotics laws are aimed at the availability of the narcotic and police solicitation may be the only way to elimi-nate that availability. However, homosexual laws are aimed largely at *unprovoked* solicitations and the entrapment doctrine should be applied more strictly to prevent solicitations provoked by the police. *See Homosexual Project, supra* note 1, at 701–02.

However, where an arrestee is involved, because of the intense personal pressure on him to make a purchase, the inference of preexisting intent to sell is less. In order to acknowledge this difference, the entrapment rules might be altered by placing the burden of proof on the prosecution to show preexisting intent where the purchase was made by an arrestee. Such a burden could be discharged by showing possession of a large amount of marijuana by the defendant, by having the arrestee make more than one purchase, or by other circumstantial evidence. The issue of preexisting intent is usually met by having the agent or informant make two to three purchases.[77]

It is not clear whether the defendant can use entrapment for sale to negate a separate charge of possession.[78] If not, the police have a powerful weapon since they can entrap a suspect into a sale, and even if the sale is thrown out, still successfully prosecute him for possession.

Unlike local agencies, the California Bureau of Narcotics Enforcement depends primarily on information from arrestees.[79] Although it has a limited number of regular informants, it does not have the manpower nor the proximity to the problem to develop a more extensive network. It gets cooperation from individuals it has arrested, but relies primarily upon arrestees of local agencies. The local agencies contact the State Bureau whenever they have an arrestee who has information on major traffic. Like the local agencies, the state claims that it gives no guarantees to cooperating informants.

4. One-Time Informants. The final source of information comes from random calls from people within the community. The police tend to ignore these calls unless there is some indication that the caller can provide a solid lead.[80] The police must be especially careful in this

---

[77] Barber Interview, *supra* note 44; FBN Interview, *supra* note 21; Warner Interview, *supra* note 17.

[78] Probably not, since entrapment in theory is treated as an implied defense to the particular crime for which the defendant is charged. United States v. Kaiser, 138 F.2d 219 (7th Cir. 1943), *cert. denied,* 320 U.S. 801 (1944); Donelly, *supra* note 72, at 1110. However, if it can be shown that but for the illegal police conduct (entrapment), the marijuana would not have been discovered, then it is arguable that the marijuana is "tainted" evidence and therefore inadmissible against the defendant, to show possession. *See* Wong Sun v. United States, 371 U.S. 471 (1963); Silverthorne Lumber Co. v. United States, 251 U.S. 385 (1920).

[79] Warner Interview, *supra* note 17.

[80] The police get a surprising number of calls from people who have "heard that someone down the street is smoking marijuana," from people who won't give their names, and from obvious cranks. The State Bureau gets numerous calls from sheriffs and concerned citizens of small communities who have found one of the local youths with a marijuana cigarette and demand that the Bureau do something to eradicate the problem.

situation to look for the possibility of marijuana planted by someone with a grudge to settle. One informant who is not ignored, however, is the parent who reports finding marijuana in his child's possession. This is a large source of juvenile contacts.[81]

B. Field Operations

1. Field Investigation Units. Most police forces do not have a field investigation unit because of limited manpower.[82] The Los Angeles Police Department's Special Field Investigation Unit is composed of five two-man teams, all sergeants with extensive experience in narcotics enforcement. They operate out of the Central Division and, unlike the average investigator, they do not respond to information coming into the office, but instead are engaged in continuous independent field investigation. The key to such an operation is the investigator's ability to evaluate and connect pieces of information, insignificant alone, into a picture of a major dealer and how he operates. The investigators work continuously at developing a network of reliable informants. One informant, for example, may have information that an individual is receiving and dispersing large shipments of marijuana. If this information is corroborated by other informants, the individual may be put under surveillance. If he is a major dealer, he will usually establish a systematic pattern, such as visiting places like a supermarket or a gas station with greater regularity than the average individual. While the suspect is under surveillance the investigators are continuously rechecking with their informants. After what may be an extensive period of time, the investigation will have uncovered enough information to give the investigator probable cause to make a "bust." However, the investigator will usually wait until he believes the dealer has just received a shipment in order to arrest him before he unloads it. Because of the precise timing involved, the investigators ordinarily do not obtain a search warrant.[83]

2. Undercover Agents. Most agencies at some time employ undercover agents, although many of the smaller forces borrow them for a limited period from the Los Angeles Police Department or the Los Angeles Sheriff.[84] Prior to 1950, undercover work usually invoved a

---

[81] Out of 204 juvenile arrests studied, 22 were initiated by the juvenile's parents.

[82] Of the nine enforcement agencies responding, only the Los Angeles Police Department and the Los Angeles County Sheriff had a special field investigation unit.

[83] In only 25 of the 738 adult cases studied was a search warrant used.

[84] Of the nine enforcement agencies responding, seven used undercover operators at some time. Three of these agencies—the Los Angeles Police Department, the Los Angeles County Sheriff, and the Pasadena Police Department—used their own personnel. The other four agencies occasionally used agents supplied by the Sheriff.

disguised agent making two or more purchases with marked money from a suspect, who was then arrested. This limited the use of the good undercover worker, since once the arrest was made his name became known throughout the neighborhood and his effectiveness was destroyed. In 1950, the Los Angeles Police Department organized their present "buy program" which has been widely copied by large agencies all over the country. In this program the police send an agent into the field for a period of approximately three months, during which time he makes buys from numerous individuals. None of these people are arrested until "roundup day" at the end of this particular agent's period of work. This extended period enables the agent to become integrated into the community and facilitates the apprehension of a great number of pushers.

Undercover agents are recruited directly from the police academy without any prior patrol experience. Their appearance is made to conform to that of the average narcotics user in the community they will infiltrate. Agents placed in Watts will be goatee-wearing Negroes; agents on the Sunset Strip will be young looking and dressed in hippie garb; while agents in Hollywood will often wear homosexual attire. Although some agents are instructed to uncover both marijuana and heroin pushers, this is unusual since heroin users seldom buy marijuana and such a combination of purchases would immediately arouse suspicion.[85]

The good undercover agent will attempt to become an integral part of the marijuana subculture he is infiltrating. He will hang out at the local gathering spots, go to the homes of his new found friends, and participate in "pot parties." Technically an agent who goes to a party and participates in the ritual passing around of a marijuana cigarette is as guilty as those he arrests. Of course the police never file charges against him, even though he may sometimes be arrested along with the rest of the participants to protect his identity.[86]

The key element in the "buy program" is the agent's ability to identify the pusher from whom he made his purchases. This identification is crucial to the success of the program because it provides the exclusive basis for probable cause to make the arrest, and the judicial determination that such an identification constituted probable cause hinges largely on the reputation of undercover agents for accuracy. One case of mistaken identity proved at trial might have a deleterious effect on the whole program. Thus, if there is any doubt in the agent's mind about the identity of his supplier, the police prefer to drop the case. To aid in

---

[85] *See* text accompanying note 22 *supra.*
[86] Tiffany, *supra* note 1, at 258.

identification each agent is given a thorough briefing on identifying features to look for, such as scars and tattoos. He also is required to come to police headquarters after each transaction and record the details of the sale. This document is dated and later used to corroborate the agent's testimony for purposes of probable cause or proof of the charge.

The undercover agent makes three or four buys from each pusher. He then goes through police mug books and other sources attempting to identify the pusher by name. The police obtain arrest warrants on those the agent identifies and on "roundup day" they are arrested. In order to apprehend those pushers that the agent could not identify by name, the police take the agent through the area he worked in an unmarked car. The agent points out any pusher he recognizes and usually verifies his identification by approaching the pusher and calling him by the name he used when making the sale. On the strength of this identification, the pusher is immediately arrested without a warrant. A "roundup" results in the arrest of approximately 80 percent of the individuals from whom the agent purchased marijuana.[87]

C. Enforcement Through Patrol

A third means of enforcement involves arrests of marijuana users by the patrolman or traffic officer. This category of enforcement provides the overwhelming majority of marijuana arrests, particularly those for possession. These arrests do not result from systematic attempts to uncover marijuana violators, but are a by-product of routine police investigation. In areas of high marijuana use, however, patrolmen are specifically on the lookout for marijuana users.

The patrol arrest usually occurs as a consequence of one of the following police actions: (1) the stopping of a vehicle for a traffic violation; (2) confrontation of allegedly underage juveniles for curfew violations; (3) the investigation of a loud party; and (4) the "frisk" of an individual stopped under the "stop and frisk" doctrine. The nagging question in all these situations is whether the police are truly interested in the conduct justifying the investigation or whether they are using that conduct merely as an excuse for investigating some other activity for which they have no legal basis. To the extent that the police use these procedures as a subterfuge to uncover marijuana use, they have effectively created a new "method" of marijuana enforcement.

1. Stopping of Vehicles. A large percentage of the arrests for marijuana possession results from the stopping of automobiles for minor

---

[87] Barber Interview, *supra* note 44.

traffic violations, with the subsequent discovery of marijuana either in the car or on the person of one of the passengers.[88] The most common of these stops are for a missing taillight or for an unilluminated rear license plate. The police do not have probable cause for any search of the car based on the traffic violation alone. To justify the search they must have independent evidence indicating that contraband may be found in the vehicle.[89] This requirement, however, may be waived if the driver voluntarily consents to the search.[90] It is common for many drivers to grant such consent with full knowledge that the car contains marijuana, undoubtedly because of the natural impulse to avoid arousing police suspicions.[91]

The police may avoid the necessity of searching the automobile if one of the passengers tosses marijuana out of the window of the car as it is being stopped.[92] This happens quite often as the instinctive reaction of most people is to get rid of any incriminating evidence the instant they see the red light of a police vehicle. Once they find the tossed marijuana, however, the police must connect it with one of the passengers in order to show possession.

In the absence of either consent or tossed marijuana, the police must establish probable cause to search the automobile. This may be obtained by one of the passengers making a "furtive motion," the odor of burnt marijuana coming from the car, marijuana being in plain sight inside the car, or one of the occupants of the car displaying the characteristics of intoxication associated either with alcohol or narcotic use.

The furtive motion authorizing a search usually results as the officer is pulling the car over for a minor traffic violation. The arrest reports typically state that as he shined his lights on the back of the car, the patrolman saw one of the occupants make a "furtive motion" as if to hide or throw away something. A few appellate decisions indicate that

---

[88] Out of the 658 arrests studied in which this information was available, 230 were initiated through automobile traffic violations.

[89] *See* People v. Burke, 61 Cal. 2d 575, 579, 394 P.2d 67, 69, 39 Cal. Rptr. 531, 533 (1964); People v. Terry, 61 Cal. 2d 137, 152, 390 P.2d 381, 391, 37 Cal. Rptr. 605, 615 (1964). A citation for a traffic violation of itself does not justify a search of the car. People v. Anders, 167 Cal. App. 2d 65, 67, 333 P.2d 854, 856 (1959).

[90] People v. Michael, 45 Cal. 2d 751, 753, 290 P.2d 852, 854 (1955); People v. Weire, 198 Cal. App. 2d 138, 142, 17 Cal. Rptr. 659, 661 (1961). A suspect's consent may be implied from his opening of a car door which jammed when the officer tried to open it from the outside. People v. Williams, 148 Cal. App. 2d 525, 307 P.2d 48 (1957).

[91] There were 24 consensual automobile searches among the 658 arrest reports studied in which this information was available.

[92] Out of 658 adult arrests, 38 were initiated because of marijuana being thrown out of an automobile window. *See* text accompanying notes 25–28, Part III *infra*.

something additional, such as evasive action by the driver, must be present before the police have probable cause to search.[93] Usually, however, the judge accepts the furtive gesture alone as being sufficient.[94] This provides the police officer with an almost irrefutable method to "write-in" probable cause,[95] although some attorneys have successfully gone to great lengths to prove that the officer could not have seen inside the car from his vantage point.[96] Even accepting that the policeman did see the furtive motion, however, a sudden movement inside a car is open to a variety of interpretations and references. It is thus questionable whether such a movement satisfies the high degree of probability which has been required for probable cause in other areas.

Another basis for establishing probable cause to search a stopped automobile is that the officer detected an odor of burnt marijuana coming from the car.[97] While it is true that the traffic patrolman is given brief instruction on what marijuana smells like, there is considerable dispute as to his actual ability to detect marijuana by this method. However, as in the case of a furtive motion, the policeman's testimony is usually accepted by the court as a valid basis for the search.[98]

The police also search a stopped automobile if they see marijuana in plain view inside the car. This usually occurs when the officer shines his flashlight into the automobile, ostensibly to check the car registration, and sees marijuana on the seat or on the floorboard.[99] Defense attorneys claim that many police "look for registration" throughout the car and

---

[93] People v. One 1958 Chevrolet Impala, 219 Cal. App. 2d 18, 20, 33 Cal. Rptr. 64, 66 (1963); People v. Tyler, 193 Cal. App. 2d 728, 732, 14 Cal. Rptr. 610, 612 (1961).

[94] The leading case on the matter, People v. Blodgett, 46 Cal. 2d 114, 293 P.2d 57 (1956), appears to sanction the use of a "furtive motion" as sole grounds for probable cause to search. This is the usual interpretation. *See* People v. Shapiro, 213 Cal. App. 2d 618, 28 Cal. Rptr. 907 (1963) (defendant lowered her head as if to hide something); People v. Sanson, 156 Cal. App. 2d 250, 319 P.2d 422 (1957) (police noticed defendant withdraw his left hand from seat).

[95] The suspicion that this does occur is heightened by the almost total uniformity of the arrest reports. The traffic officer appears to be aware that if he tailors his report to a certain style with certain facts, he will almost certainly have it accepted by the court.

[96] One of the attorneys interviewed took the jury outside the courtroom to view the defendant's car from the same vantage point as the arresting officer. The car was an early model coupe with a small rear window, and the attorney was able to demonstrate that no one could see a "furtive motion" through the rear window.

[97] Out of 658 arrest reports studied, there were 30 instances of the police smelling burnt marijuana.

[98] People v. One 1961 Ford Falcon, 215 Cal. App. 2d 149, 30 Cal. Rptr. 110 (1963).

[99] *See* People v. Galceran, 178 Cal. App. 2d 312, 316, 2 Cal. Rptr. 901, 903 (1960). Out of 658 adult arrest reports studied, there were 42 instances where the police discovered marijuana in this manner.

that the marijuana does not become "clearly visible" until after the police relocate it from some location which was not initially in view. Occasionally, the visible marijuana used as a basis for the search consists solely of seeds. It is questionable whether a full scale search is justified merely on this evidence alone, since marijuana seeds do not differ radically in appearance from common garden variety seeds.

Another basis for the search of an automobile is the intoxication of the driver or passengers. The arrest reports usually state that the subject was intoxicated with no odor of alcohol on his breath and that his eyes became pinpointed under light—both characteristics of one under the influence of narcotics.[100] Under such circumstances the inference of recent drug use is regarded as sufficient probable cause for a search.[101] Also, since any intoxication justifies a search, if the driver or passenger is obviously drunk the police can search the car for alcohol and if they find marijuana it can be admitted as evidence on the theory of lawful discovery.

2. Curfew Violations.   A great many juvenile arrests, and some adult arrests, result from the police stopping youthful looking pedestrians for possible curfew violations.[102] The procedure is to stop the suspect, sometimes shining a search light on him. This confrontation will often cause the person to throw away a marijuana cigarette or make a furtive motion in an attempt to hide one. In the first situation, the police merely retrieve the discarded cigarette and arrest the individual. In the situation where the individual attempts to hide the cigarette, the police have probable cause to search him. The furtive motion theory in this situation is harder to attack than when the person is in a moving automobile since the individual is totally visible and his actions are not as capable of various interpretations.

There may be a high degree of discriminatory enforcement of curfew ordinances insofar as they are used for the apprehension of marijuana users. The police know that the teenager with long hair dressed in "mod" attire is more likely to be using marijuana than the "straight" appearing youth who looks about the same age. Thus, it is tempting for the officer in an area of high marijuana use to confront the youthful

---

[100] There were 68 instances of adults being under the influence of marijuana in the 658 adult arrest reports studied. However, there were only two instances in the entire adult sample where the defendant was charged with driving under the influence of narcotics. Cal. Vehicle Code § 23105 (West 1960).

[101] People v. Di Blasi, 198 Cal. App. 2d 215, 18 Cal. Rptr. 223 (1961).

[102] Five out of 658 adult arrests and 54 out of 204 juvenile arrests were initiated by stops for suspicion of curfew violation.

"hippie" with the hope that he will find more than a curfew violation.[103]
There is also a thinly veiled hostility on the part of the average patrolman to the so-called "hippies" with their natural antipathy towards
authority of any type, including police authority.[104] It is difficult to
prove any conscious discrimination in enforcement by the police, since
they do not, of course, admit to such discrimination.

3. Complaints of Marijuana Use and Loud Parties. A third source
of arrests results from an investigation, sometimes by the narcotics division, of a complaint by a tenant or neighbor that marijuana is being
used or that there is a loud party on the premises.[105] The police usually
station one man outside a window of the residence. The others go to the
door and announce themselves as required by statute.[106] To escape arrest the residents will often toss the marijuana out of the window where
the officer is waiting. He shouts this information to the other officers
which establishes probable cause to enter the residence.[107] They also
have probable cause to enter if they hear a toilet flushing or any other
indication that the occupants are attempting to dispose of contraband,[108]
or if they observe marijuana through an open window.

If the occupants open the door without giving the police cause to
enter, the police may attempt to get consent to search the apartment.
If this is refused they still have probable cause to enter if they smell
burning marijuana.

4. Stop and Frisk. A final major source of arrests for possession is
the "frisk" performed by the patrolman under the "stop and frisk" doc-

---

[103] It is difficult for the patrolman to see anything wrong in stopping a "hippie"
type youth where he would not stop a "straight" youth under the same circumstances. An experienced patrolman realizes that the possibility of a "hippie" type
youngster possessing marijuana is much greater than a "straight" looking young
person. Therefore, he feels that the efficient way to discover marijuana violations
is to stop those likely to be committing them. The fact that the law does not
always openly sanction the officer's experience as a basis for probable cause is
another example wherein police feel that due process undercuts efficiency. *See*
Packer, *supra* note 6.

[104] The police officers interviewed made no attempt to hide their dislike of the
long haired "hippie" type. There was a particular contempt for the older hippies
(generally in their 20's) who the police believe introduce many high school age
juveniles to drug use.

[105] There were 28 instances of neighbors' complaints leading to apartment busts
in the 658 adult arrest reports studied.

[106] Police, with probable cause to arrest or with a search warrant, can break
into the premises, after they have announced who they are and their reason for
being there, if they are refused admission or if there is no answer. Cal. Penal
Code §§ 844, 1531 (West 1956).

[107] People v. Padilla, 240 Cal. App. 2d 114, 49 Cal. Rptr. 340 (1966).

[108] People v. Fisher, 184 Cal. App. 2d 308, 7 Cal. Rptr. 461 (1960).

trine. In California, an individual can be stopped for questioning as long as the prudent officer would consider such a step necessary to discharge his duties.[109]

The usual justification for the stop is the presence of the suspect late at night under "suspicious circumstances."[110] These circumstances may include individuals parked in a car in a residential area or pedestrians on foot who appear to be engaged in some sort of suspicious activity. What constitutes "suspicious circumstances" seems to depend largely on the experience of the individual officer involved. For example, one officer may consider a parked car on a dark residential street with youths inside as being suspicious. Another officer, under the same circumstances, may require an additional element before his suspicion is aroused. These highly individual judgments of the police are traditionally encompassed in general phrases such as "present under suspicious circumstances in a high crime rate area." This phrase appears time and time again in the arrest reports studied, with the judge usually accepting it as being sufficient to justify the stop.[111] There has, as yet, been no real definition of either the phrase "under suspicious circumstances" or "high crime rate area."[112]

Incidental to a valid police stop, the officer often submits the suspect to a brief "pat-down" search, known as a "frisk," for the purpose of uncovering concealed weapons. The frisk is designed solely to protect the officer. Defense attorneys, however, claim that if the officer believes he might find marijuana, the frisk strains the limits of its definition. For example, in confronting a "hippie" type youth after curfew, if the police fail to establish grounds for a full scale search, they allegedly will submit him to a frisk in which every thread of his clothing is carefully gone over. If during this frisk the police feel what appears to be a cigarette, then, depending on the circumstances surrounding the stop, they may have probable cause to reach inside the individual's pocket and extract the suspected marijuana cigarette.[113]

---

[109] People v. Mickelson, 59 Cal. 2d 448, 450, 380 P.2d 658, 660, 30 Cal. Rptr. 18, 20 (1963); People v. Currier, 232 Cal. App. 2d 103, 106, 42 Cal. Rptr. 562, 564 (1965); People v. Hilliard, 221 Cal. App. 2d 719, 723, 34 Cal. Rptr. 809, 811 (1963); People v. Ellsworth, 190 Cal. App. 2d 844, 846, 12 Cal. Rptr. 433, 435 (1961). *See* Note, *Stop and Frisk in California,* 18 *Hastings L.J.* 623, 625 (1967); Comment, *Constitutional Limitations on Pre-Arrest Investigations,* 15 *U.C.L.A. L. Rev.* 1031, 1031–46 (1968).

[110] There were 72 adult arrests out of 658 studied where the individuals were stopped because of "suspicious circumstances."

[111] *See* Comment, *Constitutional Limitations on Pre-Arrest Investigations, supra* note 109, at 1039 n.33, 1040 n.34.

[112] *But see id.* at 1040 n.35.

[113] People v. Machel, 234 Cal. App. 2d 37, 44 Cal. Rptr. 126, *cert. denied,* 382 U.S. 839 (1965). The court ruled that the circumstances surrounding the ques-

It is difficult to distinguish between a valid frisk for weapons and an alleged illegal search for marijuana under the guise of a frisk. If the recent Supreme Court "stop and frisk" decisions [114] are applied carefully by the lower courts much of this problem will be avoided. Those cases require the policeman to be able to point to particular facts that led him to believe the person was armed and dangerous. [115] In addition, the scope of the search must extend only to the extent necessary to uncover dangerous weapons. [116] But if these safeguards fail to deter the police from making searches for marijuana under the guise of a frisk for weapons, only two solutions remain. One, which is clearly undesirable, would be to do away with the frisk altogether. The other would be to refuse to admit as evidence any contraband found as a result of the frisk. [117]

V. SELECTIVE ENFORCEMENT

Selective enforcement results from conscious police decisions not to invoke the criminal process against certain classes of violators. These decisions, in marijuana enforcement, are premised on the realization that it is not possible to enforce the laws against all violators. [118] Selective enforcement of the marijuana laws, unlike that of homosexual offenses,

---

tioning and frisk of the defendant gave the police probable cause to believe he was in possession of marijuana. Those circumstances included the officer's knowledge that the defendant was a known narcotics user, the fact that the defendant came to the apartment where the officer had just arrested two other individuals for marijuana possession, the defendant's failure to answer when asked what was in his pocket, and the fact that he sweated profusely. It is unclear whether the mere feeling of a cigarette during a frisk, without the suspicious circumstances present in *Machel,* would give the police probable cause to reach inside the suspect's clothing.

[114] Terry v. Ohio, 392 U.S. 1 (1968); Sibron v. New York, 392 U.S. 40 (1968); Peters v. New York, 392 U.S. 40 (1968).

[115] Sibron v. New York, 390 U.S. 40, 63–64 (1968).

[116] *Id.* at 65.

[117] For an exposition of both sides of this argument *see* Comment, *Constitutional Limitations on Pre-Arrest Investigations, supra* note 109, at 1047–48.

The Supreme Court has yet to decide the issue of the admissibility of evidence other than weapons found through a frisk. *Peters* raised the issue, but the Court dodged it by finding probable cause for arrest. 392 U.S. at 65.

[118] Professor Joseph Goldstein of Yale divides police enforcement of any law into three levels: total enforcement, which occurs when the police successfully apprehend all violators; full enforcement, where the police actively follow every lead up to the full level of their authorization; and actual enforcement. Goldstein, *supra* note 53. Obviously total enforcement of the marijuana laws is impossible because of the extent of the problem and the legal boundaries placed on investigative techniques, such as search and seizure and interrogation. Interviews with police officials indicate a general consensus that actual marijuana enforcement operates at a level considerably below what Professor Goldstein would class as

does not appear to be conditioned on the undesirability of enforcing the laws under certain circumstances.[119]

All enforcement agencies interviewed indicated that marijuana enforcement was, by necessity, selective. This selectivity stems from police determinations regarding the necessity of uncovering one type of narcotics offense rather than another; police discretion in the geographical distribution of patrolmen resulting in de facto discrimination against some groups; police discretion in the arrest of juvenile offenders; and attempts by the police to persuade the courts to deal more severely with some individuals.

Because of manpower limitations the police must decide which type of narcotics offender they are going to place the highest priority on uncovering. This decision may vary from agency to agency. For example, one agency may place the highest value on the apprehension of a major marijuana dealer, while another agency would favor the apprehension of a heroin pusher. This type of decision is influenced by four factors: (1) the type of activity involved (*e.g.,* sale or possession); (2) the volume of the drug or narcotic involved; (3) the individuals involved; and (4) the drug or narcotic involved.

The Federal Bureau of Narcotics, the California Bureau of Narcotics Enforcement, and the police narcotics investigation units claim to be solely interested in professional marijuana importers, dealers and pushers rather than the individual user.[120] It is clear that this is true for the federal and state agencies. But some defense attorneys claim that the police special units use informants to entice ordinary users to commit sales.[121] The smaller police departments, without special narcotics squads, generally have the same priority of sale over possession, although the smaller the community, the more likely it is to respond to any reported activity.[122] The state and federal narcotics bureaus are solely interested in major traffic and do not respond to other types of leads.[123] The local units attempt to apprehend all pushers, although they are primarily interested in the regular pusher who is a consistent link in the overall traffic.[124]

---

full enforcement. This is the result of numerous factors such as manpower limitations and financial considerations, but apparently not from any reluctance to enforce the law.

[119] *See Homosexual Project, supra* note 1, at 734.

[120] FBN Interview, *supra* note 21; Warner Interview, *supra* note 17.

[121] Cahn Interview, *supra* note 11.

[122] Pettit Interview, *supra* note 11.

[123] FBN Interview, *supra* note 21.

[124] Barber Interview, *supra* note 44. Sergeant Barber indicated that less than one-third of those arrested through the efforts of a single undercover agent on the "buy" program are consistent pushers. The rest are only occasional sellers.

It is apparent that small pushers are pursued more vigorously if juveniles are involved. While both the Los Angeles Police Department's Narcotics Division and Juvenile Narcotics Division do field investigations, the latter is more likely to engage in a full scale investigation to apprehend a small scale pusher than is the former.[125]

Finally, the decision of an agency to follow up a lead may depend on whether the narcotic is heroin or marijuana and this, in turn, depends on the individual agency. The California Bureau admits that all other things being equal, it would prefer to get two ounces of heroin rather than 10 kilos of marijuana.[126] But this feeling is not shared by the majority of local police forces who generally consider marijuana an equal or greater threat than heroin.[127] In fact, since heroin comes in smaller amounts than marijuana and is easier to destroy, the police may prefer to concentrate on making marijuana arrests.[128] The attitude of the smaller police forces depends on the attitude of the individual primarily responsible for narcotics enforcement. Generally, although there are some notable exceptions, these smaller communities have little problem with heroin.

The juvenile narcotics officer likes to view himself as part policeman, part juvenile counselor. His implementation of this latter role is especially important since it affects his decision whether to exercise his statutory discretion to counsel and release an arrested juvenile, or to file a formal arrest report, requiring the juvenile to attend a hearing with a probation officer.[129] His decision will be based on how effective he believes a simple lecture to the juvenile on the evils of marijuana will be toward deterring future use.[130] The factors going into this decision are generally the same as those considered by a juvenile court judge in deciding whether to release a juvenile to his parents.[131] They include past record, family stability, school record, and general willingness to cooperate.[132] The type of case most amenable to counsel and release occurs when the parent reports the juvenile's activity and comes with him to the police station for consultation.[133] In other cases the narcotics offi-

---

[125] Zappey Interview, *supra* note 36.

[126] Barber Interview, *supra* note 44.

[127] This feeling was particularly prevalent among police forces in smaller communities where a heroin problem is virtually nonexistent.

[128] McKissick Interview, *supra* note 22.

[129] Cal. Welf. & Inst'ns Code § 626 (West 1966).

[130] Zappey Interview, *supra* note 36.

[131] *See* text accompanying note 114, Part III *infra*.

[132] Zappey Interview, *supra* note 36.

[133] Despite the alleged antipathy of minority groups toward the police, the Los Angeles Police Department claims to get as many calls from Negro and Mexican-American parents as it does from White parents. Zappey Interview, *supra* note 36.

cers will go to the juvenile's home to inform his parents of the problems and observe firsthand the potential for rehabilitation. The juvenile officer's role as a counselor might be attacked as an undesirable encroachment upon the probation officer's field of concern. But it seems desirable to avoid exposing the juvenile to the entire criminal process if it doesn't appear necessary. This may be particularly true in small communities where the police often know the juvenile personally and have a more thorough familiarity with the family situation than any probation officer could attain.[134] It is difficult to judge the effectiveness of the counsel and release since there are no accumulated statistics showing the number of juveniles released who are later arrested for drug use.

The police decision on where to concentrate their routine patrol activities, although not necessarily motivated by marijuana usage,[135] nevertheless may cause greater enforcement in one area than another. Since the majority of arrests come from routine patrolling, the heavier patrolling of areas with higher incidences of violent crime will undoubtedly result in a higher percentage of marijuana arrests in proportion to actual use than in more lightly patrolled areas. This may be part of the reason for the high percentage of Negroes and Mexican-Americans arrested.[136]

There is no evidence of any conscious discrimination against one group based solely on marijuana use, with the possible exception of the aforementioned "hippie" type youth.[137]

There is no evidence that the extent of the arrestee's marijuana involvement affects a decision whether to arrest. The police, however, often try to influence the court's disposition of convicted offenders. This is usually done by police contribution to the probation report to encourage the judge to give a stiffer sentence to the professional pusher.[138] The police may also attempt to influence the court's disposition by refusing an offer of cooperation by an individual they desire to see given a stiff sentence.[139]

---

[134] Pettit Interview, *supra* note 11.

[135] The only area where heavy police patrolling is partially attributable to marijuana usage is in the Hollywood area. The usual cause for heavy police patrolling of a particular area is a high incidence of violent crime. Barber Interview, *supra* note 44.

[136] Out of 738 arrests studied, Negroes and Mexican-Americans accounted for 402 (304 Negroes, 98 Mexican-Americans), a percentage far higher than their respective percentages of the Los Angeles County population.

[137] *See* text accompanying notes 103–04 *supra*.

[138] Barber Interview, *supra* note 44.

[139] *Id.*

COMMONWEALTH V. LEIS AND WEISS

Chief Justice Tauro's Opinion

1. Prior Proceedings

The defendants, Joseph D. Leis and Ivan Weiss, are here on appeal
from convictions in the East Boston District Court of violations of
Gen. Laws. ch. 94, s. 205, illegal possession of a narcotic drug,
and of s. 213A of the same chapter, conspiracy to violate the narcotic
drug laws of the Commonwealth. They have also been indicted for
illegal possession of a narcotic with the intent to sell it in violation of
Gen. Laws. ch. 94, s. 217B.

2. Stipulated Facts

The parties have stipulated to the following facts:

The defendants were arrested at Logan International Airport in
East Boston on March 11, 1967 by Sergeant Edmond Griffin and
members of the Boston Vice Squad when one of the defendants pre-

---

Commonwealth v. Joseph D. Leis and Ivan Weiss, Findings, Rulings and Order
on Defendants' Motions to Dismiss, Chief Justice Tauro's Opinion, Commonwealth of Massachusetts, Suffolk Superior Court, December 19, 1967. Copy provided
by John F. Burke, Executive Clerk to the Chief Justice.

sented a claims check for a trunk at an airline baggage terminal. The trunk contained fifty pounds of sand and five pounds of marijuana, which is classified as a narcotic in Gen. Laws. ch. 94, s. 197. Upon their convictions in the East Boston District Court on March 29, 1967 for violations of s. 205 and s. 213A of chapter 94 of the General Laws, each of the defendants was sentenced to one year in the House of Correction on each complaint, such sentences to run consecutively. It was further stipulated that neither of the defendants has been convicted previously for any violation of the narcotic drug laws of this Commonwealth.

3. Defendants' Motions

The defendants filed amended motions to dismiss and motions to substitute their amended motions to dismiss on August 28, 1967. The motions to substitute were allowed by this court on September 18, 1967, at which time a hearing on the amended motions to dismiss was commenced. The hearing was concluded on October 3, 1967.

The defendants claim that the statutory scheme of regulation relating to the possession, use and sale of marijuana in this Commonwealth, Gen. Laws. ch. 94, s. 197 to s. 217E inclusive, is unconstitutional because it is arbitrary, irrational and unsuited to the accomplishment of any valid legislative purpose. They further contend that it violates the defendants' rights secured to them by the Ninth Amendment to the Constitution of the United States and by the Due Process and Equal Protection Clauses of the Fourteenth Amendment. Finally, they argue that these statutes impose cruel and unusual punishments upon users, possessors and sellers of marijuana in violation of the Eighth Amendment as applied to the states by the Fourteenth.

4. Standing

Because of their convictions in the East Boston District Court for violations of s. 205 and s. 213A and also because of their indictment for violation of s. 217B, the defendants assert standing to attack the validity of the entire statutory scheme as it relates to the possession, use and sale of marijuana in this Commonwealth. In support of this contention, they rely primarily on *Griswold v. Connecticut,* 381 U.S. 479 (1965) and cases cited therein.

In Griswold, the defendants, the Executive Director of the Planned Parenthood League of Connecticut and its medical director, a licensed physician, were convicted of violating a general accessory statute for abetting the violation by a married couple of Connecticut's anti-contraception statute. In that case, the Supreme Court recognized the right of the defendants to invoke the rights of their patients to use contraceptives as a defense to the accessory charge. *Griswold,* therefore, is proper authority for the logically necessary proposition that a person charged with being an accessory "has standing to assert that the offense which he is charged with assisting is not, or cannot constitutionally be a crime." *Id.* at 481. It is not authority, however, for the proposition that a person charged with a violation of a specific section or sections of a comprehensive, statutory scheme, whose parts are legally separable, has standing to attack the constitutionality of the entire scheme. Neither is *Barrows v. Jackson,* 346 U.S. 249, (1953) which dealt with the enforcement of racially restrictive covenants in real estate transactions, authority for any such proposition.

5. Scope of Inquiry

In ruling on these motions, I limit myself to a consideration of the constitutionality of s. 205, s. 213A, s. 217B as applied and those other sections of chapter 94 of the General Laws upon which the validity of the foregoing three sections necessarily depends. I do not rule on the validity of any section of chapter 94 whose consideration is not essential to a determination of the constitutionality of s. 205, s. 213A or s. 217B as applied in the case at bar. *Bowe v. Sec. of Comm.,* 320 Mass. 230, 245–246 (1946).

6. Propriety of Proceedings

There is ample authority for raising the question of the constitutionality of a statute by means of a pre-trial motion to dismiss (quash the indictment) when the alleged defect is apparent on the face of the record. *Comm. v. Pentz,* 247 Mass. 500, (1924), *Comm. v. Oliver,* 342 Mass. 82, (1961), Gen. Laws. ch. 278, s. 17. Yet, in cases such as this, where the defect cannot be ascertained from the face of the record, the usual procedure has been to raise the objection to the statute during the course of the case in chief. However, Gen. Laws. ch. 277, s. 47A specifically states that "(a)ny defense or objection which is capable of determination without the trial of the general issue may be raised before trial by motion."

Both the Commonwealth and the defendant agreed that these motions could be heard most expeditiously in a pre-trial hearing. To have proceeded otherwise, in view of the correctly anticipated length and publicity of the hearings, would have been extremely impractical and inconvenient.

The practice of hearing motions to dismiss for constitutional defects not apparent on the face of the record, where the taking of evidence not related to the offenses charged would be necessary, was advocated in *People v. Utica Daw's Drug Co.,* 16 App. Div. 12, 225 N.Y.S. 3d 128, 4 A.L.R. 3d 393 (App. Div., 1962). There, the court, without any explicit statutory authorization, proposed that hearings on motions of this type be conducted in the same manner as pre-trial hearings on motions to suppress evidence. See Superior Court Rule, 101B; *Comm. v. Penta,* 1967 Adv. Sh. 535, 540–541.

I conclude that the instant proceedings, while unusual and possibly unique, were conducted in accordance with the law and represented the most practicable method of treating the contentions raised by the defendants' amended motions to dismiss.

7. Fundamental Rights

The defendants maintain that among the hierarchy of individual rights guaranteed by the Constitution of the United States, there are certain fundamental rights which may be abridged by the states only upon the showing of a compelling state interest. These rights encompass those "privileges long recognized at common law as essential to the orderly pursuit of happiness by free men." *Meyer v. Nebraska,* 262 U.S. 390, 399, (1923). In addition to those specifically enumerated in the Constitution, they also include the right to travel freely, to contract, to acquire useful knowledge, to marry, establish a home, raise a family, and educate children to earn a livelihood, to exercise the franchise, to read, to inquire, to teach, to associate and to privacy in one's associations. See *Meyer v. Nebraska, supra; Aptheker v. Sec. of State,* 378 U.S. 500, (1964); *Spevak v. Klein,* 35 L.W. 4140, (1967); *Griswold v. Connecticut, supra;* and cases cited at 482–483. *Harper v. Va. Bd. of Elections,* 383 U.S. 663, (1966).

Although no decision appears to have attempted to propound an all inclusive list of fundamental rights, an examination of those cases cited by the defendants indicates that only those rights are to be considered as fundamental whose continuation is *essential* to ordered liberty. In other words, fundamental rights are those without which democratic society would cease to exist. Furthermore, those rights which are recognized as fundamental are also, in many instances, closely related to some commonly acknowledged moral or legal duty and not merely to a hedonistic seeking after pleasure. No claim of any such duty which would demand the possession, use or sale of marijuana has been advanced in this case. See *People v. Woody,* 40 Cal. Rptr. 69, 394 P. 2d 813, (1964).

I conclude that the alleged rights of the defendants to possess, use or sell marijuana, which I find to be a harmful and dangerous substance, is neither essential to the preservation of ordered liberty or to the orderly pursuit of happiness by free men nor required by any commonly recognized legal or moral duty. I rule that these alleged rights do not rise to the level of fundamental rights nor fall within the periphery or penumbra emanating from such rights. Therefore, it is not necessary that a compelling state interest be shown in order to subject them to regulation under the exercise of the state's police power.

8. Extent of Police Power; Burden of Proof; Presumption of Validity; Test of Validity

The non-fundamental right to possess, use or sell intoxicating substances such as marijuana or alcohol can be regulated or even absolutely prohibited by the state in the exercise of its police power, provided such statutory restrictions are reasonably suited to achieve a valid legislative purpose. *Clark Distilling Co. v. West. Md. Rwy. & State of W. Va.,* 242 U.S. 311, (1917); *Crane v. Campbell,* 245 U.S. 304, (1917); *Hornsby v. Allen,* 326 F.2d 605, 609, (1964).

A properly enacted statute is presumed to be constitutionally valid and the burden is upon its assailants to demonstrate its unconstitutionality.

> "Unless the act of the Legislature cannot be supported upon any basis of fact that can reasonably be conceived to sustain it, the court has no power to strike it down as violative of the Constitution." *Sperry & Hutchinson v. Dir. of Div. of Necessities of Life,* 307 Mass. 408, 418, (1940).

Thus, when enacting legislation in the exercise of the state's police power, the Legislature is presumably supported by facts known to it "unless facts judicially known or proved preclude that possibility." *So. Carolina Hwy. Dept. v. Barnwell Bros.,* 303 U.S. 177, 191, (1938); *Borden's Farm Prod., Inc. v. Baldwin,* 293 U.S. 194, 209, (1934); *U.S. v. Carolene Prod. Co.,* 304 U.S. 144, 153, (1938); *Sperry & Hutchinson Co. v. Dir. of Div. of Necessities of Life, supra; Merit Oil Co. v. Dir. of Div. of Necessities of Life,* 319 Mass. 301, 305, (1946); *Coffee-Rich, Inc. v. Comm'r of Pub. Health,* 348 Mass. 414, 422, (1965).

During the course of these proceedings, there was some reference to the legislative history of our narcotic drug laws or rather, more properly, to the lack of any such complete history. While the existence of such a legislative history may be helpful in ascertaining the intent of the Legislature when construing a statute, it is not, however, essential to a determination of the points in issue in this case. The court's function in a case such as this is not to conduct an historical survey to determine the facts known or reasonably conceived to exist by the Legislature at the time of the statute's enactment. Rather, it is to determine whether facts now exist or could now be reasonably conceived to exist by the Legislature which would sustain the statute. To rule otherwise would involve the courts in the absurd position of upholding clearly erroneous statutes on the grounds that they were reasonable in the light of the state of knowledge existing at the time of their enactment and of striking down presently justifiable statutes on the grounds that the Legislature could not have known the facts necessary to sustain them at the time of their enactment.

Since legislative regulations are of continuing effect until they expire by their own terms, they are repealed or are invalidated by the courts, I rule that they should be tested according to the facts known or reasonably conceived to exist at the time of their challenge. This is especially so in view of the fact that amendments were made to s.197, as late as 1966. St. 1966, c.71, s.1, s.2.

10.   *Inclusion of Marijuana as a Narcotic*

The defendants argued that Gen. Laws. ch.94, s.197, is irrational and arbitrary insofar as it defines marijuana as a narcotic drug in the same category with such "hard" narcotics as morphine, cocaine and heroin.

The testimony elicited at the hearing from expert witnesses indicated that the term "narcotic," as currently used, is a legal term with no precise, technical meaning, and is employed to describe a varied assortment of harmful and dangerous drugs. Section 197 makes no effort to provide a generic definition of "narcotic" but resorts to definition by specific inclusion. The fundamental question with regard to such a definition, then, is whether those drugs included in it are so distinguishable from one another as to render marijuana's classification as a narcotic so arbitrary and unreasonable as to be unconstitutional.

Despite some pharmacological differences between other drugs, such as heroin, and marijuana and despite the physiological differences in their effects, most notably with regard to physical dependence, I do not find that the inclusion of marijuana in the statutory definition of a narcotic drug is constitutionally offensive. *People v. Stark,* 157 Colo. 59, 66, 400 P.2d 923, 927 and cases cited therein.

As with the other drugs included in s.197, the use of marijuana does cause psychic disorientation. It is a hallucinogenic, mind altering drug whose common usage and usual effect is to cause a state of euphoria or intoxication and which can lead to the user's habitual, psychological dependence on the drug.

The term "narcotic" is broad enough to include marijuana as well as the other drugs proscribed by s.197. The failure to include other known drugs, such as alcohol, or yet undiscovered synthetics in this category either by generic definition or specific inclusion does not make marijuana any less of a narcotic.

11. *Reasonableness of the Legislation:*

DANGERS OF MARIJUANA

This Commonwealth's statutory scheme of regulating the possession and sale of narcotic drugs, admittedly a virtual prohibition as applied to marijuana, is predicated upon the premises that its use is harmful or dangerous and that its strict regulation and virtual prohibition is a rational means of preventing the harm and damage attendant upon its use. The next and central issue would logically seem to be a determination of whether there are facts in existence or which reasonably could be conceived to exist that would sustain a legislative conclusion that the use of marijuana is harmful or dangerous.

It is my opinion, based on the evidence presented at this hearing, that marijuana is a harmful and dangerous drug.

The effects of marijuana are not readily predictable and, to a great extent, depend upon and accentuate the psychological predisposition of the user. The drug, as it is commonly used, has as its primary and, as far as I can ascertain, its only purpose the induction of a state of intoxication or euphoria. While under the influence of marijuana, a person's mental processes are disoriented; his perception of time and space is distorted; his coordination is impaired, but his strength remains undiminished. Marijuana tends to cause the user to lose perspective and to focus his attention on one object to the exclusion of all others.

The drug has a great attraction for young men and women of college age or less during the formative years when they should be gaining the education and experiences upon which to build their future lives. Furthermore, there is widespread emotional instability among the users of marijuana. The use of the drug allows them to avoid the resolution of their underlying problems rather than to confront them realistically. In addition, users naturally associate with other users, who are also likely to have emotional problems, and compound one another's difficulties. In such persons, the use of marijuana may cause temporary psychotic episodes. They develop a drug-oriented culture which is marked by a peculiar proselytism, whereby users strive to introduce non-users to the drug. Marijuana users customarily use the drug with the specific intent of becoming intoxicated. No evidence was introduced to show any significant number of persons who use marijuana to achieve a state of relaxation short of intoxication. Even the so-called regulatory process of "self-titration" is employed to attain a desired state of intoxication, not to stop short of intoxication.

A great deal of testimony was devoted to the addictive qualities of marijuana. While marijuana is not physically addictive in the sense that heroin is, it can cause psychological dependence in the user. The user can come to depend upon marijuana as a crutch and its usage becomes habitual. It is this form of addiction which modern medical experts assert is the proper definition of the term.

Given the effects of marijuana and the character of its users, the possible dangers associated with its use are clearly discernible. Its tendency to release inhibitions, both verbally and actively, and the dependence of its unpredictable effects on the disposition of the user, marijuana can be especially volatile when used by a despondent, hostile or unstable person. Its impairment of motor coordination, coupled with the retention of muscular strength and the distortion of time and space relationships, makes its use extremely hazardous among those operating machinery, especially automobiles, and among those individuals responsible for the care and custody of other persons, such as the parents of young children.

The propensity of marijuana users to concentrate on one object, while ignoring all others, leads to a loss of awareness and frustrates the formation of rational judgments by them. This narrow, subjective preoccupation of users, especially the young, with drugs and their effects can cause irreparable disruptions of education, family ties or careers whose adverse personal and social effects can last long beyond the period of actual marijuana use. Further, by centering their attention on the attainment of a state of euphoria through drug consumption, marijuana users are apt to neglect their health and that of others in their care and to submit to a life of indolence. The effects of these patterns of living are not limited to the users themselves. Ultimately, society must assume the burden created by their use of marijuana.

Much of the testimony concerned the relationship between the use of marijuana and the progression to "hard" narcotics, between its use and crimes other than violations of laws pertaining to marijuana and between its use and sexual promiscuity. There is no allegation by the Commonwealth that physical addiction to "hard" narcotics, crime and promiscuity would disappear if marijuana use were to disappear. Nor is there any claim put forth that marijuana use necessarily and inevitably leads to addiction to "hard" narcotics, crime and promiscuity in each and every case. Nevertheless, there is abundant evidence that marijuana use is closely associated with these other social evils in a great many instances. Although no definitive link of efficient causality can be demonstrated with scientific exactness at present, the coincidence between addiction to "hard" narcotics, crime and promiscuity is too great to be passed off as merely accidental. The defendants answer that the fault lies not with the nature of the drug but rather with the user and his environment. Admittedly, in such complex and intertwined social problems, no one factor can be singled out as the sole efficient cause. Yet, it is reasonable in the light of facts now known to conclude that the use of marijuana contributes to "hard" narcotic addiction, crimes other than those related to the violation of the marijuana laws and sexual promiscuity. Furthermore, if the fault does lie with the instability of the persons prone to use marijuana, it would seem that this fact would lend added support to the laws prohibiting its use.

REGULATION VS. PROHIBITION

The defendants also contend that the prohibition of marijuana exceeds the power of the Legislature, that marijuana should be regulated, as is alcohol, not prohibited. This argument merges with the contention that our narcotic drug laws, as applied to marijuana, constitute a denial of the equal protection of the laws and will also be dealt with further in conjunction with that latter contention. However, the state may, in the exercise of its police power, absolutely prohibit the possession and use of alcohol by individuals. *Crane v. Campbell, supra.* The fact that the Legislature has chosen to regulate the use of alcohol and prohibit the use of marijuana does not deny its power to prohibit the use of marijuana. The difference in the legislative treatment of the two substances is reasonable in view of factual differences between them.

The customary use of alcohol, by the glass or bottle, is conspicuous and, thereby, susceptible of regulation and limitations regarding time, place and age. The customary use of marijuana, by smoking, is not conspicuous and is not susceptible of regulation and limitations regarding time, place and age. It can be used in public places, at work, on the streets and in vehicles without detection until its effects are manifested, whereas comparable uses of alcohol can be detected much more readily.

The social harm caused by the abuse of alcohol cannot be denied. The number of alcoholics and of highway fatalities and crimes which occur under the influence of alcohol speak for themselves, but the fact remains that alcohol has uses other than as a means of becoming intoxicated. The vast majority of alcohol users do not consume it with the intention of becoming intoxicated. It has a social value as a relaxant and, in some instances, as a therapeutic. Marijuana, on the other hand, has no generally recognized medical use and is used solely as a means of intoxication.

The history and cultural acceptance of alcohol and marijuana in this country cannot be ignored. Alcohol has been in widespread use among the general population since colonial times. It is customarily consumed with meals and on social occasions which do not center on the avowed purpose of drinking to the point of intoxication. So ingrained is its use in our culture that all prior statutory and constitutional prohibitions of its use have failed. Marijuana also first appeared in our country during the colonial period, but its use was never widespread among the general population. As has been noted previously, its use is not associated with any purpose other than to become intoxicated. Nor has its use become so ingrained in our culture as to make laws strictly prohibiting its use impractical.

In view of the undesirable effects attendant upon the use of marijuana, the state has not exceeded its authority or acted arbitrarily and unreasonably by prohibiting the use, sale and possession of marijuana, a harmful and dangerous drug, while merely regulating the use, sale and possession of alcohol, which is also capable of serious abuse.

The defendants maintain that the narcotic drug laws, as applied to marijuana, are not wholesome and reasonable, as required by the Constitution of Massachusetts, Pt.2, C.1, S.1, Art.4, in that they are criminogenic. Such an assertion by itself begs the question. Any statute which prohibits certain acts is criminogenic insofar as the commission of the prohibited act constitutes a crime. However, the defendants do raise a worthwhile point. They claim that the link between crime and marihuana use occurs because the marijuana user must resort to criminals for his supply and that this contact leads to involvement with other criminal activity. There is undoubtedly some truth in this statement. However, much of the criminal and anti-social activity of marijuana users undoubtedly arises from the instability of the user and the effect of the drug itself as well.

The Legislature is faced with a dilemma. It knows from past experience with alcohol that the prohibition of marijuana will create problems. It also knows that the toleration of the use of marijuana, even with regulation, will also create problems. The Legislature must balance and weigh the evils attendant upon prohibition against those attendant upon the toleration of its regulated use. I cannot say that the provisions of Gen. Laws. ch.94, s.197 to s.217E inclusive, as applied to marijuana, are not "reasonable and wholesome."

UNREASONABLE BROADNESS OF DEFINITION

The defendants also maintain that the statutory definition of marijuana is too broad and, therefore, arbitrary and irrational in that it prescribes the possession or sale of parts of the female cannabis plant which do not contain the hallucinogenic ingredient of marijuana, tetrahydrocannabinol, as well as the harmless male plant and other harmless species of the cannabis plant. However, there was undisputed testimony that it would take an expert to distinguish marijuana from other processed parts of the female, marijuana-producing plant or of the male plant or of other harmless varieties of the cannabis plant. This broad definition is necessary to provide for effective enforcement. The extension of the definition of marijuana in Gen. Laws. ch.94, s.197 to include all of the female plant, the male plant and harmless varieties of cannabis is not arbitrary and unreasonable. If the definition were contracted to cover only those specific portions containing the hallucinogenic substance, the enforcement of the statute with regard to marijuana would be a practical impossibility.

In their argument, the defendants set up the hypothetical situation of an individual's being prosecuted for a violation of s.213A because, unknown to him, harmless varieties of cannabis sativa grew wild on his property. I have never heard of such a case. Nor is any justiciable question in this regard raised in the case at bar. Therefore, I decline to rule on the constitutionality of s.213A and s.197 as applicable to such circumstances. *Bowes v. Secretary of the Commonwealth,* 320 Mass. 230, 245 (1946).

MEDICAL USE OF MARIJUANA

The defendants allude to the problems confronted by physicians in deciding whether they may employ a narcotic without violating the narcotic drug law. The statutes, Gen. Laws. ch.94, s.197, s.199F, s.201 and s.205, cover this area. While these problems may be real, they are not relevant. The case at bar presents no justiciable issues involving the medical, instructional or experimental use of marijuana. Therefore, I also decline to rule on the validity of these sections as applied to such uses of marijuana.

12. Equal Protection

The defendants also argue that the diverse statutory treatment of alcohol and marijuana constitutes a denial of the equal protection of the laws in contravention of the Fourteenth Amendment to the Constitution of the United States. However, the evidence produced at the hearing established that, while both substances are dangerous, there is a factual difference between alcohol and marijuana which would sustain the different treatment accorded each by the Legislature.

Attempts to compare the dangers and evils associated with these two substances are both medically irrelevant and illogical. The ordinary user of marijuana is quite likely to be a marginally adjusted person who turns to the drug to avoid confrontation with and the resolution of his problems. The majority of alcohol users are well adjusted, productively employed individuals who use alcohol for relaxation and as an incident of other social activities.

The defendants' equal protection argument would fall even if marijuana's nature and effects could not be distinguished from those of alcohol. They rely on *Skinner v. Oklahoma,* 316 U.S. 535 (1942), in which the Supreme Court invalidated a state statute providing for the sterilization of "habitual criminals," a definition including the defendant chicken thief but excluding other criminals, such as embezzlers. There, the Court stated that "when the law lays an unequal hand on those who have committed intrinsically the same quality of offense . . . it has made as invidious a discrimination as if it had selected a particular race or nationality for oppressive treatment." *Id.* at 541. The defendants also cite *McLaughlin v. Florida,* 379 U.S. 184 (1964), in which the Supreme Court invalidated a statutory prohibition of cohabitation between members of different races.

Neither *Skinner* nor *McLaughlin,* in which the denial of equal protection was an intrinsic element of the statutes in question, and which concerned basic rights, can be interpreted as exceptions to the general rule "that a state may direct its law against what it deems the evil as it actually exists without covering the whole field of possible abuses, and it may do so none the less that the forbidden act does not differ in kind from those that are allowed" *Central Lumber Co. v. So. Dakota,* 226 U.S. 157, 160 (1912). The state may reach out and treat certain evils without dealing with every related evil. See *N.L.R.B. v. Jones & Laughlin Steel Corp.,* 301 U.S. 1, 46 (1937); *N.Y. ex rel. Bryant v. Zimmerman,* 278 U.S. 63 (1928); *Whitney v. California,* 274 U.S. 357 (1926). A court cannot condemn the Legislature's failure to act in one area by invalidating prohibitions it has enacted in other similar or related areas. It would seem apparent that, if the Legislature is free to prohibit one activity and ignore another similar or related activity, then *a fortiori,* it may prohibit one and regulate the other.

The defendants attempt to rationalize this line of cases by arguing that they focus on kinds of behavior among which the Legislature is free to choose, while the essence of the marijuana-alcohol dichotomy is that the Legislature has proscribed the behavior of one class, those who use marijuana as their intoxicant, and tolerates the behavior of another class, those who use alcohol as their intoxicant. There are several defects in this argument. First of all, the law does not permit voluntary intoxication by means of alcohol. Gen. Laws. ch.272, s.44–48. Secondly, as has been stated previously, there are substantial differences between the usual users of alcohol and of marijuana. In light of the prevailing patterns of use of the two drugs, it is fair to characterize marijuana as an intoxicant and alcohol merely as a potential intoxicant. The Legislature might properly conclude that the consequences of the use of the two drugs are distinguishable and that alcohol is susceptible to regulation and marijuana is not.

In a certain sense, all penal statutes are discriminatory. They differentiate between those who engage in the proscribed forms of behavior and those who do not, but such discrimination is not vulnerable to attack under the Equal Protection Clause if any state of facts can reasonably be conceived to justify it. See *Comm. v. Chamberlain,* 343 Mass. 49 (1961); *Connors v. Met. Dist. Water Supply Comm'n,* 314 Mass. 33 (1943). On the other hand, a statutory discrimination must be found to be arbitrary unless it is based on some distinction bearing a substantial relationship to the purpose of the legislation. *Russell v. Treas. & Rec'r. Gen'l.* 331 Mass. 501 (1954); *Comm'rs of Corp. & Taxation v. Cooperative League of America,* 246 Mass. 235 (1923); *Lindsey v. Nat'l Carbonic Gas Co.,* 220 U.S. 61 (1910). I rule that the Legislature was warranted in treating alcohol and marijuana differently.

13. Cruel and Unusual Punishment

The defendants have raised the contention that the penalties attached to violations of Gen. Laws. ch.94, s.205, s.213A and s.217B constitute cruel and unusual punishments in violation of the Eighth Amendment to the Constitution of the United States and, presumably, in violation of the Declaration of Rights of the Constitution of Massachusetts, Pt.1, Art.26.

A somewhat analogous case, *People v. Stark,* 157 Colo. 59, 400 P.2d 923 (1965), considered the same contention.

> "With reference to the argument that the several offenses defined in the statute are punishable by 'cruel and unusual punishments' we hold that until some person has been convicted of a crime and a sentence has been imposed which is then asserted to be 'cruel and unusual' there is no justiciable issue presented. . . . Where there is a wide spread between the minimum and maximum punishment, whether any punishment is 'cruel and unusual' is a matter to be determined under all the facts and circumstances surrounding each offense." *Id.* at 68, 928.

Prior to sentencing, unless the minimum prescribed sentences are, in themselves, cruel and unusual, the defendants cannot be heard to say that they risk the imposition of a cruel or unusual punishment.

There is little authority to support the defendants' view, that they can raise the issue of cruel and unusual punishment at this preliminary stage of the proceedings. In *Weems v. U.S.*, 217, 349 (1909), the Supreme Court did confine its consideration to the minimum sentence for falsifying a public record in the Philippine Islands. There, however, the statute demanded a sentence of twelve years and one day in confinement at *cardena temporal,* a holdover from the Spanish penal system, under which the defendant was not only imprisoned but also forced to work at hard and painful labor in chains and without any assistance whatsoever, and subjected to absolute, perpetual civil disqualification, civil interdiction and surveillance for life upon release. Clearly, even this minimum sentence was cruel and unusual, and Weems had, in fact, been sentenced to 15 years at *cardena temporal.*

The defendants raise another argument, based on *Robinson v. California,* 370 U.S. 660 (1962), which should also be considered. In that case, the Supreme Court held that the punishment of the mere status or condition of being a narcotics addict, a sickness and not a crime in the Court's view, was cruel and unusual. *Robinson* would only be applicable if the legislation in question and as applied prohibited and penalized the status or condition of being a narcotics addict. See also *U.S. ex rel. Swanson v. Reincke,* 344 F.2d 260 (2nd Cir., 1965) cert. den., 382 U.S. 869 (1965). *Robinson,* however, is restricted to a condemnation of statutes punishing status, conditions or disease as contrasted to acts, such as use, sale or possession. Even if *Robinson* were to be extended to cover those acts constituting or compelled by the status, condition or disease, the expert witnesses have testified, without exception, that there is no status, condition or disease involved in the use of marijuana, that is, it does not cause physical addiction. Moreover, the violations with which the defendants have been charged include possession with intent to sell marijuana, Gen. Laws. ch.94, s.217B, and conspiracy to violate the narcotic drug laws of the Commonwealth, Gen. Laws. ch.94, s.213A, which involve no question of status, condition or disease, even though possession might if it could be shown that marijuana is physically addictive.

Defendants further contend that the penalties are excessive in relation to the seriousness of the offenses with which they are charged and also in relation to similar offenses regarding "hard" narcotics and alcohol. These contentions are closely related to the issues of equal protection and arbitrary classification previously discussed. The defendants attempt to read into the Eighth Amendment the proposition that punishments must not only be graduated and proportionate with regard to the particular offense charged but also in relation to penalties for other offenses. There is scant authority for such a proposition.

Weems v. U.S., supra, appears to be the only decision of the United States Supreme Court that even approaches such a result. However, *cardena temporal* for the falsification of a public record, unlike mere imprisonment for a term of years, was there viewed as so barbaric, indecent and conscience-shocking as to be classified as a cruel and unusual punishment in the abstract.

In *Gallego v. U.S.,* 276 F.2d 914, (9th Cir., 1960), the court upheld a statute imposing a minimum five year prison sentence without suspension or probation for the first offense of illegal importation of marijuana. The statute was held not to "exhibit an inclination to visit upon offenders such as appellant a penalty so out of proportion to the crime committed that it shocks a balanced sense of justice." *Id.* at 918. See also *U.S. ex rel. Swanson v. Reincke, supra,* which clearly distinguishes both *Weems* and *Robinson.*

The right of the Legislature to impose apparently disproportionate penalties so long as they are not wholly arbitrary or unreasonable was upheld in *Williams v. Oklahoma,* 358 U.S. 576 (1958) in which the defendant claimed that the imposition of a death penalty for kidnapping was disproportionate in relation to a previously imposed life sentence for the murder of his victim.

> "But the Due Process Clause of the Fourteenth Amendment does not, nor does anything in the Constitution, require a state to fix or impose any particular penalty for any crime it may define or to impose the same or 'proportionate' sentences for separate and independent crimes." *Id.* at 586.

In short, as is succinctly stated in the twin cases of *Schultz v. Zerbst,* 73 F.2d 668 (10th Cir., 1934) and *Sansone v. Zerbst,* 73 F.2d 670 (10th Cir., 1934):

> "The fixing of penalties for crime is a legislative function. What constitutes an adequate penalty is a matter of legislative judgment and discretion, and the courts will not interfere therewith unless the penalty prescribed is clearly and manifestly cruel and unusual." *Id.* at 670, 672. See also *People v. Stark, supra.* at 68, 928.

The minimum penalty for unlawful possession of marijuana is a fine of not more than $1,000.00 or a term of imprisonment of not more than 3½ (three and one half) years in the state prison or not more than 2½ (two and one half) years in a jail or house of correction. Gen. Laws. ch. 94, s. 205. The minimum penalty for conspiracy to violate the narcotic drug laws is a fine from $500.00 (five hundred) to $5,000.00 (five thousand) dollars or imprisonment for not more than 5 (five) years in the state prison or not more than 2 (two) years in a jail or house of correction. Gen. Laws. ch. 94, s.213A. The minimum penalty for the first offense of illegal possession of marijuana with the intent to sell it is a term of imprisonment in the state prison of no less than 5 (five) nor more than 10 (ten) years. Gen. Laws. ch. 94, s.217B. For subsequent offenses, the term of imprisonment is from 10 (ten) to 25 (twenty-five) years. In all of these instances, except for the second and subsequent offense of possession with intent to sell, the execution of the sentence may be suspended and parole and probation may be granted. The penalties provided for in Gen. Laws. ch. 94, s.205, s.213A and s.217B, as applied to the stipulated facts of this case are not unconstitutional as being cruel and unusual.

14. Protection of Privacy

According to the defendants, the enforcement of the virtual prohibition of the possession, use or sale of marijuana must necessarily entail unreasonable invasions of privacy by the police. Although this problem was discussed in *Griswold v. Connecticut, supra,* the holding of that case is not predicated on any invasion of privacy by police searches for evidence of the crime but rather on the absence of the state's authority to interfere with marital relations without a compelling reason.

That marijuana may customarily be used in the privacy of the home does not preclude the prohibition by the state of its use. "Crime, even in the privacy of one's quarters, is, of course, of grave concern to society, and the law allows such crime to be reached on proper showing." *Johnson v. U.S., 333* U.S. 10, 14. Thus, the citizen's right to privacy is not to be protected by excluding otherwise criminal conduct from regulation as long as it is confined to the home, but rather by a strict adherence to the statutory and constitutional provisions relating to the power of the police to arrest and search and of the courts to issue warrants. Furthermore, there is nothing in the allegations or stipulated facts of this case which raise any justiciable issue on this point.

CONCLUSION

To my knowledge, this has been the most extensive, judicial inquiry into the legal and factual aspects concerning the use of marijuana. At this hearing, many eminently well qualified experts on the subject from here and abroad have had their opinions subjected to searching cross-examination and careful analysis by learned and thoroughly prepared counsel. One of the principal factual issues presented for determination is whether marijuana is a harmful and dangerous drug.

Several legal issues are raised by defendants' motion to dismiss, but basically this is the question which requires an answer.

I found the testimony of the experts in the various branches of science very illuminating and helpful—although often controversial. On the other hand, there were areas of agreement among them, which are delineated elsewhere in this decision.

Of grave and immediately apparent importance is the growing appeal marijuana has for young people of high school and college age and for those having underlying instabilities or personality disorders of varying degrees. In many instances, the ones least capable of coping with the mind altering effects of the drug are the ones most likely to be adversely affected by its use.

The serious effects of marijuana superimposed upon mental and personality disorders have been described at length and in great detail by competent experts. I find this testimony persuasive. Actually, there is little, if any dispute, in this area between the defendants' experts and the Commonwealth's experts. Furthermore, all of them testified that they do not advocate the use of marijuana.

In its application to youngsters of high school and college age, the problems presented by the use of this drug assume tremendous proportions. There is no persuasive evidence that its use produces any beneficial results. The defense asserts that the drug causes no direct physical harm. Neither do heroin and other "hard" drugs, but few youngsters dare to experiment with these. Unfortunately, many marijuana users do not have the same apprehension or fear concerning its use, as they do of the physically addictive drugs. This, I feel, is one of the real dangers which permeates the problem. Marijuana is likely to be used, at least initially, as a lark, as an adventure without fear of serious consequences. Thus, the first and apparently innocuous step may be taken in a succession of others possibly leading to drastic results.

This phase of the problem is further complicated by those who unwittingly and perhaps unintentionally create the impression that marijuana is harmless, because it is not physically addictive. The young seize upon such utterances to rationalize their conduct.

While it is generally agreed that marijuana does not cause *physical* addiction as do heroin and the other "hard" narcotics, there was ample and compelling testimony that its use causes psychological dependence. Its users may not be driven to its repeated use by a physical craving, but they may come to resort to it habitually in order to compensate for real or imagined inadequacies or to avoid real or imagined problems. This pernicious and insidious form of addiction is sometimes the first step in the direction of the more potent or physically addictive drugs.

It is a universally accepted fact that marijuana is a mind altering drug and is used for that specific purpose. It is also a generally accepted fact that the drug has no medically recognized therapeutic value. In addition to its adverse effect on ill-adjusted persons, at best, it provides an insubstantial crutch to its user, giving him a feeling of intoxication in varying degrees. It provides a false sense of capabilities, strength and courage. This is of great importance when the drug user is faced with a problem which demands exercise of judgment and where the drug substitutes a euphoric and unreal feeling of exhilaration for the calm and logical thinking required by the circumstances.

In place of positive thinking and positive action, the user's mind is altered and distorted causing serious interference with his powers of perception and coordination and his ability to judge the passage of time and space.

The defendants assert that marijuana provides a certain amount of happiness or relaxation without harmful results. I am not persuaded by the evidence that the resulting euphoria is, in fact, a pleasurable and rewarding experience. I remain unconvinced by the evidence that the average user is made happy or contented—even for a short period of time. The normal brain function is altered or suspended, making the user more susceptible to the influence of others. The use of the drug also tends to accentuate any tendency toward improper conduct. In addition, it induces an abnormally subjective concentration on trivia. In short, marijuana produces a state which is analogous to a temporary mental aberration. Its prolonged and excessive use may induce a psychotic state, especially in those individuals with pre-existing psychological problems.

In my opinion a proper inference may be drawn from the evidence that there is a relationship between the use of marijuana and the incidence of crime and anti-social behavior. Within the limitations of our present statistical information, we can only speculate as to the precise nature and scope of the relationship. This is, to a certain degree, the hidden aspect of the problem. We cannot, at present, ascertain to what extent marijuana is a contributing factor in motor vehicle and other accidents, school dropouts, criminal activity, cases of "hard" narcotics addiction, broken homes and ruined careers, irrational and deviate acts, or losses of ambition and of the desire to become productive members of society. Although the *extent* of such results may be speculative, it is my opinion that a strong inference may be drawn from the evidence presented at this hearing that a causal relationship does exist between the use of marijuana and these assorted, social evils. In order to establish more firmly the nature and scope of this relationship, exhaustive and incisive studies must be undertaken.

In any event, there is no indication from the evidence that the user of marijuana becomes, through its use, a better student, a better worker, more dedicated to the public interest, or more efficient or productive in any undertaking. On the contrary, there is convincing evidence that the converse is true.

Many succumb to the drug as a handy means of withdrawing from the inevitable stresses and legitimate demands of society. The evasion of problems and escape from reality seem to be among the desired effects of the use of marijuana. Its use is not so much a symbol of dissent in order to effectuate changes in our social system, but rather a manifestation of a selfish withdrawal from society.

The lessons of history and the experiences of other nations teach us that such artificial alteration of the normal brain function by the use of drugs has been harmful both to the individual and to society in which he lives. The evidence clearly indicates that where a sub-culture has developed which tolerates the general use of marijuana or its derivatives, the harmful results have become clearly manifest. It is of great significance that the vast majority of nations have outlawed its use.

Although its relevancy is doubtful, there was the unavoidable comparison of marijuana with alcohol. Alcohol has some therapeutic value and its use is not limited solely to the achievement of a state of intoxication or the alteration of the mental processes. Furthermore, the use of alcohol is supported here and elsewhere by many centuries of cultural experience. Admittedly, its misuse has posed serious problems and continues to do so. But these problems, as they now exist, could be greatly expanded and compounded by the legalization of the use of marijuana. It is difficult to justify any law which would permit an expansion in the use of marijuana to the point where conceivably it would fall into the same category as alcohol and become a part of our national culture. That the use of marijuana may have results similar to those associated with the abuse of alcohol is hardly a persuasive argument for its legalization.

Marijuana users must, of necessity, consort with opportunistic pushers and other hardened members of the criminal element. In the case of youngsters, this is especially dangerous. It introduces them to and establishes a rapport with persons whose total influence is apt to be corruptive. As serious, if not more so, as the young user's association with pushers and the criminal element is the frequency, duration and intimacy of his contacts with other basically unstable users who not only involve him in their problems but compound his own.

The defendants argue that the statutes are also criminogenic in nature, as well as cruel and unusual, in that they prescribe serious criminal penalties for what may be relatively minor offenses. These arguments certainly do not apply to pushers. The legislation might profitably be reviewed with regard to the penalties provided for possessors as opposed to pushers or where the evidence indicates a first offense with the improbability of repetition. In such cases, the judge should be given wide discretionary powers so that the imposition of a criminal record may be avoided whenever warranted by the facts.

Because of the harmful and dangerous nature and effects of marijuana, the statutory prohibition of its possession, sale and, thereby, its use does not constitute a legislative interference with any fundamental right of a citizen. Nor do the specific provisions involved, Gen. Laws. ch.94, s.205, s.213A and s.217B as applied to these cases, involve any denial of due process or of the equal protection of the laws. Neither do they present any issue of cruel and unusual punishment. Nor does their proper enforcement necessarily entail any unreasonable invasion of privacy. Sections 205, 213A and 217B of chapter 94 of the General Laws bear a real and substantial relation to public health, safety, morals and the general welfare and are a valid exercise of the police power of the Commonwealth. *Sperry & Hutchinson Co. v. Dir. of Div. of Necessities of Life, supra,* at 418; *Coffee-Rich, Inc. v. Comm'r of Pub. Health, supra,* at 422.

On the basis of the findings and conclusions above, I further conclude and rule that the defendants, Joseph D. Leis and Ivan Weiss, are not entitled to have any of the indictments or complaints against them in these cases (Suffolk Superior Court Nos. 28841–2, 28844–5, 28864–5) dismissed on any of the grounds alleged in support of their amended motions to dismiss, which are hereby denied.

ENTERED: /s/ G. Joseph Tauro

December 19, 1967.   G. Joseph Tauro
                                            Chief Justice of the
                                            Superior Court

LEGISLATIVE AND JUDICIAL TRENDS IN MARIHUANA CONTROL

Donald E. Miller

Marihuana abuse is literally and foremost a legal problem. However you may choose to describe it—as a sociological, as a psychological or as a human problem—the fact remains that our society has decided to subject marihuana to controls through the use of criminal sanctions.

The prevailing philosophy in the United States, and I might add throughout the world, is based on the premise that it is better for persons to function without resorting to the abuse of a drug so dangerous as marihuana. Abuse of the drug has been considered to be a major social threat by our legislators, who have enacted and retained the anti-marihuana laws.

My topic today will lead me to consider with you some of the patterns of legal controls, the application of those controls, and the need to retain rather stringent Federal and State regulatory statutes.

Prior to the enactment of the Marihuana Tax Act of 1937 (the pri-

Presented at the Illinois State Medical Society National Symposium on Psychedelic Drugs and Marihuana, Chicago, Illinois, April 11, 1968. Printed with permission of the author and Illinois State Medical Society.

mary Federal control), Congress was possessed of quite a lot of information concerning the social and physiological effects of marihuana. By today's standards, perhaps the evidence against it was not as strong as it might have been. Mr. Joseph Oteri has made a special point of this in his discussion, "A Look at the Passage of the Marihuana Tax Act." [1] But, in developing programs, our lawmakers are not required to rely on only uncontroverted factual propositions. Nevertheless, the hearings, including the secondary reference material, provided ample support for the proposition that marihuana had harmful effects and that it contributed to anti-social problems.

Interestingly enough, medical science all over the world has long recognized the damages of marihuana. There is not a single modern, responsible medical body (to my knowledge) that supports the legalization of marihuana. The American Medical Association opposes it— and the World Health Organization opposes it. Additionally, the nations of the world have long opposed the abuse of marihuana. In fact, the Single Convention on Narcotic Drugs (1961) obligates the 65 parties to maintain special measures of control on marihuana, and to prohibit the use of marihuana for other than medical and scientific purposes within 25 years.

It is ridiculous to conclude that the public health officials who helped formulate the health policies all over the world did so without adequate knowledge of marihuana's dangers. To conclude, as Mr. Oteri seems ready to do, that former Commissioner Harry J. Anslinger duped all the world's scientists, legislators, and public officials and that he alone "turned off the world," is equally contrary to common sense.

The impression is being created that virtually nothing is known about marihuana. This is false. Also, the impression is being created that there is nothing harmful about marihuana. This is equally false. Too many people seem to think that we should not pay any attention to the old studies. Too many permissivists argue that the studies of Benabud,[2] Bouquet,[3] Chopra,[4] Gardikas,[5] Jo-

---

[1] Oteri, J. and Silverglate, H.: "In the Marketplace of Free Ideas: A Look at the Passage of the Marihuana Tax Act," *Marihuana Myths and Realities,* Brandon House, p. 136 (1967).

[2] Benabud, A.: "Psycho-pathological Aspects of the Cannabis Situation in Morocco: Statistical Data for 1956," *Bulletin on Narcotics,* v. 9, no. 4, pp. 1–16 (1956).

[3] Bouquet, R.: "Cannabis, Parts I and II," *Bulletin on Narcotics,* v. 2, no. 4, pp. 14–30 (1950); "Cannabis, Parts III–V," *Bulletin on Narcotics,* v. 3, no. 1, pp. 22–43 (1951).

[4] Chopra, I. and Chopra, R.: "The Use of the Cannabis Drug in India," *Bulletin on Narcotics,* v. 9, no. 1 (Jan.–Mar., 1957).

[5] Gardikas, C.: "Hashish and Crime," *Engephale,* no. 2–3 (Aug. 1950).

achimoglu,[6] and Wolff [7] are not valid because they were not done in America, under American standards, using American subjects, and using "American-type" marihuana. I cannot dismiss those studies so lightly, and neither should you.

The real damage being done in this crisis of confidence is that some scholarly men are more willing to attack the marihuana controls than to justify them; that these persons are more concerned with deriding the public officials who are charged with enforcing the laws than in helping them prevent drug abuse; and that they are more interested in rationalizing the use of marihuana than in presenting reasons for controlling it.

It is true that we do not possess absolute knowledge of the effects of marihuana. However, let us remember that marihuana contains a very powerful ingredient, tetrahydrocannabinol, which is capable of producing many ill effects. Various studies from the Middle East, the Near East and in the United States indicate that the mental effects are very significant. Emotional balance is disturbed—waves of euphoria are often interspersed with phases of anxiety; paranoid episodes are frequent— giving rise to disturbances of conducts; volition and initiative are impaired; sensation is changed and distorted; and even the so-called "American-type" marihuana can produce full-fledged hallucinations and delusions.

The formal list of reported physiological and psychological effects of the intake of marihuana is quite varied and lengthy. The 1965 report on Drug Dependence of the World Health Organization lists the following:

> "Among the more prominent subjective effects of cannabis ... are: hilarity ... carelessness; loquacious euphoria ... distortion of sensation and perception ... impairment of judgment and memory; distortion of emotional responsiveness; irritability, and confusion. Other effects, which appear after repeated administration ... include: lowering of the sensory threshold, especially for optical and accoustical stimuli ... illusions, and delusions that predispose to antisocial behavior; anxiety and aggressiveness as a possible result of the various intellectual and sensory derangements; and sleep disturbances."

A problem in the United States in the field of research is the lack of a potent standard product. Significantly, about 50% of novices report that they obtained no effects whatever the first time they used marihuana.

---

6 Joachimoglu, G.: *Hashish, Its Chemistry and Pharmacology*, Little, Brown, p. 5 (1965).

7 Wolff, P.: *Marihuana in Latin America, the Threat It Constitutes*, Linacre Press (1949).

They have not been the victims of a drug, but merely have been deceived with a hoax. There is so much gyping going on that it helps support the notion that marihuana is innocuous. Chemically speaking, many persons who confess on questionnaires to have been "triers" of marihuana really have done nothing more than to become partially asphyxiated from polluted air.

There is a wide variance in the potency of black market marihuana. Although hashish is readily available in many parts of the United States, the majority of the marihuana is of the less potent variety. Also, we know that marihuana varies according to where it is grown, when and how it is harvested, and its age. Nevertheless, there is little doubt that marihuana contains a very powerful hallucinogen, and when potent substances are consumed, or the dosage of a weaker substance is increased, mental and physical reactions are intensified. The results of using the natural occurring tetrahydrocannabinol of marihuana seem to be conclusive. Dr. Harris Isbell concludes that in sufficient dosage, the properties of marihuana "can cause psychotic reaction in almost any individual." [8]

The isolation of the tetrahydrocannabinols and the promise of increasing availability of synthetic substances makes it possible for us finally to perform the vitally needed pharmacologic, biochemical, genetic and behavioral research necessary to answer the questions about the long-range effects of marihuana. More likely than not, the earlier failures in finding such effects in this country resulted from the unavailability of chronic users of high quality marihuana. Even the clinical studies in the highly regarded "LaGuardia Report," [9] must be reviewed with the knowledge that marihuana of unknown potency was smoked, and that much of the research involved oral administration of a marihuana concentrate.

Hence, we find very adequate reasons for proscriptions against marihuana. Even if we were to accept the snobbish proposition that the children of our colleges today possess a superior sense of moral intelligence and are better able to deal sensibly with drugs, and even if we were to conclude that marihuana affects only the weak and the vulnerable, since when has our society stopped being concerned about a minority? The very purpose of many of our health laws is the protection of minorities. I am not impressed that a law student with a high IQ does

---

[8] Isbell, H., et al.: *"Studies of Tetrahydrocannabinol"* (Feb. 1967). A copy may be obtained from the Bureau of Narcotics and Dangerous Drugs, Washington, D.C. 20226.

[9] The Mayor's Committee on Marihuana, *The Marihuana Problem in the City of New York,* Jaques Cattell Press (1944).

not obtain a reaction from taking two or three puffs on a marihuana cigarette. I am concerned over the consequences of making the drug readily
available in a society containing millions of persons predisposed to
impulsive and aggressive behavior.

I believe that most of us here today would oppose complete legalization of marihuana. The real issue seems to be the extent to which we
should control it. The Marihuana Tax Act of 1937 [10] is a system of
registration, occupational tax, transfer tax, and transfer forms. The law
is designed to permit marihuana to be produced and used for industrial,
scientific and medical purposes only. In determining which persons may
become registered, and thereby sell or acquire marihuana, the regulatory scheme requires as a condition precedent that the applicant be
qualified to engage in the activity according to the applicable State provisions. A typical "street peddler" could not become registered, because such a person is disqualified by State law. Lawyers will continue
to argue that the Federal Government has no right to rely on such
controls. Indeed, great stress has been put on certain aspects of such
laws in recent Supreme Court decisions.[11] However, I take it that the
major concern of this symposium is in the area of penalties. So, I will
try to ventilate the fog of misunderstanding in that area.

It is true that the Federal law does have rather substantial sentencing
provisions. The penalties provide not less than 2 years or more than
10 years for a possession offense, and not less than 5 years or more than
20 years for a sale offense. Perhaps, if the law had been designed for
and applied against minor traffickers and so-called "users," there
might be a need for adjustment of the penalties to fit the gravity of the
offense. However, this is not the case. The mandate from Congress
and the Executive policy makers is to concentrate our efforts on the
larger international and interstate traffickers. Even if we were to obtain
evidence against a mere possessor of marihuana for his own use, there
are certain latitudes, such as charging the person as a "juvenile delinquent" or handling him under the Federal Youth Corrections Act
rather than sentencing him under the regular penalty provisions. I can
recall no case where a student was prosecuted in Federal court based
on mere evidence of possession of marihuana for his own use. It is
interesting to note that Congress has looked at these penalty provisions
on several occasions, and has not found a need to reduce them.

Why make possession a violation of law? Law professors will claim

---

[10] 26 U.S.C. 4741 *et seq.*
[11] *Marchetti v. U.S.*, 88 S.Ct. 697 (1968); *Grosso v. U.S.*, 88 S.Ct. 709 (1968);
and *Haynes v. U.S.*, 88 S.Ct. 722 (1968).

that in order for a law to be an effective prevention, its operation must be prompt, certain, efficient, and its threats must not be bluff—its club must not be stuffed with highly selective enforcement and frequent evasions. On the surface, this would not be true with the Marihuana Tax Act of 1937 in view of the manner in which the laws are administered. Nevertheless, it is reasonable to assume that the fear of suffering the consequences of the law does deter countless reasonable and responsible persons. Avoidance of punishment and disgrace is a very decisive reaction of normal people. It can be assumed that the vast majority of the people who have lived with the social contrivance of punishment, in the home, in the schools, at play and at work, will avoid certain courses of action which are potentially injurious. The big red apple on the tree in the field where the bull grazes may be enticing, but most of us are afraid to go over the fence after it.

This, consequently, sets up a barrier, not only to unauthorized use, but more importantly against proselytizing. We can make one generalization: marihuana abuse spreads from person to person—the users who possess it are the ones who breed new users. To condone possession is to condone a ready source of marihuana for proselytizing. The result of "legalizing" possession can only be a more permissive attitude.

I believe a case has been made against marihuana. It is a harmful and dangerous substance which must be controlled. Further scientific studies are needed, and the National Institute of Mental Health is presently carrying on a complete plan of research, covering all aspects of marihuana use. The Bureau of Narcotics has been working with N.I.M.H. to develop procedures to facilitate research, and to obtain sufficient quantities of marihuana and tetrahydrocannabinol for the research. We are hoping that continual funds will be available for the next several years in order that we will be able to find the answers to the basic research questions which are being asked.

In the meantime, pending the results of the new studies, we should not make any off-the-cuff decisions. We should not take any action which will be seized upon as approval to use a debilitating drug. We now have more than 62,000 reported active addicts, we have untold thousands of amphetamine and barbiturate abusers, and we have millions of persons who drink too much alcohol. That seems to be quite enough.